W9-AES-788

2 CYH

Sparke

42-23260   Dec 3, 1970

NO DAY OF TRIUMPH

NO DAY
OF TRIUMPH

By

Saunders Redding

With an Introduction by
Richard Wright

This is not a day of triumph; it is a day of dedica-
tion. Here muster, not the forces of party, but the
forces of humanity. Men's hearts wait upon us. . . .
—WOODROW WILSON

J. & J. Harper Editions

HARPER & ROW, PUBLISHERS

New York and Evanston

WINGATE COLLEGE LIBRARY
WINGATE, N. C.

NO DAY OF TRIUMPH.

Copyright 1942 by J. Saunders Redding.

Printed in the United States of America. All rights reserved. No part of this book may be used or reproduced in any manner whatsoever without written permission except in the case of brief quotations embodied in critical articles and reviews. For information address Harper & Row, Publishers, Incorporated, 49 East 33rd Street, New York, N.Y. 10016.

FIRST J. & J. HARPER EDITION 1968
LIBRARY OF CONGRESS CATALOG CARD NUMBER: 42-22760

For

Esther E. J. Redding

48313

CONTENTS

INTRODUCTION

IT HAS long been my conviction that the next quarter of a century will disclose a tremendous struggle *among* the Negro people for self-expression, self-possession, self-consciousness, individuality, new values, new loyalties, and, above all, for a new leadership. My reading of Redding's *No Day of Triumph* has confirmed and strengthened this conviction, for his book contains honesty, integrity, courage, grownup thinking and feeling, all rendered in terms of vivid prose. *No Day of Triumph* is another hallmark in the coming-of-age of the modern Negro; it is yet another signal in the turn of the tide from sloppy faith and cheap cynicism to fruitful seeking and passionate questioning.

Redding is the first middle-class Negro to break with the ideology of the "Talented Tenth" in a complete and final manner. Some may feel that he tears down more than he builds, but that is beside the point. Redding's main task is to expose, exhibit, declare, and he does this job in a dramatic and unforgettable manner, offering his own life as evidence. His narrative moves on a high, sensitive plane, and he depicts how one man, surrounded with falsehood and confusion, groped toward truth and dignity and understanding.

For a long time this book cried out to be written. I predict that it will rock the Negro middle class back on its heels; I forecast that it will set the "Talented Tenth" on fire with its anger; I prophesy that it will be as acid poured in the veins of the smug Negro teachers in Negro colleges. *No Day of Triumph* is a manifesto to the Negro and a challenge to America.

—RICHARD WRIGHT
Author of *Native Son*

NO DAY OF TRIUMPH

CHAPTER ONE

Troubled in Mind

I

CONSCIOUSNESS of my environment began with the sound of talk. It was not hysterical talk, not bravado, though it might well have been, for my father had bought in a neighborhood formerly forbidden, and we lived, I realize now, under an armistice. But in the early years, when we were a young family, there was always talk at our house; a great deal of it mere talk, a kind of boundless and robustious overflow of family feeling. Our shouts roared through the house with the exuberant gush of flood waters through an open sluice, for talk, generated by any trifle, was the power that turned the wheels of our inner family life. It was the strength and that very quality of our living that made impregnable, it seemed, even to time itself, the walls of our home. But it was in the beginning of the second decade of the century, when the family was an institution still as inviolate as the swing of the earth.

There was talk of school, of food, of religion, of people. There were the shouted recitations of poems and Biblical passages and orations from Bryan, Phillips, and John Brown. My mother liked rolling apostrophes. We children were all trained at home in the declining art of oratory and were regular contestants for prizes at school. My father could quote with appropriate gestures bits from Beveridge, whom he had never heard, and from Teddy Roosevelt and Fred Douglass, whom he had. There was talk of the "race problem," reasonable and unembittered unless Grandma Redding was there, and then it became a kind of spiritual poison,

3

its virulence destructive of its own immediate effects, almost its own catharsis. Some of the poison we absorbed.

I remember Grandma Redding coming on one of her visits and finding us playing in the back yard. My brother and sister were there and we were playing with Myrtle Lott and Elwood Carter, white children who were neighbors. Grandma came in the back way through the alley, as she always did, and when we heard the gate scrape against the bricks we stopped. She stepped into the yard and looked fixedly at us. Holding her ancient, sagging canvas bag under one arm, she slowly untied the ribbons of her black bonnet. The gate fell shut behind her. Her eyes were like lashes on our faces. Reaching out her long arm, she held open the gate. Then she said, "Git. You white trash, git!" Our companions, pale with fright, ducked and scampered past her. When they had gone, Grandma nodded curtly to us. "Chillen," she said, and went into the house.

Grandma Redding's visits were always unannounced. She came the fifty-odd miles up from Still Pond, Maryland, as casually as if she had come from around the nearest corner. A sudden cold silence would fall, and there would be Grandma. I do not know how she managed to give the impression of shining with a kind of deadly hard glare, for she was always clothed entirely in black and her black, even features were as hard and lightless as stone. I never saw a change of expression on her features. She never smiled. In anger her face turned slowly, dully gray, but her thin nostrils never flared, her long mouth never tightened. She was tall and fibrous and one of her ankles had been broken when she was a girl and never properly set, so that she walked with a defiant limp.

She hated white people. In 1858, as a girl of ten, she had escaped from slavery on the eastern shore of Maryland with a young woman of eighteen. They made their way to Camden, New Jersey, but there was no work and little refuge there. Across the river, bustling Philadelphia swarmed with slave hunters. By subterfuge or by violence even free people were sometimes kidnaped and sent south. Near Bridgeton, New

Jersey, the runaways heard, there was a free Negro settlement, but one night they were stopped on the docks by a constable who asked them for papers. They had none. Within two weeks after their escape they were slaves again. When my grandmother tried to run away from the flogging that was her punishment, Caleb Wrightson, her master, flung a chunk of wood at her and broke her ankle.

It was not until we were quite large children that Grandma Redding told us this story. She did not tell it for our pleasure, as one tells harrowing tales to children. It was without the dramatic effects that Grandma Conway delighted in. What *she* would have done with such a tale! No. Grandma Redding's telling was as bare and imageless as a lesson recited from the head and as coldly furious as the whine of a shot.

"An' ol' man Calub flane a hick'ry chunk an' brist my ankle-bone."

I can see her now as she sits stooped in the wooden rocker by the kitchen stove, her sharp elbows on her sharp knees and her long black fingers with their immense purple nails clawing upward at the air. Her undimmed eyes whipped at ours, and especially at mine, it seemed to me; her thin lips scarcely parted. She had just come in or was going out, for she wore her bonnet and it sat on the very top of her harsh, dull hair. Hatred shook her as a strong wind shakes a boughless tree.

"An' ol' man Calub stank lik'a pes'-house from the rottin' of his stomick 'fore he died an' went t' hell, an' his boys died in the wo' an' went to hell."

But her implacable hatred needed no historical recall, and so far as I remember, she never told the tale to us again.

But generally Grandma Redding's taciturnity was a hidden rock in the sea of our talk. The more swift the tide, the more the rock showed, bleak and unavoidable. At other times the talk flowed smoothly around her: the bursts of oratory and poetry, the chatter of people and events, the talk of schooling and sometimes of money and often of God. Even the talk of God did not arouse her. I think she was not especially religious; and in this, too, she was unlike Grandma Conway.

My grandmothers met at our house but once. They did not like each other.

2

Grandma Conway said "Good morning" as if she were pronouncing the will of God. A woman as squat and solid as a tree stump, she had a queer knurl of religious thought and character that no ax of eclecticism could cleave. She had great bouts of religious argument with whoever would argue with her. Even though her adversary sat but two feet away, she would shout out her disputes in a cracking voice and half-rise threateningly, her gray serge breast lifting and falling as if she had been running uphill. She often frightened our young friends in this manner, awed them into speechlessness; and when she had done this, her green-yellow eyes would blink very fast and her fat, yellow little fists would fly to her chest and beat gently there in laughter.

Grandma Conway was honest about God and often very moving. When she visited us, the family prayers on Sunday belonged to her. Her prayers seemed to bring Him into our dining room, transforming the flesh and blood reality of Grandma Conway into a greater reality of mystical communion. It was as if a sleep and a dream of God descended upon us all, replacing our earthly consciousness with another too penetrating to be born in wakefulness and too sublime to bear the weight of our gross senses. I would keep my gaze fastened upon Grandma for visual evidence against that awful Presence; or I looked around, feeling my elbows pressed deep into the fabroid of the chair seat, at my brother, my sisters, the quiet stillness of my mother's bent back, the upright, almost transfixed solidity of my father's shoulders. I would hear and smell the sausage frying, and the baked beans, and the hot rolls, and the coffee. But insensibly my eyes would close against the physical reality, which somehow even sight and sound and smell could not confirm, and I would be washed up onto a plane of awareness that terrified me.

"Come on feet of thunder, Holy One, but tread amongst us softly, and let us hear the rustling of your garments. It's like the sound the wind makes at night in the sycamore trees in front of my house on Columbus Street. I feel Your spirit hands uplifting me and Your Holy Presence cloaking me, Oh, Giver of all things good and perfect."

But often she talked to Him of the intimate trifles that enlivened her day, of her children and her children's children.

"Dear Father, the boy, Saunders, had a croup last night and his hacking and coughing kept me from my sleep."

So intimately and yet so reverently.

It was on one of these Sundays that my grandmothers met. Grandma Conway had been with us a month. Grandma Redding came as unceremoniously as she usually came, looking as if she had walked every step of the fifty miles from her home. When my mother went to the kitchen that morning, Grandma Redding was sitting on the back steps. Though it was August and hot, she wore the heavy black dress and the black woolen jacket which seemed to be her only garments. When she discovered that Grandma Conway was visiting us, she did not remove her bonnet, and, as I remember, there was some difficulty in inducing her to stay for prayers and breakfast.

The presence of the two old women filled us children with strange, jerky excitement. Even our mother was infected by it. I think we recognized more than the surface differences between our grandmothers. Separating their thoughts and characters was a deep gulf that could not be accounted for alone by the wide divergence of their experiences. It was something even more fundamental. It was what they were and would have been, even, I believe, had they lived through similar experiences. No bridge of time or thought or feeling could join them. They were of different earth. On the surface it looked as simple as this: one was yellow, the other black.

There was a pause of embarrassment just before we knelt for prayers. Grandma Conway, with the gracious magnanimity with which one sometimes yields to a rival, said to my father, "Maybe your ma would like to lead us in prayer this morning." My father looked embarrassed, drawing his hand over his bald head from crown to forehead and shooting an oblique glance at my mother. Mother said nothing. Then Grandma Redding said;

"No. Thank'ee. Lewis wist I ain't no comp'ny-prayin' one. Let her pray."

We knelt at chairs around the square table. The odor of the breakfast was heavy in the room—coffee, fresh bread, and the Sunday smell of sliced bananas all mingled. The sun made a heavy shaft of light through each of the two windows and flecks of it escaping through the multitudinous small holes in the green shades danced upon the wall. More than the Sunday excitement of dressing for church filled us. Beyond the hard, straight shoulders of Grandma Redding I could see my older sister silently dancing on her knees. Behind me I could hear my mother's stepped-up breathing and the sound her dress made when she moved against the chair. The others knelt on the other side of the table. Lowering my face in my spread fingers, I waited for prayers to begin. Grandma Conway sighed heavily. I set myself against the coming of that awful Presence.

"God, our Holy Father, Chastiser of sin and evil, great Maker of all things pure and good and of the creatures that here on earth do dwell, be with us in our prayers this morning. There are many who cannot rise from their beds of pain this morning— dear Lord, be with them. There are many who went last night in health to bed and this morning lie cold in death. Be with them. And be with us. Thou can be everywhere. Thou art in the sun that . . ."

It was obvious to us who knew her prayers that the spirit had not descended upon her. Her prayer was not coming with that mellifluous and intimate spontaneity with which she generally spoke to God. She was remembering perhaps too much of the Book of Common Prayer which she had studied as a child. My tension eased a little.

". . . Holy Father, these my children now, and my children's children. Mary here, and the man who made her a woman. You know all this, Father, but I'm getting old and my mind wanders. Make these children as Your Son. Keep not the cross from them, nor the crown of thorns, nor the cup of sorrow. Deny them not the chastening rod of truth if their young lives would be as lamps on the footpaths of eternity. And Redding's ma, Lord. She's with us this morning. She has her affliction, Holy One, and we can hardly notice it, but it's an affliction on her. Bless her. Teach her that affliction chasteneth a righteous heart and only the wicked are bowed down. Bless her, dear God, and bless us all. We ask it in the name . . ."

Before my father could say "Amen," as was his custom, and we could rise from our knees, Grandma Redding's hard, grainy voice whanged out beside me. I felt the room's shocked stillness. Surprised and irritated a little at this fresh delay to breakfast, I peeped at her through my fingers. She was kneeling with her long back in a hard curve and her forearms spread along the chair seat. Her black hands grasped the uprights of the chair, so that her large knuckles stood out purple. Her eyes were not closed and her face was as hard as rock.

"Lis'en, Jesus. You wist I ain't got the words fer comp'ny prayers. This is all I want t'say. I been climbin' hills an' goin' down valleys be't sixty some years, an' the hills ain't no littler an' the valleys ain't no lesser. I ain't downright complainin', Jesus. I'm jes' tellin' You the way things is, be't You ain't been here in my lifetime. You ain't been here in be't than a thousan' years. Sence You been here, Gawd's done made a new lan' an' put a whole lot o' diff'unt things an' people on it all together, an' we'se all steered up ever' which way. We had slav'ry sence You been here. That's mean business. Now we got something else, an' that's mean business too. Devilment an' hate an' wo' an' some being one thing an' some another, that's all bad, mean business. We'se all skiverin' an' steered up. It ain't t'beginnin' an' it ain't the close. You understan' what's on my mind, Jesus.

"Now, bless these young'uns. Bless 'em on earth. It don't matter 'bout us ol' ones. We'se skitterin' down the rocky hill anyhow. Bless us in the everlastin'. But these young'uns, they's climbin' up. All I ast be You keep 'em from the knowin' an' the manbirthed sins o' blackness. We'se bent on knees to Your will, Lord Jesus. Amen."

This prayer probably had no lasting effect upon the others who heard it, but, young as I was, its impression upon me was profound. In time to come it was to be as a light thrown upon Grandma Redding's character, and, by reflection, upon Grandma Conway's. It was only later, of course, that I had any intellectual comprehension of the basis of the contrast between them. For many years I continued to think of Grandma Redding as a strange, bitterly choleric old woman and that her irascibility was somehow a part of her blackness. I could not help this absurdity then, for ours was an upper-class Negro family, the unwitting victim of our own culture complexes; deeply sensitive to the tradition of ridicule and inferiority attaching to color; hating the tradition and yet inevitably absorbing it.

Grandma Redding knew and admitted the debilitating force of that tradition, and out of her knowledge had come her prayer. There were dark ones among us, but none so black as Grandma Redding. I was dark. But here again we were the victims of evasive and defensive thinking. To members of our immediate family the stigma of blackness did not apply. But Grandma Redding, whom, somehow, we never seemed to know very well, and her children—my father's brothers—were not of the family circle. And it applied to them. It was a crazy, irrational, paradoxical pattern, not made less so by those occasional upheaving disturbances in the general social order that rolled in on us in great breakers from the fathomless sea of the white world. We were a garrisoned island in that sea.

On the other hand, I thought of Grandma Conway and her kin—they were all mulattoes—as escaping the tradition. But, indeed, Grandma Conway was nearer the absurdity than I. I have always remembered with what garrulous delight she used to repeat:

"So this white gentleman, who lived in the next block, met us on the street one day. I had a big hat on Cora, you see, and you couldn't see her face without raising her head or taking off her hat. So he met us and says, bowing just as nice, 'Miss Cora'— that was to me. Your poor, dead Aunt Cora was named for me. 'Miss Cora,' he says, 'let me see this prize package under the big hat,' and he lifted her hat up. Cora was just as pretty! She was too pretty to live, dear Lord. He lifted her hat up, and when he saw her, he says, as if he'd been kicked in the stomach, 'Why, she's nearly white!' 'Yes, indeedy,' I said, 'and I intend to keep her that way.' "

And then her eyes behind her tiny oval glasses would screw up and her fat yellow hands would fly to her breast and beat there gently in laughter. Her laughter was not an exact comment, but it was only later that I realized this, for when we were young it seemed merely an amusing story.

My grandmothers did not meet again after that Sunday breakfast. It was as strained a meal as any I have ever sat through. Grandma Redding kept her bonnet on all through it. She drank only sweetened hot water and ate only the sliced bananas. As always, Grandma Conway, though silent, ate and drank heavily of black coffee sweetened almost to syrup, of the kidney stew and baked beans, and the crunchy rolls as large as buns. Even under ordinary circumstances, her appetite was amazing. My father quarreled with us a good deal that morning. My mother was silent. Eventually we all fell silent, hearing only the sucking sound that Grandma Redding's lips made on the edge of her cup and the explosive grunts of pleasure with which Grandma Conway munched into her roll.

They never saw each other again, though each lived several years longer. In 1923 Grandma Redding, her face stone-set in pain, limped defiantly to her death, and three years later death caught up with Grandma Conway while she slept.

3

Our street was caught in the embrace of the slow decline which possessed it in mellow decadence for almost twenty years. A block above us on the west stood a row of massive houses facing the Court House square. They were the clubs of the rich. Among the shining carriages and the high, big-wheeled cars, I used often to see the low, queer-shaped, foreign-made cars of the Du Pont who was "crazy about automobiles," and the square glass and metal electrically driven boxes called hansoms, which also were associated in my mind with great wealth. These hansoms were always driven by elegant women in elegant hats. Whenever I saw one, I used to think how grand my mother would look in one of them. The thought was the measure of my naivete. I thought that if my father just kept on working very hard and living according to certain moral principles, he would certainly become rich—rich enough to buy an electric hansom for my mother and a huge, high-wheeled car for us all. That is what we were taught in school and Sunday school. Were not the Du Ponts fine, Christian people, attending and supporting the church? My father was a fine Christian too. Was not John D. Rockefeller, whose little, wrinkle-lidded eyes peered out from a page of my civics book, the richest man in the world? And had he not been a Sunday school worker all his life? My father was superintendent of Sunday school. He is now. He has been for thirty-odd years; but he has never become rich. In those days I had not heard of Tarbell or Steffens.

We lived in a sort of neutral ground between the last orderly outposts of the well-to-do—their businesses, their clubs, their churches, their graveyards—and the teeming camp of the hard-faced poor. Our street was quiet and shaded with elms that in summer formed an archway over the cobbled street. There were porches and hedge-bordered patches of front yards, and deep back yards with grape arbors and flowers. But below us on the east the streets became gradually more naked and sly, until, flinging off the last rag of pride, they prowled with brutal defensiveness past the huddled houses, the big-windowed corner saloons, the dark, dirty grocery stores, and the obscene, blank-walled factories to the river. On wet, still days the stink from the morocco shops and the jute mills lay over the streets—and over ours—like the breath of putrefaction. It was a strange, compelling, lairlike neighborhood, immobilized in stilly desperation.

How my parents maintained their neutrality! What a fine balance they drew! Belonging neither to the outpost above nor to the camp below, they were yet a part of both. Their manifest standards were conservative. My father voted the Democratic ticket once, but only after agonies of soul-searching. They went to church regularly. They believed in individual initiative and in its fruits. The conservative instinct of acquisition did not grow stagnant even under the burden of debt and mortgage and taxes. They believed that one was rewarded according to his worth and that no factor—save only occasional strokes of mischance—upset the balance between honor and truth and industry on the one hand and respect, credit, and success on the other. Yet I have known my father to sit on the back steps and my mother to sit just within the screen door and listen for hours in sympathetic respect to the strange talk of Weeping Joe.

Weeping Joe was a character frequently spewed up from the gurgling entrails of the east side. A short, pallid man of Polish stock, he went barefooted and bareheaded winter and summer. School children mocked him pitilessly, though he paid them no mind. Three or four times a year, surrounded by crude home-made emblems and placards, he stood on the low wall surrounding the Court House square and railed against the "symbols of arrogance, the license of wealth, the unholy power of corrupt politics." He wept and railed. Always promptly arrested for disturbing the peace, his release was always the occasion for a one-man parade of protest, during which he was sometimes spat upon and subjected to other indignities. He was called an idiot. But Weeping Joe was not an idiot. He talked of the return of power to the masses from whom it was derived. He talked sane heresies—of equitably distributing wealth, of a people's government, of wiping out racial prejudices, of linking the spirits of men together in the indissoluble bond of Christ. He talked these things, too, on our back steps, and my parents, sitting in the silence of the warm evening, listened.

WINGATE COLLEGE LIBRARY
WINGATE, N. C.

"That is it," Joe would say.

"Yes. I know," my father would say. "But is one's own ambition and initiative to amount to nothing?"

"To one's own self and family, enough to feed them, put them in a good house, clothe them. To everybody else, everything."

"My sweat to feed others, to satisfy others? I wouldn't like it," my father said quickly, stroking his bald head.

"Ah! Of what I talk, that thing is better for the colored peoples than for me. That thing would make you equal, make everybody the same in equalness. Don't you see? It would be Christ come again. Is that not better? And do you think there are no equal men to you who are poorer than you? I know, my friend." He tapped his eyes. "I see."

He was not the weeping heretic, the burning rabble-rouser of the Court House wall. He laughed a little, a strange sound like the call of some strange bird. He stroked his coarse, straw-colored beard against his naked throat and looked up sideways at the dark face of my father.

"What has working for yourself got you?"

"Well," my father said tentatively.

In the doorway, behind the screen, my mother was bent forward listening. It had grown too dark to mend and she was leaning over a small basket of stockings in her lap.

"Answer, my friend." He made that laugh again and let go of his beard, screwing himself sideways on the step so that he faced my father.

"Well," said my father again.

"It has got you a house, which maybe you will own the next fifteen, twenty years—maybe. . . ."

"Twelve years," said my father triumphantly. "The second mortgage is paid, and it took me only eight years."

"That's twenty years, my friend. Think. Think!" His voice rose a little. "Twenty years to pay for a house that somebody built in a few weeks, a house that was paid for once already, maybe two times already. Twenty years! It is a crazy thing, a thinkless thing. And who gets paid, my friend? The peoples

who put up the house? No. The peoples who cut the boards?
No. The peoples who made the bricks? No. Who gets paid for
twenty years of your work and sweatings is the peoples who
have never seen the house and don't know you are living."

My mother stirred.

"But *we* have the house, Mr. Smoleki," she said quietly. She
had been very careful to ask him his last name, and now she
called him by it.

"Yes, my friend, you peoples have the house. But only because you are buying for those other peoples mansions. Are they
better than you that you should have lesser? Are they aristo-
cratics, like in the old country? Are they from the womb un-
born? Are they of the immaculate conception?"

My mother did not answer. Father said, "I don't mind work.
It's what a man has to do to live."

"In decency," my mother said pointedly.

Weeping Joe laughed and shook his massive head. That head
was like a weedy pumpkin on a pole. He threw one leg across
the other and swung his bare suspended foot.

"In decency," he gently mocked.

"Yes," my mother answered.

"Ah, my friend's lady, there is only one decency for peoples,
and that is here." He touched his fingers to his heart and looked
past my father to the dark-soft shape of Mother sitting in the
doorway. "Is it not so?"

My mother straightened up and sighed. "I suppose so."

Still with his cupped fingers lightly touching his heart, Weeping Joe went on. "If every peoples had equalness of decency
here, it would be the day of Christ."

"But even then," my father said dejectedly. "Even then."

"Hush, Fellow," my mother said. She always called my father
that.

"That day won't ever come, Joe."

"Ah, my friend. It is a bad thing for peoples who have no
hope."

So they talked, my father always strangely aroused, always,

it seemed to me, on the verge of something, of establishing some absolute value by which to judge the meaning of his living. And always ending in dejection. What did his living mean? What purpose had it? Perhaps he never framed the questions to himself, but heaving up from almost any circumstance he faced were these and other imponderables. There was my mother, too, mostly silent, thinking I do not know what, but in her way aroused no less than he, responding to his dejection with murmurs of gentle protest, and by a slow exercise of almost organic will blunting the cool edge of excitement which Joe's words set oscillating within her.

But my father was not usually hopeless. A man without hope does not struggle, does not work. And my father worked. He had come up from that same east side whence Weeping Joe now and then emerged. Indeed, he had come from deeper down in some spiritual east side, where his mother and all her kin had dwelt as far back as ancestral memory goes; for slavery was an east side, too, for some—a kind of spiritual ghetto of the damned. My father's emergence was more than physical, but it was not complete. It was as if a man struggling from beneath a smothering weight frees his head to breathe, but finds the rest of him pressed down and his cramped lungs unable to use the air his gasping mouth sucks in.

His hopes were high when he had gone to Howard University and worked his way through in all kinds of service. There he had met the long-legged mulatto girl who was to be my mother. They were graduated from the Normal Department, and she went home to Alexandria, and he went out to make a living. In the winter he taught a country school in Maryland for fifteen dollars a month. From spring until late fall he waited table in the old United States Hotel in Boston. But in 1898 my father's older brother persuaded him to move to Wilmington, Delaware. Here, after their marriage in 1900, my parents settled down, and here we began to be born.

For a time, my father ran a grocery store deep in the east side where they lived. (I was not yet born.) His trade was mostly a credit trade among the Negroes, and after a little more than a year, when his own credit was exhausted and his books full of bad debts, he had to give it up. He went into the postal service.

I have no remembrance of our east-side house. Grandmother Conway would not visit there because she could not bear "the stinking morocco, the jammed-up houses, and the ugly mud-flats." My brother, the oldest of us, was frequently ill there too, and when the second child was born, my mother went home to Alexandria where her children could grow in health. There was no breach in my parents' relationship. My mother's going was simply the best thing to do and she did it. They saw each other frequently, and on one of her visits to Wilmington I was born prematurely. I was born in the house on the east side.

Grandma Conway used to say of us who were born down there that we were marked for life. All through my childhood the east side had strong and unpleasant associations in my mind. It seemed that everything anti-social happened there. There lived the whores and the pimps, there happened the shootings and the stabbings, and there in the night one could smell the hot breath of violence. Frequently the papers carried editorials on the "east side element," the Negroes and the foreign-born poor, who, it seems, were most undesirable. When I was a schoolboy, the hurled epithet "dirty eastsider" cut to the soul, and even now has an edge to make me wince.

In its purely physical aspects my father could and did cope with the east side. He moved. Moving was not so simple, for it was not a matter merely of having the money to buy or to rent the house of one's choice. It was made very dark and complicated by the fact that we were a Negro family. I have never got the details straight, but moving was almost like stealing.

It has always seemed to me that I have some recollection of that moving. I was not then four years old, and it is likely that part of my memory is ancestral. I remember the hushed quality of that night, the subdued and yet excited air of conspiracy. I remember the two-seated, rubber-tired carriage which my

father had hired skipping over the cobbled road, past the dark
factories and the houses huddled in the night. I remember the
feel of my mother's arms as she held me in her lap, and my
sister's bubbling excitement. "Shush, honey. Shush," my mother
said. Baggage was piled all around us. My brother sat on the
front seat with my father. Out of the narrow streets into a broad
street with a carbon light on every corner and a gas lamp in
every block. Wonderful lamps! The light from them flecking
the leaves of the trees and making dancing patterns on the road.
Out of the east side, the horses trotting smoothly now and fast,
with the carriage lights shining on their flanks and leather and
wood creaking and the night air streaming into our faces. Then
a turn to the right, up a cobbled, slanting street that somehow
looked free and clean even in the dark. In the very middle of
the hill, dim under the tree that spread to its roof, stood the
house. It, too, was free. There were no houses joined to it on
either side. It seemed alive with the light from the gas lamp
playing on its four front windows and the glass-fronted door.

I remember how my father's jaw stood out like a hard fist in
the light of the match he struck to find the keyhole in the back
door. He went in first, and we could hear him picking his way
among the litter of furniture that had been sent in broad daylight—for furniture has no race. My mother stood trembling,
waiting for the lamp to be lit. Then she stepped in, and we all
stepped in, and there was my father holding the lamp above
his head.

"This is home, Girl," he said.

And my mother sat down on a packing box and lifted her
veil and removed her hat. Her hair was already whitening,
though she had just turned thirty. "Thank God!" she said, and
broke into uncontrollable weeping.

That night trembles down the crowded corridor of my memory as a light seen at the end of a long tunnel.

My father was right. It was home. Here life laid siege to us,
and we built our walls of family-feeling, of love and talk, inviolate, we thought, against the flux of time and the change of

circumstance. Here the other four children were born, and two of them died in infancy.

4

But what a struggle it was! As far back as I can remember, it was necessary for my father to eke out his small government salary by doing all sorts of odd jobs after his regular hours and in his vacations. He belonged to a waiters' association, and frequently he served at dinners, banquets, and parties from early evening until dawn. On these occasions he wore the swallow-tailed coat in which he had been married and the black broadcloth trousers which he had picked up at a secondhand shop. This outfit always amused us, for the trousers did not cover his ankles and his big feet spread beneath them in a truly monumental fashion. The coat had a greenish tinge and fitted across his thick shoulders like a harness. My mother had to sew up the shoulder seams after every use. My father cared little about the appearance of his clothes. "So long as they're clean, children," he used to say, when for reasons of pride we used to fidget with his tie, fold down his collars, and see to it that he was wearing a proper belt in his trousers. Our attentions amused him, and he would wink at our mother and say, "Girl, they've all got your side's pride."

Sometimes he would bring from these parties a satchel bulging with steaks, chicken, butter, rolls, and ice cream; and then we feasted—not because we ever went hungry, but because all this was extra and had to be eaten before it spoiled.

My father always took his annual vacation in the late summer or early fall, for then he could find employment among the farmers a few miles outside the city. He would contract to cut corn or harvest potatoes. Sometimes he stayed in the country, but when he did not, he was always back long after we were in bed and gone again before dawn. Often my brother and I, in the room next the bathroom, would wake up in the night and hear my father thrashing about in the tub and murmuring wearily to my mother, who always waited for him late in the night.

As I look back upon it now, I know that my father was driven by more than the necessity to provide a living for his family. Surrounded by whites both at home and at work, he was driven by an intangible something, a merciless, argus-eyed spiritual enemy that stalked his every movement and lurked in every corner. It goaded him every waking hour, but he could not get at it, though he felt it to be embodied in almost every white man he met. Because of this, he moved with defensive caution, calculating the effect of every action and every utterance upon his unseen enemy. Every day he won defensive victories, but every day the final victory seemed more impossible. He was up at dawn, painting the trim, repairing the roof, putting out ashes, shoveling snow from the sidewalk. In fifteen years he was never late for his work, and only once did he allow an illness to keep him home. His endurance was a thing of the spirit.

But the other necessity was there too, the physical need to provide for a family that soon increased to seven. We were a problem. We helled through our clothes, and especially our shoes. My father mended our shoes with thick leather patches that balled clumsily on the soles. He trimmed our hair. When it seemed safe, he avoided doctor's bills by purging us with castor oil, plastering us with goose grease, and swathing us in flannel. I myself was often sick with ruinous colds that threatened a serious illness. I was almost constantly under the care of Dr. Elbert, who spent his time thumping my chest and giving me nauseating medicines. But no saving was too trifling, no economy too stringent for my father to make. Sometimes it was a joking matter. Our garbage pail seldom contained anything but vegetable parings and bones, for my mother, too, knew the value of a penny. Indeed, her thrift was generally more effective and yet less severe than my father's. She had a reasonableness in the matter which he lacked. Sometimes she raised objections— futilely, for instance, to my father's spending his vacation harvesting potatoes or cutting corn. She argued the point of his health, but my father's answer was always the same: "Work wouldn't hurt a man."

When I was fourteen or fifteen, I spent a Saturday on one of these corn-cutting expeditions with him. It was the last week end of his two-weeks vacation, and he had been working on a farm eight miles out of the city. We left home before daylight and reached the farm just at dawn. It was a large farm, and only a part of it was under cultivation. Before we set to work, the farmer joined us. He was a buck-toothed post of a man, with a skin raw and peeled-looking by the sun. The corn field lay some distance from the house and the land sloped away gently to a flat, rocky strip beyond which the corn field rose abruptly. The brown corn stood in marching rows on the side of the hill. The field had not been cared for. High weeds tangled the rows.

"Well, you overstretched yourself, looks like," the farmer said, looking at the uncut corn on the hill.

My father took off his coat and drew his corn knife from the ground, where he had left it the evening before. I saw his jaw tighten like a fist.

"I'll need a knife for my boy here," he said. "We'll get it done. The weeds will hamper us some, but we'll get it done."

"Maybe you will at that," the farmer said, kicking in a mat of weeds. "Didn' have no time to do nothin' with this crop out here myself. Had another colored feller workin' for me, but he ups an' quits 'bout the time I needed him most. Wasn' much of a loss to me, I don't reckon. He sure was a lazy one. This your boy, hunh?"

"Yes," my father said. He looked past the man. "We'll get it done all right."

"I'm from Missouri," the farmer said.

When he came back with the long-bladed corn knife, he stood for a while and watched us work. I had never cut corn before, but it was simply a matter of bending one's back and swinging one's blade as close to the roots as one could. When an armful of stalks was cut, we bound them together and stood them up to finish drying for fodder. The weeds were already giving us

tautness that sometimes kept her strained for days, she said to my father:

"That's all it takes, Fellow. Today our house is worth one-third of what it was last night. When those people . . ." She shrugged her wide shoulders and stared at my father.

"Oh, Girl! Girl!" my father said gently. "You mustn't be so hard on them. They may be respectable people."

"Hard! Hard! And respectable people!" She laughed brittlely. "What has respectability got to do with it?"

Then she tried to find the words for what she felt and thought, for we children were present and she did not wish to appear unreasonable before us. The subject of race was for her a narrow bridge over a chasmal sea, and the walking of it was not a part of her daily living. Only when she felt she must save herself from the abyss did she venture to walk. At other times she ignored it, not only in word, but I think in thought as well. She knew the speeches of John Brown and Wendell Phillips, the poetry of Whittier and Whitman, but not as my father knew them; not as battering stones hurled against the strong walls of a prison. She was not imprisoned. Stones, perhaps, but dropped into a dark sea whose tides licked only at the farthest shores of her life. She took this for reasonableness.

I remember she laughed a brittle laugh and said, "The first thing they moved in was one of those pianola things. Oh, we shall have music," she said bitterly, "morning, noon, and midnight. And they're not buying. They're renting. Why can't they stay where they belong!"

"Belong?" my father said.

"Yes. Over the bridge."

"They are our people, Girl," my father said.

My mother looked at him, tears of vexation dewing her eyes. She blinked back the tears and looked fixedly at my father's dark face shining dully under the chandelier, his bald head jutting back from his forehead like a brown rock. As if the words were a bad taste to be rid of, she said;

"Yours maybe. But not mine."

"Oh, Girl. Girl!"

But Mother had already swept from the dining room.

It is strange how little my deep affection for my mother (and hers for all of us) taught me about her while she lived. I have learned much more about her since her death. It is as if the significance of remembered speech and action unfolded to me gradually a long time after. My mother was the most complex personality I have ever known.

But no will of my mother's could abate the heave of the social tide just then beginning to swell. Our new neighbors were the first that we saw of that leaderless mass of blacks that poured up from the South during and after the war years. It was a trickle first, and then a dark flood that soon inundated the east side and burbled restively at our street. Within five months of the time my mother had raged, the whites were gone. But rents and prices in our street were too high for the laborers in morocco and jute mills, shipyards and foundries, the ditch-diggers, coal-heavers, and the parasites. They crowded sometimes as many as eight to a room in the houses below us, and I knew of at least one house of six small rooms in which fifty-one people lived.

Our street and the diagonal street above it were a more exclusive preserve. A few middle-class Jews, a clannish community of Germans clustered about their Turn Hall, and some Catholic Irish lived there. But they were nudged out. The Germans first, for they became the victims of mass hatred during the war, and the last German home was stoned just before the day of the Armistice. Landlords and realtors inflated prices to profit by Negro buyers who clamored for houses as if for heaven. Into our street moved the prosperous class of mulattoes, a physician and a dentist, a minister, an insurance agent, a customs clerk, a well-paid domestic, and several school teachers. Nearly all of these were buying at prices three times normal.

The atmosphere of our street became purely defensive. No neighborhood in the city was so conscious of its position and none, trapped in a raw materialistic struggle between the well-being of the west side and the grinding poverty of the east, fought harder to maintain itself. This struggle was the satanic bond, the blood-pact that held our street together.

But there was also the spiritual side to this struggle. It remained for me for a long time undefined but real. It was not clear and cold in the brain as religion was and taxes and food to eat and paint to buy. It was in the throat like a warm clot of phlegm or blood that no expectorant could dislodge. It was in the bowels and bone. It was memory and history, the pound of the heart, the pump of the lungs. It was Weeping Joe making bursting flares of words on the Court House wall and murmuring like a priest in funeral mass on our back steps of summer evenings. It was east side, west side, the white and the black, the word nigger, the cry of exultation, of shame, of fear when black Lemuel Price shot and killed a white policeman. It was Paul Dunbar, whose great brooding eyes spirit-flowed from his drawn face in a photograph over our mantle. It was sleeping and waking. It was Wilson and Hughes in 1917, Harding and Cox in 1921. It was a science teacher saying sarcastically, "Yes. I know. They won't hire you because you're colored," and, "Moreover, the dog licked Lazarus' wounds," and getting very drunk occasionally and reeling about, his yellow face gone purple, blubbering, "A good chemist, God damn it. A Goddamn good chemist! And here I am teaching a school full of niggers. Oh, damn my unwhite skin! And God damn it!" It was the music of pianolas played from dusk to dawn. And it was books read and recited and hated and loved: fairy tales, *Up From Slavery*, *Leaves of Grass*, *Scaramouche*, *Othello*, *The Yoke*, *Uncle Tom's Cabin*, *The Heroic Story of the Negro in the Spanish-American War*, *The Leopard's Spots*, *Door of the Night*, *Sentimental Tommy*, *The Negro, Man or Beast?*, and the rolling apostrophes of the *World's Best Orations*.

And on this plane allegiances were confused, divided. There was absolute cleavage between those spiritual values represented by Grandma Conway, who thought and lived according to ideas and ideals inherited from a long line of free ancestors and intimates (her father had been white, her mother part Irish, Indian,

Negro. Her first husband was a mulatto carriage maker with a tradition of freedom three generations old) and those ill-defined, uncertain values represented by Grandma Redding and which, somehow, seemed to be close to whatever values our neighbors on the east held. What these were I never knew, nor, I suspect, did Grandma Redding. Certainly she would have cast equal scorn on the east side's black Lizzie Gunnar, who ran a whore house and who two days before every Christmas gathered up all the Negro children she could find and led them to the Court House for the city's party to the poor, because, "Niggahs is jus' about de poores' folks dere is," and white and foreign-born Weeping Joe, who spoke of linking the spirits of men together in the solvent bond of Christ. Her closeness to them was more a sympathetic prepossession than an alliance. They were her people, whether their values were the same as hers or not. Blood was stronger than ideal, and the thing that was between them sprang from emotion rather than mind. It was unreasoning, and as ineluctable as the flight of time. Grandma Redding was the outright inheritor of a historical situation.

But not so Grandma Conway. She had assumed—not to say usurped—both the privileges and the penalties of a tradition that was hers only disingenuously, and therefore all the more fiercely held. The privileges gave her power; the penalties strength. She was certain of her values and she held them to be inviolate. She believed in a personal God and that He was in His heaven and all was right with the world. She believed in a rigid code of morality, but in a double standard, because she believed that there was something in the male animal that made him naturally incontinent, and that some women, always of a class she scornfully pitied, had no other purpose in life than to save good women from men's incontinence. In her notion, such women were not loose any more than rutting bitches were loose. A loose woman was a woman of her own class who had wilfully assumed the privileges and shunned the penalties of her birth. Such women she hated with face-purpling hatred. She believed in banks and schools and prisons. She believed that the world was so ordered that in the end his just desserts came to every man. This latter belief was very comprehensive, for she thought in terms of reciprocal responsibility of man and his class—that man did not live for himself alone and that he could not escape the general defections (she called it "sin") of the group into which he was born.

These beliefs must have been conspicuous to Grandma Conway's most casual acquaintance, but to me—and I have no doubt, to the rest of us long familiar with them—they were past both realizing and remarking, like the skin of one's body.

But realization of her most occult belief must have come quite early. Perhaps it came to me in 1917, when, on one of her visits, she first found the lower boundary of our neighborhood roiling with strange black folk and brazen with conspicuous life. It may have come to me imperceptibly, along with the consciousness of the stigma attaching to blackness of skin. But this stigma was a blemish, not a taint. A black skin was uncomely, but not inferior. My father was less beautiful than my mother, but he was not inferior to her. There were soot-black boys whom I knew in school who could outrun, outplay, and outthink me, but they were less personable than I. And certainly we did not think in any conscious way that Grandma Redding was a lesser person than Grandma Conway. The very core of awareness was this distinction.

But gradually, subtly, depressingly and without shock there entered into my consciousness the knowledge that Grandma Conway believed that a black skin was more than a blemish. In her notion it was a taint of flesh and bone and blood, varying in degree with the color of the skin, overcome sometimes by certain material distinctions and the grace of God, but otherwise fixed in the blood.

To Grandma Conway, as to my mother, our new neighbors on the east were a threat.

In our house a compromise was struck. No one ever talked about it. In the careless flow of our talk, it was the one subject avoided with meticulous concern. My parents were stern disciplinarians, and this subject was so fraught with punishable possibilities and yet so conscious a part of our living that by the time the three older ones of us were in grammar and high school our care for the avoidance of it took on at times an almost hysterical intensity. Many a time, as we heard schoolmates do and as we often did ourselves outside, one or the other of us wished to hurl the epithet "black" or "nigger," or a combination, and dared only sputter, "You, you . . . monkey!" For being called a monkey was not considered half so grave an insult as being called the other; and it was at least as grave a sin to avoid as using the Lord's name in vain. My parents, of course, never used either black or nigger, and avoided mentioning color in describing a person. One was either dark or light, never black or yellow—and between these two was that indeterminate group of browns of which our family was largely composed. We grew up in the very center of a complex.

I think my older brother and sister escaped most of the adolescent emotional conflict and vague melancholy (it came later to them, and especially to my brother, and in decidedly greater force) which were the winds of my course through teenhood. For me it was a matter of choices, secret choices really. For them there was no choice. And yet I had less freedom than they. They went off to a New England college in 1919. Up to then their associates had been first the white and then the mulatto children on our street. Even the children whom they met in high school were largely of the mulatto group, for the dark tide of migration had not then swept the schools. Going to school was distinctly an upper-class pursuit, and the public school was almost as exclusive as the summer playground which Miss Grinnage conducted along stubbornly select lines for "children of the best blood" (it was her favorite phrase), almost as exclusive as the Ethical Culture lectures we attended once each month, or the basement chapel of St. Andrews Episcopal church, where Father Tatnall held segregated services for us twice a month. For my older brother and sister, the road through childhood was straight, without sideroads or crossings.

But by the time I reached high school in the fall of 1919, life was undergoing a tumultuous change. It was as if a placid river had suddenly broken its banks and in blind and senseless rage was destroying old landmarks, leveling the face of the country farther and farther beyond the shore line.

The migrants not only discovered our neighborhood, they discovered the church where we went to Sunday school and where my father was superintendent. They discovered the vast, beautiful reaches of the Brandywine where we used to walk on fair Sundays. They discovered the school. I remember the sickening thrill with which I heard a long-headed black boy arraign the mulatto teachers for always giving the choice parts in plays, the choice chores, the cleanest books to mulatto children. He called the teachers "color-struck," a phrase that was new to me, and "sons-of-bitches," a phrase that was not. He was put out of school. Many black children were put out of school, or not encouraged to continue. Two incidents stand out in my mind.

In my first oratorical competition, I knew—as everyone else knew—that the contestant to beat was a gangling dark fellow named Tom Cephus. He had a fervor that I did not have and for which I was taught to substitute craft. His voice, already changed, boomed with a vibrant quality that was impressive to hear. Moreover, he was controlled, self-possessed, and I was not. For days before the competition I was unable to rest, and when I did finally face the audience, I uttered a sentence or two and from sheer fright and nervous exhaustion burst into uncontrollable tears. Somehow, bawling like a baby, I got through. I was certain that I had lost.

Cephus in his turn was superb. The greater part of the audience was with him. Beyond the first rows of benches, which were friendly to me, stretched row after increasingly dark row of black faces and beaming eyes. It was more than an oratorical contest to them. It was a class and caste struggle as intense as any they would ever know, for it was immediate and possible of compromise and assuagement, if not of victory. Mouths open, strained forward, they vibrated against that booming voice, transfixed in ecstasy. The applause was deafening and vindicative. In the back of the crowded hall someone led three cheers for Cephus (a wholly unheard-of thing) and while the teacher-judges were conferring, cheer after cheer swelled from the audience like the approaching, humming, booming bursting of ocean waves.

A pulsing hush fell on them when the judges returned. They watched the announcer as leashed and hungry dogs watch the approach of food. But the judge was shrewd. She wanted that excitement to simmer down. Flicking a smile at the first rows, she calmly announced the singing of a lullaby and waited, a set smile on her face, until three verses had been sung. Then icily, in sprung-steel Bostonian accents, she announced to an audience whose soft-skinned faces gradually froze in spastic bewilderment, "Third place, Edith Miller. Second place, Thomas Cephus. First place . . ." My name was lost in a void of silence. "Assembly dismissed!"

Stunned beyond expression and feeling, the back rows filed out. The front rows cheered. Cephus's lips worked and he looked at me. I could not look at him. I wanted to fall on my knees.

I was truant from school for a week. When my parents discovered it, I took my punishment without a word. A little later that year, Cephus dropped out of school.

But I was stubborn in my resistance to these lessons. My stubbornness was not a rational thing arrived at through intellection. It was not as simple and as hard as that. I was not a conscious rebel. I liked people, and, for all the straitening effects of environment, I was only lightly color-struck. A dark skin was perhaps not as comely as a brown or yellow, but it was sometimes attractive. In matters of class morality and custom and thought I was perhaps too young to make distinctions. I liked people. When I was sixteen and a senior in high school, I liked a doe-soft black girl named Viny. After school hours, Viny was a servant girl to kindly, dumpy, near-white Miss Kruse, the school principal, who lived across the street from us. I saw a good bit of Viny, for I ran Miss Kruse's confidential errands and did innumerable small things for her. There was nothing clandestine about my relations with her servant girl. We talked and joked in the kitchen. We sometimes walked together from school. We were frequently alone in the house.

But one day Miss Kruse called me to the front porch, where in fine, warm weather she ensconced herself in a rocker especially braced to support her flabby weight. She sat with her back turned squarely to the street. She was very fair, and because she ate heavily of rich, heavy foods, at forty-five she was heavy-jowled, with a broad, pleasant, doughy face. A sack of flesh swelled beneath her chin and seemed to hold her mouth open in a tiny O. She was reading.

"Sit down," she said.

I sat in the chair next to hers, but facing the street, so that we could look directly at each other. Both sides of the street were still lined with trees at that time, and it was June. Hedges were green. Miss Kruse read for a while longer, then she crumpled the paper against herself and folded her fingers over it.

"You like Viny, don't you?" she asked, looking at me with a heavy frown.

"Yes, ma'am," I said.

"Well, you be careful. She'll get you in trouble," she said.

"Trouble?"

"How would you like to marry her?"

I did not answer, for I did not know what to say.

"How?"

"I don't know'm."

This provoked her. She threw the newspaper on the floor. The network of fine pink veins on the lobes of her nose turned purple.

"Well, let her alone! Or she'll trap you to marry her. And what would you look like married to a girl like that?" she said bitingly. "No friends, no future. You might as well be dead! How would you like to spend the rest of your life delivering ice or cleaning outdoor privies? Don't you know girls like her haven't any shame, haven't any decency? She'll get you in trouble."

I stared stupidly at her. I do not know what my reaction was. I remember being confused and hotly embarrassed, and after that a kind of soggy lethargy settled in my stomach, like indigestible food. I distinctly remember that I felt no resentment and no shock, and that my confusion was due less to this first frank indictment of blackness than to the blunt reference to sex. Boys talked about sex in giggly whispers among themselves, but between male and female talk of sex was taboo. In the midst of my embarrassment, I heard Miss Kruse's voice again, calm and gentle now, persuasive, admonitory.

"You're going to college. You're going to get a fine education. You're going to be somebody. You'll be ashamed you ever knew Viny. There'll be fine girls for you to know, to marry."

She sighed, making a round sound of it through her O-shaped mouth, and rubbing her hands hard together as if they were cold.

"Viny. Well, Viny won't ever be anything but what she is already."

And what is she? And what and where are the others? One, who wore the flashy clothes and made loud laughter in the halls, is now a man of God, a solemn, earnest pulpiteer. Cephus, the boy who won and lost, is dead. And Pogie Walker's dead. It is remarkable how many of those I came to know in 1919 are dead. Birdie, Sweetie Pie, and Oliver. Viny? After she quit and moved away, she used to write me once a year on cheap, lined paper. "I'm doing alrite." (She never learned to spell.) "I'm living alrite. I gess I'm geting along alrite. How do these few lines fine you?" And Brunson, the smartest of that migrant lot, who outran, outfought, outthought all of us. He was expelled for writing a letter and passing it among the students. Most of the things he said were true—the exclusion of the very black from the first yearbook, the way one teacher had of referring to the black-skinned kids as "You, Cloudy, there," and never remembering their names. Well, Brunson is a week-end drunk. At other times he's very bitter. Not long ago I saw him. I spoke to him. "You don't remember me," I said. "Yeah. I remember you all right. So what?" He lives down on the east side, way down, where in the spring the river comes.

6

Miss Kruse was right in this: I did go to college.

My mother was recently dead, and a temporary sentimental weakness settled on my father. He did not wish me to go far from home. He considered me too young in 1923 to go off alone to the college in New England from which my brother had just been graduated. I had first to spend a year at Lincoln University, a Negro college run by a white Presbyterian church board in Pennsylvania, only twenty-odd miles from home. That I should go to college was a matter of course. I was just seventeen, and I felt no compelling drive. There was nothing in particular that I wanted to learn, and I had given no thought to a career. The driven, sharp ambition of some of the chaps (and especially those from the South) I met there surprised and bewildered me. They seemed to me to have a brazen, articulating cunning. They thought of education exclusively in terms of prestige value. They wanted to be doctors and lawyers—doctors mostly —professions to which they referred as "rackets." There was money in them, and they were motivated by the desire to possess, as indeed they put it, yellow money, yellow cars, and yellow women. They studied textbooks to that end. Almost none of them did any reading beyond the requirements of courses. Each had a singleness of purpose that seemed to me even then as ruthless and as uninspired as the flame of an acetylene torch. It was deadly. It was unmixed with either cynicism or idealism. All their instincts, all their forces were channelized to flow in one swift, hard, straight stream, to settle at last in a kind of dull gray lake of fulfillment.

Perhaps this would have been better for me. But I could not see life with such baneful certainty. There stirred sluggishly

in me a consciousness of certain incommensurables that could
not be measured out in the scales of personal ambition, a certain
imponderability that could not be weighed in terms of biology,
chemistry, civics, and Greek—or in any other terms of which
I knew. I could not spin in a whirring cosmos of my own crea-
tion, as the others did. I could not create a cosmos; I haunted
others. I could not even spin; I wobbled.

I was lonely a good deal. I studied enough, but with no other
purpose than to put a face on things, to make a pretense of
ambition that I did not have, for I was ashamed of my groping
uncertainty. I read with indiscriminate avidity. The library was
open only two hours a day, but I got special permission and a
key and spent greedy hours there. Most of the books were old,
and three-fourths of them on theology, but in a tumulus of dust
I found Stendhal, Meredith, Thackeray, Trevelyan, Bierce,
Miller, William James, Dreiser, Henry George, and a half-
dozen paper-bound plays by Sedley, Wycherley, and Congreve,
which, I am certain, Professor Labaree did not know were
there. On Sunday nights I walked four miles to a mission church
and listened to the singing of such starkly primitive and beautiful music as I had never heard. At the end of my first year, I
transferred to Brown, in Providence, and no one at Lincoln
missed me.

There were two other Negroes at Brown, both seniors at the
time, and Clyde Bastrop came in my second year. Bastrop and I
could have roomed together at a saving, but we did not, for we
took elaborate precautions against even the appearance of clannishness. I had found this peculiar behavior in the two seniors,
and apparently it had come down to them from a long, thin line
of Negro students. Yet among them there must have been a
terrific consciousness of kind, just as there was between Bastrop
and me. Our denials of this consciousness sometimes took the
most exaggerated forms. We made a great show of not seeking
each other's companionship, meeting always apparently by accident, and never in the Union or the Commons or the library,
and only in each other's rooms at night with the shades drawn.

We never ate together. We recognized no snubs or slights from white associates. We did not even talk of them to each other in the secret of our rooms at night with the shades down. Once in a biology class, the instructor, a man from Tennessee, referred to "niggers" in a humorous, insulting way, but I said nothing. Once a professor committed an act of discrimination so flagrant that even one of his assistants rebelled, but I pretended not to notice. Bastrop and I underwent a kind of purge, but we denied any sense of martyrdom. We were lost in the sacrificial, foreordained, pitilessly wretched way in which the not-quite-saved are lost. But we were not alone. Negro boys in colleges all over New England were also lost; and on occasional very rowdy, very unrestrained parties in Boston we cemented with them a desperate bond of frustration.

These parties were the measure of our tense neurosis, our desperation. I see that now. With an abiding strain of puritanism, I was inclined in those years to put an undue weight of moral significance upon the sins we committed. For days after a week end saved from utter beastliness only by a certain controlling melancholy cynicism, a sort of soul-sickness, I suffered an agony of remorse. I reviled and despised myself. I hated the housemaids, the elevator girls, the hairdressers, and the occasional college girls who shared our unrestraint. But I went again. I always went, as a sick dog returns to his vomit. That shameless bitchery! Those shoddy, temporarily freeing, hysterical bacchanalia!

We thought we had the strained, fine courage of strong men who are doomed and know they are doomed. In reality we carried on a sort of blind quest for disaster, for demotic and moral suicide outside the harbors of sanity.

It was following one of these parties in the late winter of 1926 that Bastrop left. Still red-eyed with sleeplessness, he came to my room in Hope College. He was a round-faced boy, extroverted, I thought, and with a capacity for playing practical jokes of a complicated nature. But this day he was subdued, looking inward upon himself and not liking what he saw.

"I'm leaving," he said, without preliminaries.

"Leaving school, you mean?"

"Yes," he said, and fell silent. He sat on the bed and leaned backward on his elbows. Then he turned over and lay with his chin on his fist, staring at the wall. Around his eyes the skin was almost white, as if he had worn dark glasses in the hot sun for a long time. He raised his head and said, "Yes. I'm leaving."

"But why?" I asked. "What's eating you?"

With a sudden twisting movement he was up and sitting on the edge of the bed, hunched over, hard-drawn. I knew he was not joking.

"There must be some place better than this. God damn it, there must be! I can find a place somewhere. This isn't the place for me. I feel like everybody's staring at me, all these white guys, waiting for me to make a bad break. Things I'd do without thinking about them, I do now like they were the most important things in the whole damned world. How the hell do you stand it? We're always talking about being casual. All right. But what do we do?" He got up nervously, but sat down again almost at once. "I'll tell you good and damn well what we do! We put on the damnedest airs in the world. We're showing off. Casually, casually, by Christ! And yet everything comes so hard you can hear us breathing way over on George Street. I'm sick of being casual! I want to be honest and sincere about something. I want to stop feeling like I'll fall apart if I unclench my teeth. Oh Christ!"

He looked wretched. He sat there on the edge of the bed with his hands in his pockets and his shoulders drawn in a hard curve, as if he were out in the cold without an overcoat. The religious medallion which he wore on a silver chain around his neck had worked through his shirt and he seemed to be staring at it.

"Listen, Bastrop," I said.

He looked up. "Listen, hell! I'm tired of listening," he said angrily.

It was just as well, for I do not know what I would have said. There is no answer to truth. I do not know what I thought or felt other than the need to retreat from the truth against which all my defenses had toppled. Suddenly all my resiliency was gone. I started to make some tea, but even as I made it, I knew that tea-making was another bluff, a flimsy protective device, like our careful speech, our careful avoidance of clannishness, and I knew at the same time that these things were necessary to us in the same way a sheath is necessary to a sword. I did not want to lose my hard, fine edge, as Bastrop was doing, I thought cynically.

"That was a hell of a party in Springfield," I said.

Bastrop looked up with angry eagerness. "Did you see Jerry?" Jerry was a girl we knew from Philadelphia who was a student in Boston.

"Yes. Sure."

"Listen. Do you enjoy those breakdowns? Do you really have fun?"

"Sure. Yes," I said.

"All that hog-wallowing?"

"It's something to do. You got to do something."

He looked at me with strange aversion, I thought. But his thoughts were not on me, for he said:

"Jerry enjoyed it. She actually got a kick out of it," he said, as if he could not believe it. "And when a girl like that enjoys that . . . Well, we were dancing," he said, as if he were wretchedly eager to get something off his mind. "We were dancing and she said she was enjoying it, said she was going to be herself. She wasn't drunk then either. She didn't get drunk until later. You saw how drunk she got. She got pie-eyed."

"Why did you take her in the first place?" I said. "You knew what kind of party it was going to be."

"I don't know," he said miserably.

"Did you . . . ?"

He looked at me for a wild, frightened, shamefaced moment and dropped his head. I diverted myself in sham anger.

"So that's the real reason you're leaving. You're afraid," I said.

He stood up. "Afraid? Afraid? Yes, God damn it! I'm afraid.

But I'm not afraid of what you think. I'm afraid of getting like the rest of the guys. I'm afraid of not having anything inside, of getting so that if anybody touches me I'll fall apart. I've still got enough left to know that there's something wrong with this, and I'm leaving before that goes too!"

That night Bastrop left on the night boat. I never saw him again, for in the late spring he killed himself in the bathroom of his parents' home in Cleveland. He was the first of five suicides in a half-dozen years from that group I knew in New England. Two of them were girls. By any reckoning, this is a high percentage. Excluding that numerous crowd of fourflushers who took an evening course here and there in the various colleges in Boston, there were not more than fifteen of us who knew each other intimately as fellow collegians.

7

In my senior year I met Lebman. For several lonely months I had been the only Negro in the college, and the sense of competitive enmity, which began to develop slowly in me in my second year, was now at its height. It was more than a sense of competition. It was a perverted feeling of fighting alone against the whole white world. I raged with secret hatred and fear. I hated and feared the whites. I hated and feared and was ashamed of Negroes. (The memory of it even now is painful to me.) I shunned contacts with the general run of the latter, confining myself to the tight little college group centered around Boston. But even this group was no longer as satisfying as once it had been, and I gradually withdrew from it, though the bond of frustration was strong. But my own desperation was stronger. I wished to be alone. My room in University Hall had almost no visitors, but it was peopled by a thousand nameless fears.

Furtively trying to burn out the dark, knotted core of emotion, I wrote acidulous verse and sent bitter essays and stories to various Negro magazines. One editor wrote, "You must be crazy!" Perhaps I was. I was obsessed by nihilistic doctrine. Democracy? It was a failure. Religion? A springe to catch woodcocks. Truth? There was no objective ground of truth, nothing outside myself that made morality a principle. Destroy and destroy, and perhaps, I remember writing cynically, "from the ashes of nothingness will spring a phoenix not altogether devoid of beauty." All my thoughts and feelings were but symptomatic of a withering, grave sickness of doubt.

And then I met Lebman.

He was a Jew. He had lived across the hall from me since the fall, and I had seen him once or twice in only the most casual way. Then late one night he knocked at my door. When I opened it, he was standing there pale and smiling, a lock of damp, dark hair falling across his wide, knotty forehead.

"I saw your light. Do you mind if I ask you something?" he said diffidently.

"Come in," I said automatically; but all my defenses immediately went up.

Still smiling shyly, he came into the room and stood in the center of the floor. He carried a book in his hand, his longer fingers marking the place. He was wearing pajamas and a robe. I remember I did not close the door nor sit down at first, but stood awkwardly waiting, trying to exorcise my suspicion and fear. He looked around the room with quiet, friendly curiosity.

"I've been reading your stuff in the *Quarterly*," he said. "It's good."

"Thanks," I said. And I remember thinking, 'Don't try to flatter me, damn you. I don't fall for that stuff.' Then I tried to get ahold of myself, groping at my tangled feelings with clumsy fingers of thought in an action almost physical. "Thanks."

"I think you're after something," he said. It was a cliché, and I did not like talking about my writing. It was always like undressing before strangers. But Lebman was sincere, and now unembarrassed.

"You do?" I said, trying to say it in a tone that would end it.

"Yes."

"Why?"

"Oh, it's plain in your writing. You know, I correct papers

in philosophy too. Your paper on Unamuno, it was plain there. That paper was all right too."

"I wish I knew what I was after, or that I was after something," I said defensively, cynically. I closed the door. Then in the still, sharp silence that followed, I moved to the desk and turned the chair to face the other chair in the corner. Lebman sat down.

"What I came in to see you about was this," he said, holding the book up. And in another moment, without really asking me anything, he had plunged into a brilliant, brooding discussion of Rudolph Fisher's *Walls of Jericho*, the book he held in his hand, and of men and books. I listened captiously at first. He did not speak in the rhapsodic way of one who merely loves books and life. He spoke as one who understands and both loves and hates. He sat in the chair in the corner, where the light from the reading lamp fell upon his pale face, his narrow, angular shoulders. Through the window at his elbow we could see the mist-shrouded lights outlining the walks of the middle campus. Lebman talked and talked. I listened.

I do not remember all he said between that midnight and dawn, but one thing I do remember.

"I'm a Jew. I tried denying it, but it was no use. I suppose everyone at some time or other tries to deny some part or all of himself. Suicides, some crazy people go all the way. But spiritual schizophrenes aren't so lucky as suicides and the hopelessly insane. I used to think that only certain Jews suffered from this —the Jews who turn Christian and marry Christian and change their names from Lowenstein to Lowe and Goldberg to Goldsborough and still aren't happy. But they're not the only ones. Fisher makes a point of that. I thought so until I read him. You ought to read him, if you haven't."

"I've read him," I said, trying to remember the point.

"Schizophrenia in the mind, that's the curse of God; but in the spirit, it's man's curse upon himself. It took me a long time —all through college, through three years of reading manuscripts for a publisher, through another two years of graduate school—it took me years to realize what a thing it is. I'm a thirty-six-year-old bird, and I've only just found my roost.

"That's what you want, a roost, a home. And not just a place to hang your hat, but someplace where your spirit's free, where you belong. That's what everybody wants. Not a place in space, you understand. Not a marked place, geographically bounded. Not a place at all, in fact. It's hard to tell to others," he said. "But it's a million things and people, a kind of life and thought that your spirit touches, absorbed and absorbing, understood and understanding, and feels completely free and whole and one."

That midnight conversation—though it was scarcely that—recurred to me many times in the years immediately following.

When I came up for graduation in 1928, it still had not occurred to me to think of finding work to do that would turn my education to some account. My brother had been graduated from Harvard Law, and I thought randomly of earning money to follow him there. My credits were transferred. But I earned very little and I could discover in myself no absorbing interest, no recognition of a purpose. The summer blazed along to August. Then, out of the blue, John Hope offered me a job at Morehouse College in Atlanta. I took it. I was twenty-one in October of that fall, a lonely, random-brooding youth, uncertain, purposeless, lost, and yet so tightly wound that every day I lived big-eyed as death in sharp expectancy of a mortal blow or a vitalizing fulfillment of the unnamable aching emptiness within me.

But Morehouse College and the southern environment disappointed me. The college tottered with spiritual decay. Its students were unimaginative, predatory, pretentious. Theirs was a naked, metal-hard world, stripped of all but its material values, and these glittered like artificial gems in the sun of their ambition. An unwholesome proportion of the faculty was effete, innocuous, and pretentious also, with a flabby softness of intellectual and spiritual fiber and even a lack of personal force. They clustered together like sheared sheep in a storm. They were a sort of mass-man, conscious of no spiritual status even as men, much less as a people. They were a futile, hamstrung group, who took a liberal education (they despised mechanical and technical learning) to be a process of devitalization and to be significant in extrinsics only. They awarded a lot of medallions and watch charms. Try as I might, I could feel no kinship with them. Obviously my home was not among them.

I thought often of Lebman in the pre-dawn quiet of my room, saying, "Not a place in geography, but a million things and people your spirit touches, absorbed and absorbing." I did not want sanctuary, a soft nest protected from the hard, strengthening winds that blew hot and cold through the world's teeming, turbulent valley. I wanted to face the wind. I wanted the strength to face it to come from some inexpressibly deep well of feeling of oneness with the wind, of belonging to something, some soul-force outside myself, bigger than myself, but yet a part of me. Not family merely, or institution, or race; but a people and all their topless strivings; a nation and its million destinies. I did not think in concrete terms at first. Indeed, I had but the shadow of this thought and feeling. But slowly the shadow grew, taking form and outline, until at last I felt and knew that my estrangement from my fellows and theirs from me was but a failure to realize that we were all estranged from something fundamentally ours. We were all withdrawn from the heady, brawling, lusty stream of culture which had nourished us and which was the stream by whose turbid waters all of America fed. We were spiritually homeless, dying and alone, each on his separate hammock of memory and experience.

This was emotional awareness. Intellectual comprehension came slowly, painfully, as an abscess comes. I laid no blame beyond immediate experience. Through hurt and pride and fear, they of this class (and of what others I did not know) had deliberately cut themselves off not only from their historical past but also from their historical future. Life had become a matter of asylum in some extra time-sphere whose hard limits were the rising and the setting sun. Each day was another and a different unrelated epoch in which they had to learn again the forgetting of ancestral memory, to learn again to bar the senses from the sights and sounds and tastes of a way of life that they denied, to close the mind to the incessant close roar of a world to which they felt unrelated. This vitiated them, wilted them, dwarfed their spirits, and they slunk about their gray astringent world like ghosts from the shores of Lethe.

I tried fumblingly to tell them something of this, for my desire for spiritual wholeness was great. I yearned for some closer association with these men and women, some bond that was not knit of frustration and despair. In impersonal terms I tried to tell them something of this. They snubbed me. They looked upon me as a pariah who would destroy their societal bond, their asylum. They called me fool—and perhaps I was. Certainly I was presumptuous. Their whispers and their sterile laughter mocked me. They were at pains to ridicule me before the students. They called me radical, and it was an expletive the way they used it, said in the same way that one calls another a snake. For three years I held on, and then I was fired.

But my seeking grew in intensity and the need to find became an ache almost physical. For seven, eight years after that I sought with the same frantic insatiability with which one lives through a brutal, lustful dream. It was planless seeking, for I felt then that I would not know the thing I sought until I found it. It was both something within and something without myself. Within, it was like the buried memory of a name that will not come to the tongue for utterance. Without, it was the muffled roll of drums receding through a darkling wood. And so, restricted in ways I had no comprehension of, I sought, and everywhere—because I sought among the things and folk I knew—I went unfinding.

CHAPTER TWO

Don't Be Weary, Traveler

I

IN 1940, with funds provided by the Rockefeller Foundation, the University of North Carolina invited me to do a job. The assignment was so simple and direct that Mr. Couch and I had to talk it over a half-dozen times. Sitting in his cool office in Chapel Hill, Mr. Couch said, "Go out into Negro life in the South. Go anywhere you like." It was as simple as that.

"All right," I said. "But I can't promise you what I'll find." I was still questing, still lost.

"If you could, there'd be no need to send you," Mr. Couch said.

I knew what they wanted and I thought I knew vaguely what I wanted, and the two things were not the same. Their wants were simple and direct. Mine seemed neither. I had no trouble getting a leave from teaching. "Good luck," Mr. Couch said, and I went up into Delaware to take leave of my family.

"Be careful," my father warned. My brother said, "Watch those crackers down there." My son put his five-year-old hand in mine, gave me a wet kiss, and went scooting off. My wife held me close for a moment and whispered, rather tensely, as if she were charging me, I thought, "It's all right. This time you're going to find it."

I was not so sure. I think I was frowning and disturbed as I meshed the gears and headed south through Maryland—Elkton, Havre de Grace, and Baltimore. Once through Washington, I thought, I would not care what road I took, so long as it led south. I did not even consult the maps. I was looking for people, for things, for *something*.

Who were these people? What were these things, this something? I did not know. My mind was uneasy, bedeviled by vague doubts. It seemed to me that I was looking for stability in a world that had been slowly disintegrating for a dozen years, and now, half of it at war, was breaking up very fast. No one seemed to know the values that would be preserved, or even those worth preserving. The depression seemed a final paralysis before the death of a way of life that men had thought enduring. The first rantings of a national political campaign were like a monstrous death rattle. Perhaps, I thought, what you will find in this already dying world will not be valid for the world that comes after. The world *I* know, I thought. So? Well and good.

But even as I thought this defiance, I felt my courage dwindle and the long fingers of my memory reach for a saving straw in the dark sea of the past. I had long since forgotten nihilism. Destruction there was and would be. But always there was building, too, however inept, and always something better, finer. This was platitudinous thinking, pretentious thinking, and I did not like it; but it was my thinking all the same, and there was nothing I could do about it.

The world is dying, I thought; think back over the values you were taught and see if there are any worth saving. Think! I thought. There were the bread-and-butter values, the Rockefeller and Morgan values. There were the intellectual values, about which my notions were hobbled with certain irritating inconsistencies. There were the Christian values, all turned into formulas for material success. And there were those uncertain values memorably represented for me in the brilliantly colored stereopticon slides of famous paintings that were the delight of my childhood. As one who held these things valid, I was an atom of humanity, a man, a public-schooled American, conscious of having in these things a common bond with other Americans. But if the disturbed days of my youth had taught me any lesson it was that I was also a Negro, that as such, there were other values, other validities (no one ever told me what these were), and that these must be, had of necessity to be, I was taught, prescinded from the consideration of my manhood, my common heritage, my Americanism. One was never told, "You are a man." It was always, "You are a Negro." I knew no more now what these values were than when I was a wide-eyed child. Everyone spoke of them and I had seen men weep over them, but no one seemed to know what they were. I was doubtful of ever discovering.

What validity? What reality for this dying world of men and Negroes? It was the old question, but asked myself with the impatient urgency of necessity, for if there were such values, then the discovery of them seemed the very core of the job I had to do.

Lost in Washington late at night, so that I had to inquire my way from a policeman, who asked me very appropriately where I was going, and who said suspiciously, "It's pretty late, ain't it, buddy?" I became platitudinous. "Courage and brotherhood and justice are eternally valid," I remember thinking. "And goodness of heart—the full round sum of the fixed values of humanity." By this means I shut out reality a little longer.

Like an opiate, this sufficed me in that slow, night-long drive. But when the east turned milky and things that had been shadows took on the solidity of form and substance, I approached reality.

In the early morning I found myself climbing a long hill. It had been beautiful country for many miles through the milky, pink-gray dawn, and now dawn was full and the land loped out in many hills and rolled away to other hills that one felt must lie beyond. As I climbed the slope into the town and the first gray houses began, my memory stirred, for surely I had passed through Fairfax and Bull Run in the dark and this was Warrenton, and somewhere around the curve at the top of the hill must be the shop where Grandfather Holmes had made fine carriages so many years ago. I did not see it. Perhaps it was no longer there. I put that kind of memory away. I saw the low-walled, new-brick fronts of chain grocery and drugstores, filling stations, and shops. High-raised above the narrow pavement and crowning the hill were the long flank and the first high columns of the Court House.

A dozen Negro men sat on the steep steps of the Court House in an attitude of expectancy. They were not talking, but sitting tensely, their heads turned to watch the approach of my car. One or two of them had blankets draped around their shoulders, and one of them had risen and stood watching, poised to leap. When they saw the car, they seemed to relax a little. Wondering why they were there, I drove past them down the main street. The narrow, stony streets of the town fell away from the main street in all directions. The short business section and the houses beyond it were still quiet with sleep, and the pathlike streets, flanked with trees, were gray and damp in the morning. The sun had not yet sliced through the hills. I went back to the Court House to inquire for a place to eat.

There was a truck at the curb now, and three or four of the men were down on the pavement talking to the red-faced driver, who sat looking carelessly down on them from the cab of the truck. The driver was not talking, just looking down on them and smiling carelessly. Voices were loud but indistinct. They made sharp sounds in the empty morning. Most of the men on the steps were standing now, and all of them were listening. As I approached, the men on the pavement scrabbled for the cab door, pushing, pulling, and cursing each other. Their words were quite clear now. Their faces were distorted with angry effort. The driver, grinning, raced the motor premonitorily and opened his mouth and laughed. Finally, one of the men, pushing off his fellows, scrambled to the cab and held on precariously, kicking out with his feet as another clutched wildly at him and the truck lumbered and then raced past me down the hill. One of the men ran a few desperate steps after the truck. The driver was grinning sardonically.

Curious, I pulled up to the curb, but already the men were settling back into an attitude of expectant waiting and the talk of what I had just seen was dead. They eyed me with hard-eyed, resentful unconcern. The length of the street was beginning to move now; a car or two and a truck went by. The men's eyes followed these things until they disappeared around the curve and down the hill. I did not know whether to join them or to call. I called, and finally, after looking at the others and back at me, one of the men whom I recognized as having fought for a place on the truck pulled himself together and came down. He was a young, hard-faced, brown fellow.

"Is there a colored hotel in this town?" I asked. "Any place to eat?"

"Hoe-tel? Naw," he said. "On'ies' place I know of's maybe Shepard's. Been there?" He told me that Shepard's place was in Fishtown. Then, mumbling, "I ain't doin' nothin' noway," he climbed in beside me. The men watched without a word as we pulled off.

"What do those fellows do, sleep there all night?" I asked.

"Some of them, near 'bout."

"Why?"

He gave me a queer, sidelong look, and a hard smile curled at the corner of his thick mouth. "Not meanin' to give you no short answer: 'cause they's crazy as hell. Me 'long with 'em."

He did not smell very good. His hands were crusty with dirt and there was dirt ground into his slick-looking trousers, and his throat was lined with clean lines between patches of dirt. He smelled as if he had slept in his clothes for several nights. I judged him to be in his early twenties.

"The white folks has got us beat, man. Got us beat," he said ruefully, with resentment, but without emphasis.

I made no comment. At his direction we turned left into a steep, pebbly street between the blind side of a low building and a weed-grown field. As we went down, the field rose higher on our right until we were riding under the lip of it. The houses of the main section of the town had disappeared and no others were in sight. It was very quiet in the undisturbed morning and the town seemed far away. Then suddenly I saw the first Negro dwelling, a shanty. It was built against the hill, on high spindling

piles. Other dwellings similarly built lay on insecure shelves
farther down. The street had become little more than a cattle
path. There were no pavements, just rutted, pebbly footpaths a
few inches wide. The shanties looked as if they had been built
to meet an emergency and the emergency had lasted fifty years.

"There we set on our tails. Set there from two or three in the
mornin'— Chilly! My God, you don't know how chilly it can
git settin' on your tail that time o' mornin' an' the win' slippin'
off'n the hills. Set there waitin' for some white man to come
along an' ast us, 'Boys, want a day's work?' He ain't talkin' to
nobody in perticuler, so we all rushes down. We don't ast him
no questions. He jus' tell us. Then he takes the one that 'grees to
the less money."

"What kind of work is it?"

"Truckin' stuff up the country. You gather an' load all day,
then drive all night an' unload when you git to Philly or New
York. Then you drive back. You might pick up a coupl'a bucks."

"And sometimes you squabble over that?"

"Yeah," he said.

"Why don't you get together on it?"

"Hunh!" he grunted disdainfully. "D'you ever hear tell o'
niggahs gittin' together on anything?"

We stopped in front of the shanty he indicated. It did not
look like a restaurant, except that there was a new Coca-Cola
sign painted over the sagging door. The flight of steps leading
up from the path looked dangerously rickety, and the whole
place appeared quite lifeless. Inside, a rough makeshift counter
ran along one wall, and there was a table with a cracked enamel
top and three cane chairs. The wooden walls were bright with
soft-drink ads, but soot and dust hung in feathery plumes from
the ceiling and from the screen over the only window. A slatternly woman with the twisted mouth of a paralytic brushed
through the cretonne curtain that separated the dining room
from the kitchen.

"What you got this mornin'?" my companion asked.

"Same thing," the woman answered, her voice coming wet and flat through her twisted lips.

"Ain't got no sausage meat?"

"You ain't fixin' t'eat, is you?"

"I brung you some trade," my companion said, smiling crookedly.

I could not tell whether the jerked movement of the good side of the woman's face was meant for a smile. The left side of her face was drawn as if it had been burnt, hiking the corner of her mouth away from her teeth in an unsightly sneer and the corner of her eye down so that the inside of the underlid showed a tumid red.

"That ain't what I ast you. I ast you was you fixin' t'eat."

" 'Cordin' to what you got," he said shortly.

"Marie was here," the woman said. "An' my ol' man was in here when she come."

"So what?" His brows thickened. "So what?" he said again.

"Aw, nothin'," the woman said, shrugging and turning to me.

She did not have what I wanted, so I told her to bring me what she had. She brought me the hard curled rind of fried bacon and bacon grease poured over a glutinous mound of gray grits and an egg black from frying in stale grease. She also brought a heavy cup of thick coffee and a cold slab of short-bread.

"What did Marie say?"

"She was talkin' to him," the woman said, sitting down in the third chair at the table.

"Well, what did he say?"

The woman leaned forward suddenly, looking at him. "You know me, Leon. I'd feed you in a minute. But I gotta check with my ol' man. He know how much o' ever'thing's back there. He say white folks checks an' double-checks. That's why they gits along."

"He ain't no white folks," Leon said resentfully.

Diffidently, I suggested that I would pay for his breakfast, but he neither accepted nor rejected my offer. He pushed his cap back from his forehead, revealing a tangled mat of hair. My mind was clutching at every word spoken, trying to wring out its meaning. "He ain't no white folks" and "White folks got us beat" linked up in my mind. I saw in these the unreasoning, pragmatic acceptance of a situation that was the core around which his life was wound. And this acceptance was one of the absolutes of his existence. This was reality for him, and valid. Instinctively he resented any attempt to transgress that validity, for it brought order into his world. In this he had peace. It limited his choices and his decisions, the things he could want and want to be.

"Well, what did Chumby say?"

"He beat up his gums some," the woman said. "He said you was ackin' funny agin. 'Gittin' ready to blow agin, I reckin,' he said. Like you done before. You bes' eat. The man say he pay for it."

She went into the kitchen and brought him a more generous serving of the same food I had. Then she sat down again.

"You fixin' t'leave, sho' nuff?"

"Maybe."

"Marie mus'a tol' him something, 'cause he beat up his gums 'bout you not knowin' when you was good off. He said you couldn' eat no more less you could pay."

Leon ate steadily, like a clumsy automaton of mouth and grasping, lifting hands. For a while he looked neither to right nor to left, and the woman waited. Her red, tumid, crooked eye dropped water almost constantly. She wiped the drops away with the back of her hand. The sun fell in a broken stream through the feathery window.

"Your ol' man can go to hell. Him an' Marie both. Only thing is, when I lef' before, I couldn' git no job. I b'lieve I can git a job this time, if I go far enough. They can go to hell!"

"Git a job doin' what?"

"Any damn thing."

"Settin' on the Court House steps in some other town, waitin'?" the woman said.

"Damn you," Leon said.

"I think jobs are opening up," I said.

"I don't know what gits to ailin' me," Leon said, talking, it seemed, neither to the woman nor to me. "Ever' little bit, I git to feelin' like I got ants in my pants an' I don't want no parts o' Marie. Don't even want to see her. If I didn' set up there on them Court House steps tryin' to make a dollar or two . . ." He broke off abruptly and stared straight at me. "Sleepin' with a woman ain't chow-earnin' work, is it? It ain't ought to fill your belly. Hell!" He gulped the rest of his coffee and jerked his cap down on his head.

"You is ackin' funny," the woman said. "You's lucky, niggah."

Leon looked at her, and spoke through his teeth. "I'm tarred sleepin' with that snuff-dippin' woman jus' t'git me something t'eat."

"Yeah?" the woman said sarcastically.

But Leon did not answer her, and when we opened the door and went out, she was still sitting at the table with the dirty dishes crowding her elbows. The sun lay everywhere outside, as if the earth had been suddenly, gloriously doused in golden paint. Down the row, the shanties trembled in this glory of morning sun, and behind the shanties the hill dipped and then rose liquidly to the streaming light.

"And are you going away?" I said, when I had turned the car and we were going back up the cattle path.

"Maybe," he answered slowly. "There ain't no percentage in stayin' here." But I could see that his mind was not made up and that his resilience was gone. Would there be any "percentage" in going away?

"Where would you go?" I asked.

He turned his eyes slowly upon me. There was no conviction in them. "This is a big country," he said.

I told him I was heading south and asked him if he wished to go along, but the idea did not appeal to him. He seemed to have lost faith in getting a job if he went far enough.

town's old slave-built houses and churches. I walked down Charles Street in the hot evening sun, and along quiet Amelia Street, with its elms and low stone walls and the Confederate cemetery at the end, where a passing Negro told me, "You kin't go in dere. No suh. Dat's white folks." But I went all the same, not in a spirit of defiance, but because I did not wish to feel that the historical dead belonged to white folks any more than to me. I was an heir to history too.

Sitting in my hotel room later, I laid aside *The Negro in Virginia* and looked out the window. My room faced Route 1, fluid with north and south traffic flowing through the heart of the town. Opposite me was a row of old houses, upon which the sun slanted mellowly. I was not thinking—only trying to feel history and looking at the houses across the street. I saw a Negro woman drag a chair out onto the narrow porch of one of the houses. She placed the chair near the door and sat down in the flush of the sun. Then a man came out, bringing a chair with a broken back. Except for the door through which they came, the house was shut and the shades drawn. It was thirsty for paint. There were two small windows, shuttered, and farther down the porch there was another door. It was over this second door that I saw a streaked and dirty legend. It read:

TOURIST WELCOME

HOME

OF

PRESIDENT MONROE

I could not credit my sight. I went down and walked casually to the corner and crossed the street, walking slowly, and read it again. I was not eight feet from it. The man looked at me suspiciously, but the woman's eyes followed me with the sprightly curiosity of a bird's. She looked happily half-witted.

"Have you always lived here?" I asked.

"Born here. And so was she," the man said, nodding toward the woman. He looked about fifty. She was much older. Both were yellow.

"And was this really Monroe's home?"

"You read the sign," he said. "White folks have tried to dispute it, too, but we got proof." He clenched his hand as if the proof were in his hand and he did not intend to let it go.

"I wasn't disputing it," I said.

"Her own father left it to her, and *his* father helped to build it. We got proof," he said truculently.

He answered my good evening with a grunt.

Back in my room, I did not pick up *The Negro in Virginia* again. It was a good book, but it was not history. It was a much better book about Negroes than many I had read before. A spurious, emotionally based dichotomy was one thing, the ignoring of the individual, the denials, the restrictions hampering his civil life had only a perishable significance and was one thing, though a not very good thing. But this separation of a people from its history, this intellectual denial of a people "something to look backward to with pride and forward to with hope" was another thing.

I looked out of the window and saw the old woman sitting in a narrowing swath of sun on the porch of the home of President Monroe. She had moved her chair to follow the sun, and the sunlight bobbled on her as the big vans went by on the highway. She sat in the lax attitude of the old, her hands turned listlessly upward in her lap, her head shaking visibly, and the weight of the years rounding her shoulders.

When I awakened in the early morning, it was already hot. Up the street, where the white hotels and tourist homes began, a white-coated Negro was watering the pavement. The first truck rumbled by toward Washington. Sticking through a little door in the cab behind the driver's head was a pair of black, horny feet. The green, sweet smell of melons and the hot smell of concrete that has not cooled in the night filled the air.

"Did the trucks keep you awake last night?" asked the man who ran the hotel. He laid my place on the table and stood looking down at me with sober-miened solicitude.

"I don't think so," I said. I remembered waking up several times in the night and hearing the traffic, but I do not think it awakened me. All night my head was like a clock that had been wound too tight and would not tick.

"That's good. Route 1 is bad that way with traffic. You have to get use to it. But we live on it. This town lives on tourist trade. We do a wonderful tourist business here."

"You mean the town?"

He stepped back while the girl put the food before me. "Yes. This time of year you can't count the cars. The cars is all right. But them trucks! Us hotel people have been agitatin' around to have a belt line run around for the trucks, not allow 'em to come through the city. But the service stations kicked on that. City council didn't let it go through. It wouldn't hurt us hotel people none. But live and let live, I say. Is everything to your satisfaction?"

He looked over the table, touched the sugar bowl, fiddled the cruets. Then he brought the evening-before paper from behind the counter and left.

In the midst of breakfast, the screen door rattled and a voice full of pleasant raillery spoke to me, calling me "Comrade." I looked up briefly, nodded, and went on reading the paper. The man came to the table and pulled the chair facing me. I looked up now, curious and annoyed, and mocking eyes looked back into mine.

"I hate to drink morning coffee alone," he said, in that derisive tone. "May I join you?"

"You already have," I said.

He laughed outright at that, showing fine teeth and brushing his hand over his hair. Slouching at the table, he looked about my age, road-free, perhaps irresponsible, and yet with a certain tough and sensitive grain in him. There was a deep, new-looking scar on his right cheek. The waitress came in with silver, but he waved it away.

"Coffee, toast," he said. "I eat light. Besides, these joints gyp you."

"This ain't no joint," the girl said.

"All right. Toast and coffee."

"Motoring?" I asked him.

"I left Washington this morning on an empty truck."

"Hitchhiking," I said.

"Anything wrong with that?"

"No," I said. "Going far?"

"You ask a lot of questions, Comrade," he said.

He ate slowly and in silence. His features were thin and mobile. His deep-set eyes were lighter than his crisp brown face. They were the light hazel color of the button eyes of a teddy bear, and just as shallow looking, and just as hard.

"You've called me comrade twice," I said.

"Resent it?" he mocked.

"No."

He laughed. The flesh ridged beneath his eyes, almost closing them, for he laughed with his whole mobile face and scarcely made any sound at all.

"It's a joke I know. I know a feller who thinks anybody with a mustache is a Red. He hates Reds. He's afraid of them. Can you imagine a nigger hating Reds because he's afraid? What's he got to lose?" A note of hard seriousness underlay the mockery. "Look. This feller is a darky in a southern town, and he hates Reds. Can you imagine that?"

"Don't most people hate and fear the radical?"

He wiped his mouth on the paper napkin. "Radical! Listen, Comrade," he said sarcastically, "a nigger can't be radical in this goddamn country."

I was looking at the map for a road to follow from Fredericksburg when he finished breakfast. Route 1 was not the way to go. It led straight to the heart of the mercantile South of factories and warehouses and morning and evening newspapers, and this is not the South in the way that the little towns and farmlands are.

"Going south?" the man asked.

"Yes," I said. "But I don't know which way."

He took the map and turned it across the table. His long finger pointed out the red line of a road running beside the Rappahannock River through villages with unusual names. Beyond a place called Gloucester the road ended in a narrow curve of Chesapeake Bay.

"Why don't you go this way?"

"That's your route?"

"Maybe," he said, grinning.

In fifteen minutes we were going over the route he had suggested. It was hot on the road. The air smelled of baked earth and sun-dried vegetation. There were many scorched thickets and dribbling creeks. Thick and fat, but earless, the corn was beginning to turn brown and the blades to curl. We passed through Return, Loretto, Occupacia—paralyzed villages whose names meant nothing to me. But there were a good many iron markers on the shoulder of the road, and I knew we were in historical country.

"Well, Comrade," he mocked, "this is as good as any other road."

"Don't call me comrade. Call me by my name," I said. I think he sneered. But I told him my name. "What's yours?"

"Call me Mike. Mike Chowan."

"O. K."

"For Christ's sweet sake, don't offer to shake hands. That's a lot o' baloney."

Anger spurted up in me, but I said nothing. I did not seem able to get far with him. Evidently he was a Communist, and evidently he was cynically amused at me and what he thought I stood for. I stole glances at him as he leaned against the door, exposing his sockless ankles, his long fingers drumming on his knee. I decided to go after him directly.

"I'm going to ask questions," I said. He looked at me with what I thought was amused condescension.

"You're giving me a lift, so you're entitled to my guts. The world is full of perverts," he said.

I was trying to think of an answer to this, when suddenly, with an inexplicable change of mood, Mike said:

"All right. Maybe you won't have to ask questions. Maybe I want to talk. You're safe to talk to. A coupl'a hours more and you'll go one way and I'll go another. It won't matter. Talking'll probably keep me ahead of myself for a while. You gotta keep ahead of yourself. Once you catch up with yourself, it's your tail. I got caught up with myself in Spain, and I know it's your tail."

"Spain?"

"Yeah. But I don't want to talk about Spain. Jesus, it's hot!"

I accelerated up to fifty-five, but the breeze was only hotter and stronger. The sun lay like a stroke on the land. Way off to the left, where low hills rose abruptly from the plain, we could see a green haze of heat breaking and washing up the hills. The pungency of sun-scorched pine and the hot smell of baked earth were absorbent fingers in our nostrils.

"Come to think of it, I haven't done a hell of a lot of talking since I've been back either. I've only felt like it once, back in April. I was home in April. Home's a town here in Virginia. My old man's been in school work there for twenty-five years. I only go home once or twice a year now. It saves embarrassment. But every time I go, some damn thing or other comes up.

"When I was home in April, my folks had a woman in to dinner. She runs a school, and she was talking about a book she was writing on etiquette. It seemed so goddamn silly to me. She runs a finishing school. Can you imagine that? The whole idea of her school and her book on etiquette seemed so goddamn silly. She made me feel like I used to feel before I went to Spain and when I was organizing in Boston and New York and Corpus Christi.

"She was beefing about the book she was writing about the correct thing to do, and my folks were eating her up. How to dress, how to eat, what to say. She griped my guts. I told her that the trouble wasn't learning how to eat; it was getting something to eat. And do you know what she said?" He laughed scornfully. "Listen. She said, 'I wasn't thinking of those who encounter difficulties about getting food.' Encounter difficulties! My God, that's rich! Ain't that a honey?

"Then I said, 'You didn't write your book for niggers.' After she went, my folks gave me hell."

I think that the essential characteristic of Mike Chowan was that he was completely without affectation, altogether stripped of distracting decoration. His character stood out with a certain starkness, simple and yet complex. He was ungracious, he was hard, he was without pretense.

"My folks always give me hell. They're absolutely middle-class Americano. There's a combine that can't be beat—American, middle class, Negro."

"Can't be beat for what?"

"For everything American stands for. For everything middle class stands for. For everything Negro stands for."

"I don't get it," I said.

"I'd like to be a good American without being either middle class or Negro. You can't be a good all three. You can't be a good two."

"So you're a good Communist," I said.

He did not answer. He had kicked off one shoe, lifted his bare foot to his knee, and was picking at a monstrous corn on his little toe.

"Why can't you be American, middle class, and Negro? I still don't get it. It's too metaphysical," I said.

"A Greek's a Greek, a Russian's a Russian, and a Limey's a Britisher. They're that. And what are we?"

"Americans."

He laughed. "O. K."

We stopped a little farther down and left the car on the shoulder of the road and went down into a wood where there was a small stream. The banks of the stream were cracked with dryness, but the water ran swift and cool-looking in the bed of the stream. We doused our heads and lay on the bank in the shade. Mike kicked off his shoes. It was cooler here, but breezeless, and soon the heat would penetrate the shade and drop on us like a steaming blanket.

Mike was thirty, he told me. As a youngster out of high school, he had won a fraternity scholarship to a Negro state college, but he had rebelled against the system of hazing, of cleaning fraternity brothers' rooms, running errands, and confining his associations to a clique. After several fights over these matters, Mike resigned the scholarship. But this was not the reason for his expulsion from college. He was expelled for refusing to divulge his knowledge of a prank.

For a while after his expulsion he worked in a winter-resort hotel in Hot Springs, Virginia. The food that was served the help was sometimes rotten, always unfit for human consumption. Mike complained of it, but he complained alone. It seemed that the help thought things were the way they should be. They also seemed to think that because things were the way they were, they had a moral right to steal whatever good food they could. He complained to the headwaiter, but the headwaiter merely shrugged. "You can quit," he said. "The headwaiter could eat anything he wanted to eat. That's the way it's worked. The white folks find some old pussy-footing nigger, make him boss, give him anything he wants, and tell him to keep the other niggers quiet."

From Hot Springs he went to Boston, where in the previous summer he had worked on the Eastern Steamship Lines. He liked the life. Before taking ship, he joined the International Seamans Union, and under its influence he began to realize something of the importance of organization. He was still terrifically race-conscious, and when he thought of organization it was in terms of Negro workers. "I didn't realize that all workers live in the same world, that all workers, white and black, should be organized."

On the first trip out, Mike's ship went aground off the coast of Maine, and for three weeks he was on the beach in Boston. During this time he was approached by union agents and asked to help organize the steward's crew on his ship. He worked very hard, he said, for the sort of lethargy he found among the cooks, waiters, and cabin boys could not be broken with cold reason. All the organizers worked. Within five months they had lined up solidly the marine employees of the E.S.L. They were the best-paid marine employees in the country.

Then, suddenly, without consulting the men, union officials signed an agreement with the American Steamship Owners Association. The agreement was a good one, but it had been made without consulting the men. Dave Grange, president of the Marine Stewards and Cooks, Erickson, president of the Eastern and Gulf Sailors Association, and Joe Ryan, president of the International Longshoremen, simply rode roughshod over the men and made the agreement, forcing a closed shop and compelling unorganized men to join at ten dollars a head.

"The whole thing smelled stinking rotten," Mike said, getting up suddenly and dousing his head again, and then standing with his feet spread wide in the water. "It was lousy! But we would probably have fallen in line if it hadn't been for some pamphlets. I didn't know where in hell those pamphlets came from. I didn't see anyone handing them out. They were just there, all over the docks and scattered over ships' quarters. You couldn't miss 'em. Those pamphlets wanted to know if we were free men or slaves. 'Who,' they wanted to know, 'gave Grange and Erickson and Ryan the right to speak for you without consulting your wishes?' It was pretty plain that we'd been made suckers of, even if the agreement was a good one."

When the summer runs on the E.S.L. closed late that fall, Mike went to New York. He was on the beach. He seemed unable to get a ship. He bummed around in sailors' flophouses and around the headquarters of the International Seamans Union on Fourteenth Street waiting for a ship. But coastwise shipping was pretty dead. He had no money. He had no real address. One day he wandered into a meeting.

"Roy Hudson was chairman of that meeting. He was just another seaman then. There were about a hundred of us there, and we decided to set up within the A.F. of L. a union in opposi-

tion to Ryan's. The intercoastal fellers hadn't been helped any
by that Boston agreement, and we wanted them in. We called
our union the Marine Transport Industrial Workers Union.

"Somebody at that meeting knew about my work in Boston,
and they decided to keep me on the beach as an organizer for the
new set-up. I got no wages, but every Saturday somebody would
hand me fifteen or twenty dollars. I didn't know where the
dough came from, but it always came. I still didn't know anything about communism, never thought of communism. But I
was learning something about labor."

The first job of the new union was to line up the American
Hawaiian Lines, which it did in a matter of weeks. Then the
union went to the company for an agreement. It was this con-
troversy, Chowan said, that led to the first sit-down strike in
modern times. "Roy Hudson imported that one. I didn't know
for a long time where he got it from, but it was one of the
strike techniques that I was to learn a lot about later in a party
school. That was in 1932."

The crew of the S.S. *Texan* of the American Hawaiian Lines
sat down in Brooklyn. Not a winch turned, not a hatch opened,
not a gangplank moved. Mike was on the committee that went
to negotiate the agreement. They got it with some difficulty.
Then the union went to work on the intercoastal companies.
Meantime, Mike was getting thirty-five dollars a week.

"I was a blind cluck. The agents and other union workers
used to meet about once a week in a loft on Fourteenth Street.
They were a pretty good bunch of men, mostly hard workers
and not smart, with some grafters and signifiers in the bunch—
but not many—out looking for what they could get. One night
after our regular meeting, I and about thirty others were asked
to stay. Roy Hudson talked to us. We were locked in, and we
made a circle and Hudson sat in the center of the circle and
talked to a fare-you-well. He said he asked us to stay because
he believed we were men of sense and wisdom. He wasn't just
creaming us down, handing us baloney. He wasn't that kind of
a man. He talked about social justice in a way I'd never heard a

man talk before. Living and working with those men had opened my damned eyes to a lot of things, and I knew old Horse-face Hudson was making plenty sense. When he got done, everybody to a man joined the party."

Chowan stopped, as if expecting a comment from me. He lay flat on his back, his knees drawn up, staring up into the trees. His hair had knotted tight from the wetting and fast drying, and the skin was drawn hard over the bony structure of his forehead and temples.

"Go on," I said, after a while.

"That was the only way the party could work in those days. We bored from within. The union was Communist-led, but the workers didn't know it. They had no political or class consciousness. They had to be taught. They had to be milk-fed. They had to be taught gradually. I was one of those selected to teach them. I was cut off the pay roll, along with some others, and put in school. We got living expenses and spending money, and we were kept pretty much together. For six months the school was called the Marine Training School, and after that the name was changed to the National Training School for All Industries. We studied Marx and Engels. We learned Communist philosophy, Communist strategy, and Communist lingo. There was a hell of a lot to try to learn. But I got something. I lost what was left of race prejudice anyway. I got human."

After ten months of school, Mike was made an editor of the *Pilot*, a Communist organ. They flooded the ships with every issue. They printed their paper in a half-dozen languages and shipped thousands of copies of each issue to ports all over the Americas.

Finally, in 1934, came the great dock workers' strike on the West Coast and the rise of Harry Bridges. Mike's union was in the thick of that fight, supporting Bridges. In the East, Mike's union refused to service the ships until Bridges, who had become the West Coast official of the International Longshoremen, broke through with an agreement calling for a dollar and twenty cents an hour. It was a great victory, Mike said.

It was about this time that Mike was elected to the top group in the party in the East. He served on the education committee, the organization committee, on the policy committee, and as an editor of the *Pilot*. The depth of his circle grew.

"The men I met!" he said, with strange, disrupting intensity. "The decency of some of those steerage bums! I think that when society has robbed a man of all he's entitled to as a human being, then from somewhere he gets a sense of—of—of something. Call it humanity."

He sat up, and I saw him smile. "When you start filling that kind of gut, it's time to quit, ain't it? I was beginning to spout like a goddamned curbstone artist. Let's go." He slipped on his shoes.

The sun seemed not to have moved since noon. The heat reflected from the hood of the car and blazed back into our faces. Where it ran beyond the woods, the road shimmered like a shallow kiln of water with the sun on it.

"There's nothing much more to tell," Mike said, when I urged him to go on. "I was always on various strike-strategy committees. Always as a member of the union, of course, but working for the party, boring from within. We broke off from the A.F. of L. and organized an independent, which we later turned over wholesale to C.I.O. I worked the Gulf Coast from Mobile to Corpus Christi for that outfit. We had strong units down on the Gulf Coast. But I got back to Boston after a while, and from there I went to Spain."

"And you don't want to talk about Spain?" I said.

We drove on for perhaps five miles. The road ran in and out of parched patches of browning woods. Whole stretches of road were absolutely without character, and nothing in the landscape attracted the eye. One mile was like the next.

"We had a unit called the Maritime Committee for Spanish Democracy. We bought three ambulances. We bought them from Studebaker, because it was the only company under agreement to U.A.W. at the time."

"And you drove an ambulance?"

His features fixed themselves expressionlessly, so that it was impossible to tell what he was feeling, or whether he was feeling anything.

"Three of us went over. A white boy from Mobile and one from Los Angeles. The union found berths for us, and then we were told just to miss ship at Le Havre. It was a cinch. The Workers Confederation of France fixed our passage to Gijon. Everything was turned out like a machine turns things out. No fuss, no questions, no nothing. But the fighting was different. There everything was just the opposite. Nobody knew anything much. It was more like a free-for-all than a war. The cracker from Mobile had his guts ripped out.

"Coming back, some American writers met us at Le Havre and gave us some money. I don't know why. When we got to the States, the immigration people held us. There were thirteen of us. After two days they decided to release us in fifty dollars bond, and an agent came down from party headquarters and bonded us, and then I just disappeared."

"Disappeared?" I questioned.

"Oh, a lot o' long-hairs were gawking us. People who hadn't been, wanted to talk about it. They sounded like they'd fought the damned war. Spain was bad. Dead men. Dead hopes. But I've got faith still. Losing a war don't end it. I'm with the party. I'm on the State Committee of the party."

After we had passed through Gloucester, making the half-circle around the town square, which was stricken by the sun in spite of its fine trees, and gone down the short length of street into the open country again, Mike became something of what he was in the morning in the hotel. The mockery came back to his hard eyes.

"Sure. I'm a Communist, Comrade. I can't be an American."

I parked the car at the top of the hill overlooking the ferry slip at Gloucester Point and walked down to the wharf with him. We could see the little ferry just pulling out from York-town across the river and swinging around with the tide. On its hill, Yorktown looked white and hot and quaint and not at all cool because of the beach and the river. Curiously, though one knew that it was an old historic town and that a lot of men who had been with Lafayette and Washington had descendants there now running antique shops and preserving monuments, one did not think of it in that way; for one was somehow now separated from all history and moving loose-endedly in a sterile and confusing present. Yorktown was only a place one went to on a ferry.

Just before the ferry slipped in, Mike Chowan said, with pleasant raillery:

"I'd give anything to be an American, like you. A damn middle-class American nigger. Can you imagine it?"

Then he held out his hand. "Thanks, Comrade," he said. His thin figure made a quick shadow, and then he was gone through the passage and up the steps to the deck, where he stood leaning against the rail with his back toward me. Though I stood there until the ferry was halfway across the river, Mike Chowan did not turn to wave good-by.

3

On what is the northwestern edge of the South's black belt there is a town that is something to remember. You will know it if you come to it. Its Negro inhabitants have a way of speaking of the factory in the town in a manner deferential and on every possible occasion. If you ask a direction, they will say, "Do you know where the factory is?" the implication being that from that point any place can be found. If you speak of a female acquaintance, they will ask if she works in the factory, and if she does not, you will know from the tone of voice that she is scarcely worth knowing. There is really no professional class in the town. Only one of the two physicians is married, and his wife and the wife of the dentist prefer the society in towns as much as a hundred miles distant, "a piece" they drive for bridge and gossip and the movies. They do not count any more than the school teachers, whose pay is lower than the factory girls';

and even when the talk turns spitefully and condescendingly to the "dicktie niggers," it comes back inevitably to the factory.

There is no need to name the town. Nor is there any need to name the physician whom I met there. He made me wish somehow that he was less brazenly and defiantly what he was. He (and other men I have met from time to time) reminds me of a show dog that has been extremely bred to one characteristic, which is not necessarily a canine characteristic and which, therefore, seems abnormal to one who knows nothing about dog breeding. The doctor seemed bred in such a fashion to a characteristic that, though undoubtedly human, had lost all of its humanity through excess. In this way he was as brazen as a new and ungreased gun.

I told him this—it was after he had said many of the things which surprised and baffled me. I told him that he was the symbol of a peculiar element in our racial life, and that no one had ever really told the truth about him and his kind. I was after truth and understanding. "The truth of life?" he asked, smiling patronizingly. "That, perhaps," I said, "but less comprehensive than that. Essentially, the truth of living as a Negro in America. Some basis, as a spiritual matter, for my faith in all the fine ideals that are American."

He questioned my faith in those ideals. He questioned any Negro's faith in them. "Negroes just go on living," he said, "without faith in all that stuff one way or another." Then I told him of Mike Chowan, but he used him as evidence that the Negro had no idealistic faith.

"Communism?" he said, arching his brows. "I hate communism. I hate all the isms. Are you patriotic?"

"It has nothing to do with patriotism."

"Well, I'm patriotic," he said. "I fought in the last war. I enlisted. But I'm not interested in any frigging ideals. I'm just a patriotic, law-abiding citizen. I get along all right, and I'd fight again for this country."

Nevertheless, the doctor and his kind are a sort of separating body, like an impervious membrane, in American life. Masses of Negroes look to his kind for courage and encouragement, faith and hope—moral sustenance. But the juices of idealism cannot flow through him. I told him something of this. By reason of education, first, and then of wealth, he was closer to the springs of idealism. . . . He interrupted to ask if I was still talking "the bushwah about democracy and equal rights." Yes. But what has happened is that the doctor has mistaken one set of values for another. He thinks that getting education, or wealth, or social and political power is the ideal, when, in fact, they are but the derivatives of the ideal. They are the income (he could understand these terms. He grinned. It was impossible not to like the doctor, though you abhorred all he stood for) from the principle of democracy.

We were getting into deep, hot water.

"Listen, son," the doctor said, grinning and not taking me at all seriously. "I'm doing like the white folks are doing. I'm looking out for number one. That's one thing about this country, you can devote all your time to looking out for number one. That's what democracy is, son. All this other stuff you're talking about"—he waved his thin, womanish hands impatiently —"that don't amount to a phart in a windstorm. I'm looking out for number one."

And that is where the factory came in. And the factory is the doctor's symbol, all that he and many others stand for. I am surprised when I remember how many others.

All those others who are represented by the doctor and symbolized in the factory do not have the same history; nor are they all bred to the doctor's exact character. They do not have a medical education and a mill. There is one in Texas who has a woman with oil wells. Another in my town has politics and the numbers racket. Some have newspapers, some have churches, some have schools. But by some process of Americanization, very like the one the doctor went through, they have come to be what they are. They are a group apart; almost another people.

They prove nothing, perhaps, but they are evidence of a great deal.

The doctor was not always paunchy. In his office there hangs a photograph of him taken in 1917, when he was a slim lieutenant in the medical corps. There is a touch of elegance in that photograph, for the doctor carries a swagger stick and a pair of gloves. And in the office in which that picture hangs there are even now some fading traces of preciosity in the delicate prints of Harley, Ehrlich, and Benson; in the dim, handpainted decorations on the buff-colored walls; in the tarnished silver fittings on the desk. But there is no elegance now in the graying, sag-bellied man that the doctor has become; and the typewriters, checkwriters, and adding machines do not seem out of place on the table against the wall. The time since the war has wrought great changes, and it is hard to see the physician of twenty-five years ago in the hulking, squint-eyed man that he is now.

But even twenty-five years ago, when he was not a doctor but a school teacher, what he is now had begun to be. He had got a girl in trouble, "in the family way," and she wanted him to marry her. (He told me this when I had been his guest for three days and had become used to his brazenness.) She threatened suicide. He went away. He studied medicine and afterwards came to the town, where he was the only Negro physician, and where he made less than five hundred dollars his first year.

A little money went a long way in those days. Besides, he had studied in a missionary school, where students were told that their education must be used to lift the fallen, succor the poor, strengthen the weak. He had not entirely forgotten those lessons.

I looked at him when he told me this, expecting to see his eyes lit with sly, sardonic humor. But they were not.

"Did you think much about the—you know, the girl?" I asked.

"I couldn't forget her, could I, as long as I was taking care of the child?"

After the first year money came faster, but he was far from affording the automobile that he needed more than did the white physician, who had come to the town in the same year and who was already sputtering over the roads in a Maxwell. Most of the Negroes lived on farms out in the hills. There were one or two furniture factories and a textile mill, but they employed no Negroes. The doctor was sometimes paid with vegetables and often with thanks. The white doctor had an annoying way of beating him to the Negro sick who could afford to pay in cash. "His ethics were rotten," the doctor said. "But he had a car, and he used to canvass for patients in the hills!"

When the war came, the doctor volunteered and spent nine months overseas with the medical corps. He volunteered out of a spirit of adventure. Though his medical experience should have been tremendously broadened by this episode, he spoke of his military service only in terms of romantic adventure and the French "hot mamas," of whom, I gathered, he saw a good deal. There were no war stories of either hospital or heroism. He did speak with some bitterness of the propaganda, which he believed spread by the army intelligence among the French. He thought it was designed to defame and dehumanize the Negro soldier. I had heard stories of this dozens of times, but the doctor unsmilingly told them again. His bitterness over this matter was out of character now, a regurgitation, as it were, of the emotions of his young manhood.

He returned to the town after the war. He did not say so, but I think he had no difficulty picking up the threads of his civil life again. He showed me a picture of himself taken shortly after his discharge. He was standing proudly beside the car he had begun to buy with his back pay. He had changed physically only a little. He was heavier. There were faint beginnings of creases around his mouth. But in other ways, he said, he had changed. When he began to speak of these changes, I was embarrassed in the same way I was once embarrassed by a prostitute who told me with what religious strictness she had been reared and how she had been betrayed. It was as impossible to believe the doctor as it had been to believe the whore. After the war he was essentially what he had been before.

I did not look at him while he told me of the changes. He said, in effect, that the war had betrayed him, that it had lost him his ideals and earthbound his spirit of service. The missionary sense with which he had been imbued in medical school now appeared so much baloney. He said that the war had brutalized him, made him selfish and cynical, taught him to look out for number one.

The town had changed when he got back. It had grown. Cotton factories had sprung up everywhere, giving employment to three-fourths of the population of nine thousand. Whole families of whites worked in the factories and employed Negro women in their kitchens. "When Negro women work, Negro men eat." Prosperity raged in the town. Negroes moved in from the hills. The doctor made money, for that was all that medicine had come to mean to him. He built a drugstore, a café, and a poolroom. Later, in the even more lush days of 1927-29, he opened an athletic park and built a cabaret near the drugstore. When the depression struck, he was fortified against it. Indeed, he began making a great deal of money in 1936.

It was when he came to this part of his life that I began to see in the doctor the monumental significance of his representativeness. It was the familiarity of the pattern and the realization of the twisted completeness with which he had adopted it that dawned on me first. One sees the pattern endlessly repeated in American life, until it has become as acceptable and as meaningless as last week's comic strip. I used to think about it in a negative fashion, wondering what life in America, the general life, would be without it. When Lebman, an acquaintance of my senior college year, used to talk about it, it seemed to me to be a thing that impinged upon the consciousness—and especially upon the Negro's—very little. It was an unimportant detail in the living sculpture of democracy. But now, looking at the hunched hulk of the doctor, I felt suddenly the importance of this thing to Negro life. The pattern contorted itself suddenly with menacing vitality.

We were at table, and the doctor's elbows rested on the arms of his chair, the weight of his broad shoulders on his arms. The last of daylight fell through the wide window behind him. It was quiet except for the doctor's heavy voice. He was big and gray and like a buffalo at rest. Frequently he pushed his false teeth outward with his tongue and sucked them in again. The maid set the dessert.

The doctor told me that when things got really bad in 1931-32, the Negroes in the town wished to do something about them. They were suffering. He had bailed them out of jail, lent them trifling sums of money, and occasionally kept up their burial insurance, but he had not thought of himself as their leader. He looked out for number one. He was the richest Negro in town, and the best educated. But it was because of this that he found himself being dragged into considerations of group problems for which he felt no real responsibility but which he nevertheless enjoyed for the sense of a new kind of power it gave him. He admitted that he felt none of the spiritual qualities of leadership, no real concern, no honest humility. On the other hand, he did not say that he was motivated by a desire for self-aggrandizement.

But when he began speaking of the factory, something entered his voice that had not been there before. It made me think of the opening scene of *The Emperor Jones*. He spoke of "dumb niggers," and it was easy to see that he, their leader, held them in disdain, and that he now believed the acquisition of wealth had given him the right to direct their activities, make decisions for them, and control their group life. And the whites thought so too, for any matter affecting the Negro in the town's civic life was referred to the doctor.

I murmured something about the old pattern, and the doctor looked at me, his brows ridged with puzzled annoyance.

"What do you mean?" he asked.

"Well, the wealth status and the hero status affect Americans peculiarly," I said, recalling as nearly as I could Lebman's argument. "I once saw a newspaper interview in which Jack Dempsey, then heavyweight champion, discussed the World Court." (And, indeed, I had. Lebman had shown it to me.) "Once you get money, or become a hero, no matter how, your opinion on all sorts of matters becomes important. That's the pattern," I said.

He sucked his plate in with a smacking noise.

"But it's more dangerous for Negroes," I added quickly, my own thoughts piecing themselves out with snatches of Lebman's. "The whites don't take such fellows too seriously. They have counteracting forces in their political and social institutions. They publish books and newspapers. They give each other the right to speak their minds, and then generally don't pay any attention, or not too much. They have the democratic sense of fundamental equality with each other. If they make a mistake and elect a fool to Congress or to the presidency, their institutions operate to save them. And then there're so many of them, divided by so many free opinions and possessed of the means to give expression to them, that one man's opinion is no better than another's, unless he happens to be a very great man indeed.

"But we! It's different with us. We've taken on the pattern and it's become something vicious. There are so few of us to whom democratic institutions and privileges seem a natural right, so few of us who can speak our minds, you understand, that those who can are venerated. And they ought to be straight! The Negroes—well, those here in your town, for instance, say, 'Oh, the doctor, he's educated. He's got money.' You've got two of the things that this society, so everybody thinks, is supposed to make men free and equal enough to get. So they ask you to lead them. They ask you to go to the white folks for them. You have these things, you see. You have them just like the white folks have them. Your opinion is really worth to them . . ."

I had gone on ruthlessly, in spite of the impatient gestures he made with his hands. He had finished his dessert while I talked, and now he sat smiling condescendingly, patiently scratching his cheek.

"Do you want to hear about the factory?" he asked.

I bent to my dessert. I felt very hot. I swallowed. In that moment I hated the doctor.

When he began talking again there was still that in his voice which reminded me of the Emperor Jones. I did not interrupt again. Perhaps some day I would learn to hold my tongue. But the doctor was not offended. Nothing I could say would either offend or embarrass him. He was talking now with a kind of careless, godly disdain. One word described him: shameless. He was as completely shameless as an obscene god.

The factory had not just happened. It was the most substantial result of a campaign to better conditions among the Negroes in the town. Other results were a short, laudatory editorial in the white paper and the organization of a Negro civic group, at whose first two meetings the doctor himself presided. But the poor, discouraged women (there were few men besides the doctor, the undertaker, and the county school principal) turned the meetings into praying and hymn-singing assemblies.

It was the undertaker who first thought of going to the management of the shirt factory and asking for jobs for Negro girls. It was intended to be a gesture merely, the doctor said. Similar tactics had been employed in other places with encouraging results, but there was no hope of tangible results in this case. Negroes were not direct consumers of the company's goods. They had no claim upon the company's good will, and the company had no need of theirs.

But there was one unexpected circumstance, and the conference with the management revealed a real opportunity to give at least temporary employment to a few Negro women. The company was experimenting with some new machines, and two dozen old but serviceable machines were idle for want of space to operate them. The management would not mind setting up those machines in a separate building and putting Negro women to work on them, but it could not go to the expense of renting a building for that strictly charitable purpose. The management hoped the delegation understood. He hoped the doctor understood. Besides, the management did not know whether Negro women *could* operate. The women would have to learn first. They would have to take apprentice wages. The company really could not afford to lose money on an experiment. If, however, the company could get machine space rent-free for a couple of months . . .

The doctor lifted his shoulders and threw out his hands in a clumsy imitation of the way the management did.

It was the undertaker, also, who remembered about the dance hall in the doctor's depression-closed athletic park. The doctor consented to its use, and the machines were installed. The experiment was begun with thirty Negro women, who for three months received apprentice wages while they learned to operate the machines. Meanwhile the doctor and the management got together. The management had received a huge and unexpected order for uniforms. Before the three months were over, a two-story, fireproof factory, costing twenty-five thousand dollars, was going up on the site of the doctor's athletic park.

It took the doctor a long time to tell me about this. It seemed to me that he began to justify himself, and I wondered if perhaps I had embarrassed him a little after all. We were sitting in his office late at night. The drugstore was closed. The music from an automatic phonograph somewhere in the building pulsed softly through the walls. The light from his desk lamp gleamed softly on a glass case of surgical instruments against one wall. These instruments, a framed and crinkling diploma, and three prints of famous medical men were the only indications that this was a physician's office. The doctor's heavy voice dropped very low. I felt as if I were a party to a conspiracy.

The new factory was a very simple arrangement. If there were factory space rent-free for a period of five years—a period long enough, that is, to pay for new equipment—the company could afford to expand by at least two hundred machines. After five years the company would buy or lease the building. In the meantime, perhaps even that five-year period would not be entirely unprofitable to whoever built the factory. And then, think of it! (It was in these words that the doctor began to justify himself.) Steady employment for at least two hundred Negro women. Among them they could support half the Negroes in town.

But the management knew of no one who would finance such a scheme, such a charitable scheme. Perhaps the doctor knew where the money could be raised? Perhaps the Negroes themselves, led by the doctor, of course? Or there could be an issue of stock. The workers could buy stock at a dollar a week, deducted from their wages. They would not question it. They would not be interested in the stock. Besides, would not thirteen-fifty less one be better than two-fifty and three from the white folks' kitchens? Perhaps the doctor knew?

The doctor knew.

We came back through the darkness to the doctor's house on the quiet hill. We walked in the road, for there were no lights in the bottom and the sidewalk was unpaved until we came within a few yards of the doctor's gate. Down below us we could see the whitish blur of the factory on a lower hill and the bunched shadows of Negro homes clustered in the bottoms around it. The doctor's house stood alone, surrounded by a shoulder-high picket fence. The air inside was thin and sweet with the odor of azaleas. We went upstairs to the wide hall.

"When I get here, I feel like a new man," the doctor said, yawning.

"And I can see the factory tomorrow?"

"Sure. Sure." Yawning, he went down the hall to the door of his room. "Theresh naw . . . shion spare," he yawned. "Well, good night."

"What did you say?"

"There's no use everybody being full of passion and despair. Good night."

"Good night."

I do not know why, but the general manager himself conducted me through the factory. He was a Jew, dark, with an almost Asiatic cast of face, expensively and rather conspicuously dressed. A short, round man, one stooped to converse with him, so that one got the odor of sour cream from his breath. He seemed pleased to show me everything.

"Anything the doctor says is okay with me," he said.

We entered the first floor, which was below the level of the ground, and crossed a vestibule heavily placarded with safety signs. On the left of the inner door a young white girl sat at a high desk. She was idle at the moment. A young white man, who had been idly swinging his legs from the first of many long tables, jumped down when we entered. My guide ignored them.

"All-Negro?" I said.

"Did the doctor tell you that? He likes that, that feller." He laughed. "To be honest with you, the doctor ain't put his foot inside the place in two years. He don't know what we do here."

We faced an immense many-windowed room lined with long tables piled high with cloth. The tables stretched to infinity. Lint drifted about in the air and rolled in downy draft-blown whorls over the cement floor. The high ceiling hummed with invisible motion.

"We cut a surplus, an' the cutters ain't working here today."

"Does that mean that when the girls catch up, they'll have a slack time?"

"They been off this week two days a'ready," he said.

"Do the girls in the other factory share the slack?" I asked him.

He looked at me and grinned. "I don't want you should get the wrong impression. When things is slow, or we cut a surplus o' cut goods, we slow up here an' keep the other place going. After all . . ." He shrugged his shoulders expressively.

In the clumsy elevator, the hum became a deafening clatter, the walls shook, and as we crept slowly upward the confused sound resolved itself into the clack and slam of high-speed machinery and the rumble of power-driven shafts. Lint and cotton thread blew about us. As our eyes came level with the floor, they gazed at a packed forest of legs and treadles, and finally bodies and heads bent over ranks of speeding machines mounted on long tables. The din now was a disciplined, purposeful, and power-saturated hum. The air was full of floating lint.

"There they are!" the Jew shouted.

And, indeed, there they were; but I could not tell whether he spoke of the machines or the girls. Perhaps they were indistinguishable to him. The girls did not look up, but a quiver of awareness passed over them, like a wind across a grassy meadow. That one sign that they were aware of our presence, and they became again a part of the machinery, so much expert motion, so many automata of arms and treadling limbs. All movement in the vast room seemed confined, concentrated, tight.

"They work with the same conditions as the white girls in the other place, and they get the same pay," my guide shouted in my ear.

We strolled down one side of the room and up the other. Not a head turned to look at us. Each set of a dozen or so girls performed a different operation. Some sewed the pockets, some stitched the neckbands, some bound the seams. They worked at high speed. Lint quivered on their bare arms and in their hair and eyelashes. Now and then runners appeared and laid great bundles of cut cloth on racks at the end of each table. At every second table a white man stood guard.

"I've never seen anything like this," I shouted.

"Ha," the Jew said appreciatively. He pulled out a cigar and stood twirling it in his chubby fingers. We watched a little longer, and then he beckoned me to follow him through an open fire exit. It was cooler on the iron balcony.

"The girls own this building by now, don't they?"

He put the cigar in his mouth and chewed it and jammed his hands in his pockets. It was easy to see that he was considering his answer well.

"I tell you. I don't want you should get the wrong impression. I run the production. These are our machines, and we pay the girls to run 'em. What else?" But it was not exactly a question. He was merely closing the subject, politely, firmly. I looked at him and he looked steadily back at me. He took the cigar slowly from his mouth.

"I tell you. I ran a fact'ry in New York. I had experience in this business for thirty years. I always used colored in my other places. I want to help the colored, but also it's a business proposition with me. You see my point?" He hunched his shoulders and spread his hands, drawing down the corners of his thick mouth and shaking his head. Then suddenly his contortions were over, and he said:

"These girls are good business."

"How?"

"They give good production. Over here I got four bosses for these girls. Over in the other place? Ha! I got a boss for every twenty. Here I got lots o' high-school girls. Over there? Bums." He threw out his hand in a gesture of disgust.

Across the roofs of the houses beyond the naked space surrounding the plant I could see the water tank on the roof of another factory and a part of the huge lettering bordering the roof. UFACTURING CO. What could be seen of the town beyond that was shaped like a wedge of pie. Just below us squirmed the galled and gullied Negro quarter.

"All right," the Jew said, tapping me on the chest so suddenly that I started. "Say it ain't all nice an' even like that."

"You're a mind reader," I said.

"No, I ain't no mind reader. But two an' two equals four, and you look like a smart feller. Is it my fault that things ain't nice an' even? What did they have before? A coupl'a lousy bucks a week. We helped the colored in this town. I don't want you should get the wrong impression. It's a business proposition with me."

"Sure."

"I don't owe the colored nothin'," he said. "They don't owe me nothin' neither."

After a while we went in and walked to the elevator. The girls did not look up. It would not take long, I reflected, to think of them as one thinks of machinery. As our descent cut off little by little first the limbs and then the bodies and heads of the girls and the noise became again an undisciplined roar, the little Jew took the cigar from his mouth and shouted in my ear.

"They're good workers." He winked and nodded his head solemnly. "What do you think of it?"

I stooped. There was lint caught in the hair that grew in his ear. His shoulders were white with lint.

"I don't know," I shouted. "After all, it's a business proposition, and I don't know much about business."

He took his cigar out of his mouth, turned toward me, and grinned.

When we stepped off the elevator, the young man whom I had seen on the way up came with a whisk broom. He whisked the Jew off vigorously. "Okay. Okay," the Jew said impatiently. When the young man was done, he started away.

"Hey, you," the Jew said.

The young man turned. His face was already flushing, the flush spreading from his ears and across his forehead. The girl at the desk watched.

"Ain't he all over lint too?" my guide said, speaking through teeth clenched over his cigar.

The young man hesitated. Then the brush began to flick lightly at me. The girl turned her eyes to the desk.

Outside, grinning, moving with jerky, swaggering gait, the Jew said, "I want to help the colored."

I looked at him, wondering if he referred to the whisking incident, and if he was as gross and insensitive as *that*—or if he thought I was. My stomach knotted.

"That bum!" he said, squeezing under the wheel of his car.

"Thanks a lot," I said. "It was quite an experience."

"You don't owe me nothin'," he said, and I knew he would go on thinking that I was talking about the young man with the whisk broom, and that at some later time he would probably relate the incident as proof that he wanted to help the colored.

"Well, thanks, anyway."

"Okay. Okay. But you don't owe me nothin'."

I did not go to the doctor's office. My hair was full of lint, and it needed cutting anyway, and I remembered the barber shop between the drugstore and the theater. There were a lot of young men on the street. They lounged in ragged groups about the corner entrance to the drugstore, in front of the theater, and in the shallow doorways up the street. They all seemed dressed alike in the wide-brimmed felt hats with feathers in the band, coats that hugged the hips, and trousers blooming at the thighs and draping softly to narrow cuffs at the ankles. There were some older men among them, too, chronic loafers with the futile look of men who do not know what to do with time.

The barber shop was narrow and dark and smelled of dust. Beside the barber, four men sat on the long bench against the wall. One of these, whom I later heard called Chris, was talking, but he stopped and looked me over casually. He sat with his shoulders against the wall, his hands stuffed in his pockets, and his legs outthrust. I got in the chair and submitted to the dirty neckcloth.

"So you likes this town, hunh, Chris?"

"Yeah, man," Chris answered indolently. "This town's all right wid me. In a town full'a time-makin' broads like this, a man don' hafter work if he's got any stuff a-tall. I don't even down write numbers no more. Niggahs don't play numbers much when they's prosperous, an' this town's sure that. That fact'ry's bloomin', man! I been to Roanoke an' Richmon', an' I seen niggahs starvin' on South Street in Philly, an' I'll take this town ever' time. Yes, sur, ever' time!"

He was the very picture of satisfied indolence. He talked in a lazy drawl that yet managed somehow to have the effectiveness of a dramatic monologue. With only slight emphasis he managed to convey force. With no gestures at all he drew pictures.

"That all the further you been, Chris? Hell! I thought you'd went some place. You ain't been no place," one of the men said.

"You ain't seen no starvin' niggahs, Chris. Niggahs allus goin'a git som'pin t'eat," another said.

"Don' tell me I ain't seen niggahs starvin'! I liked to starve myself. An' as for you, little niggah, I been in more cities then you's seen people. I been clean to Mobile, an' I come up from there to Chattanooga—'at's in Tennessee—an' I worked on the El n' En. I worked, then, 'cause I didn' know no better. I didn' learn no better till I was a full-growed man. I was up North then. Man, I come near starvin' to death. Them niggahs up there jes' like white folks. They don' keer nothin' 'bout you. You got to have plenty stuff wid you up there. But I hadn' learnt nothin' then."

"You sure got plen'y stuff wid you now, boy."

"Solid stuff!" another said.

"Aw, I ain't got no stuff," Chris said.

I could see him in the mirror. His eyes were closed and he was smiling with proper modesty. Though he was still a young man, there was a bun of flesh on his stomach which pulsated obscenely, contentedly, as if it had a life of its own.

"Lis'en to him. He ain't got no stuff."

"Man, you got more stuff 'en a Chris'mus turkey."

"What I want to know is where at you learnt it," the short man said plaintively.

"Yeah. 'At's solid jive you handin' us now, 'bout you ain't got no stuff," another said.

"I'm partial to barber shops," Chris said, still smiling modestly. "I was hangin' 'round a shop on South Street. The man lem'me sleep in the back, an' on Sadees I hit a lick o' shoe-shinin'. Other times I jes' clean up the place some. It was a big shop wid six barbers an' six cheers, but only fo' was workin' reg'lar, an' I

kep' all that stuff shined up an' all. All the big-shot niggahs
come to Les's place. I seen Ethel Waters there once. One night
Bojangles come in, too, an' any time the Philly shots was there.
Les had him a place o' business, man, what I mean!

"There was a broad use to come in Les's, a pretty broad. One
o' these broads so pretty she look like she goin'a melt right on
down. There was a lot o' them pretty yaller broads, doctors'
wives an' all like that. But this broad come so reg'lar an' always
at the same time o' evenin' that you jes' had to notice her. One o'
the boys tol' me she been comin' there three or fo' years. But
seem like nobody could git close to this broad. Man, when she
walked in, it was like a razor cuttin' yo' th'oat. You'd'a thought
she was the pope's wife. She'd come in an' set down in the cheer
an' have her neck shaved, pay the man, an' leave on out. One o'
the boys tol' me she worked in some white folks' office downtown. Man, she was pretty! Minded me something o' that yaller
Stutz ol' man Tead's boy use t'have. You 'member, don' you,
Rabbit? Ever' week she come in, ever' Tuesday evenin', an'
didn' nobody but Bert shave her neck.

"Boys 'round the shop started kiddin' me 'bout her. You know
how some guys is. Tryin' to make me take low, an' I couldn'
took no lower then I was. No, sur! I mean I was low. They
come kiddin' me 'bout they bet I wouldn' ast her if she wanted
a shine. They was skeered theyselves t'say anything to her a-tall.
Even Bert didn' say nothin', only 'Good evenin',' an' ever'-
body'd git all drawed up when she come in.

"She was the damndes' woman in the worl', man! When Bert
got th'ough shavin' her neck, he'd take that 'er powder thing
to dust her neck. He'd do it ever' time, an' ever' time she'd
sckrowge an' say, 'Don' put that dirty thing on me,' an' the
way she had o' sayin' it was like callin' him a sonofabitch. Yeah,
man. But Bert didn' have no sense. He done it ever' time. He said
he wanted the duster to stroke her jes' once to see what she'd do.
He said he b'lieved she'd kill him. She'd sckrowge her neck
down in her shoulders an' say, 'Don' put that dirty thing on

me,' an' then she'd th'ow fifty cent on the ledge an' leave on out,
tippin' like a maltese kitten.

"Les an' Bert an' all the boys kidded me 'bout her for a munt'
or more, tellin' me I wouldn' ast her if she wanted a shine. But
I didn' want 'at stuff outa them guys. I figgered they knowed
something, see? I figgered maybe astin' her if she wanted a shine
got her water on, an' they knowed it an' jes' wanted to see her
gim'me hell. Then they was low-ratin' me too, see? They was
barbers an' I was jes' clean-up an' shoe-shine boy, sleepin' nights
in the back room. They had me right by the nuts, so they
wasn' no use o' me gittin' mad. That was only hurtin' m'ownself.
But, man, did I git tarred o' that kiddin' jive!"

"You shoulda kidded right 'long wid 'em," the short man said.
"I don' see what you-all hard-arsed niggahs was skeered o'
her fer."

"Let the man finish," the barber said, clicking his scissors in
my ear.

"One evenin' she come in, an' the guys had been ridin' me
sence early that mornin', an' when she come in ever'thing got
jes' as quiet. I was shinin' a man's shoes settin' in Les' cheer.
Les was done workin' on the man an' the man was jes' settin'
'er waitin' for me to git done, an' I was kneelin' there shinin'.
Jes' when I was fixin' to give him the rag, I happen t'look up an'
this broad settin' in Bert's cheer was lookin' at me. Her neck was
bent so Bert could git at it good, an' she was lookin' straight
down at me. I hadn' never seen her real good befo', but she
didn' look like no man-killer. I said to myself, 'Hell, she ain't
Miss Jesus!' She sure was some pretty though.

"I got up an' brushed the man off an' got down agin to put my
stuff away, an' I kinda looked up agin, an' damn if she wasn' still
lookin' at me. She gunned me an' I gunned her slightly, an' then
she histed her foot an' said, 'Okay.' "

"Jes' like dat?"

"Jes' like that," Chris said. "She jes' histed her foot an' said
okay, an' I started dustin' her boots.

"Mos'n gen'ally, when I shine a broad's shoes, natcherly, I tries t' peep. But this here broad . . ."

" 'At's a funny thing," one of the men said. "Don' make no diff'ence how many a man's seen, he allus want to see another one."

"You guys got dirty minds," the barber said.

"But, man, I didn' hist my eyes no higher 'en this broad's shins. I could feel her still gunnin' me, an' I wanted to look at Les an' 'em an' kinda wink; but, man, I was skeered to look. Right then I didn' do nothin' but dust her boots.

"After while, she says, 'Slug.' Jes' like that. She said it a coupl'a times. But hadn' nobody never called me that befo' an' I didn' know she was talkin' to me. Then she histed her foot off'n the box an' touched me on the shoulder wid it an' said 'Slug' agin. I looked up then, an' she say—like she was goin'a smile, only she didn'—she say, 'Slug, if I had your kinda hair, I wouldn' mind gittin' it wet.' I didn' say nothin', 'cause there wasn' nothin' to say.

"After she lef' on out, the boys foun' something to kid me 'bout anyhow. They kidded me 'bout the name she gim'me. Ol' man Braxton was a school gradcheate, an' he said a slug was some kinda worm. An' then did them guys jaw at me! 'I wouldn' let no woman call me no worm,' they said, an' all. Them guys was solid kidders!

"T' nex' time she come in, I wasn' goin'a pay her no mind. But she called me. I was in the back, where I slep', when she come in, an' she sent Bert back there for me. She didn' say nothin' while I was shinin' her shoes, an' when I got done, I went on back in the back.

"I hadn' been back 'er no time 'fore I heard Les say something, an' then her say something back. It sounded like she was close back there where I was at; an' then I heard her say, 'Here?' an' the do' opened, an' there she was. There was a ol' barber cheer back 'er, an' a ol' high-ended sofa, what I slep' on, an' I had my clo'es hangin' on the cheer, what clo'es I had. She looks all aroun', an' looks like she's smellin' something bad, an' she ast me didn' I take no tips from women. Then she th'owed a ten-cents piece on the flo'. When she seen I wasn' goin'a pick it up, she says, 'Look here, Slug . . .' an' right then, man, I got her tol' 'bout callin' me that. I cussed her comin' an' goin'. An' she jes' lis'ened, same's if I was preachin' a sermon. She was the damndes' broad I ever seen! When I got done cussin', she ast me was I all th'ough. An' what the hell was I goin'a say? Then—I'm tellin' you the truth, man—she hawled off an' slapped the livin' piss outa me."

"Done what, Chris?" an astonished voice asked.

"You heard the man!" the barber said.

"I'd a beat hell outa her," another said.

"I started to lay fis' on her so fas' she'da thought she was bein' beat automatic," Chris said. "I drawed back to sock her, an' then I seen she was kinda smilin'; only it wasn' no smile. Her lips was drawed like a smile, but her eyes was squoze up like it was already hurtin' her. I drawed back an' she had that funny look on her face, an' you know what she say? She says, 'Hit me. I dare you to hit me, you snake!' She kind'a whispered it, like she had a sour ball stuck in her th'oat an' couldn' talk very good.

"I don' know what kep' me from hittin' 'at broad, but when she seen I wasn' goin'a hit her, she opened her eyes an' looked me up an' down, gunned me, what I mean, an' say t' me now she's goin'a take me out an' gim'me something to eat. She said I looked like I ain't et for a munt'.

"She was the damndes' broad I ever seen."

Chris paused. I strained under the barber's hands to see what had happened. But nothing had happened. Chris sat with out-thrust legs, his almost white hat with the red and yellow feather in the band tilted over his eyes. The men sat forward on the bench, their expressions a blend of suspense and lasciviousness.

"Well, sur, when I went outa that place wid her, nobody said nothin'. The boys jes' gunned us, that's all. I thought I had their water on. I didn' know when I lef' on outa there that I wasn' never goin' back. I didn' know what the broad's racket was, but I figgered I'd be back in that shop the nex' day. I 'member 'bout a munt' later, when I was all outa the barrel 'n ever'thing, I said something to the broad 'bout seein' the boys at the shop. She tol' me she'd kill me if I even went down on South Street. She pitched a fit, man! Said I jes' wanted to go down 'er an' brag an' low-rate her, an' all. I never said no more t' her about it, an' I didn' go down there neither. She meant that thing.

"Man, I'll tell you, a ignerunt woman's bes' anytime; women like the broads 'round here, who'll work for you an' not ast no whole lotta questions. This broad was smart. She wasn' no floogie. The whole time I lived wid her, I didn' fine out where she worked at nor how much she made. An' she made plen'y. But what I'm tellin' you is a dumb broad, who only draws down a few bucks a week, is better to live with 'an one who fingers long green. Don' pick no kitchen broad, though. 'At damn heat, man, makes 'em mean. 'Course, in the North 'at's 'bout all them broads do, work housework. Once 'n a while you might run 'cross one doin' something like my broad was doin', or teachin' school, or something. But you don' hardly meet them kinda women. Niggahs like y-all wouldn' hardly meet 'em noway, even if there ain't enough 'a their own kinda niggahs to go 'round."

"Humph! Ain' no niggah better'n I is," the short, argumentative one said. "They ain't no better'n nobody else."

"You damn right dey ain't."

"Go'n, Chris," the barber said.

"Take my broad," Chris continued. "I figgered I was jes' lucky. What she shoulda had was some eddicated niggah. She mighta married a niggah like that, if she coulda foun' one. She was a niggah woman, but all niggahs ain't alike. I'm tellin' it like it is. Y-all know that.

"That night me an' her walked on outa the shop, it was snowin' like hell, an' we took a taxi clean out to her place on Fifty-eighth Street. In the taxi she kep' poundin' me on my arm an' callin' me Slug an' blacksnake, an' all. She owned that house an' she had a flat downstairs an' somebody else lived upstairs.

She had her a nice camp there, man, but I never could feel to home. She never let me feel to home.

"But she took me right on outa the barrel. She laid dough on the line for new drapes an' shoes an' all, till it looked like it was a shame. But the funny thing about it was, she didn' drape me down like that to take me no place. Onlies' place I went wid her was once 'n a while over to a show on Girard aroun' Sixtieth. She didn't carry me no place, man, an' I didn' have no place to go. I didn' know nobody, 'cept them boys in the shop down on South, an' she double-dared me to go there. I foun' a poolroom over on Fifty-secon' below Hav'aford, an' a barber shop, an' I use to go there. But when it come down to knowin' nobody, I didn' know a soul. 'Course, I could loaf in hell if I had somebody to talk to.

"But the thing about it was that half the time this cat wouldn' say nothin' to me. We'd set down t'eat, an' she wouldn' say nothin' to me the whole damn time. She'd set there wid her eyes sckrowged up, like something was hurtin' her, an' not say boo. When we'd git done eatin', she'd git a book an' set an' read. She didn' like lush none, an' she didn' smoke, an' she didn' seem to have no friends. She was all by herself wid me. An' there we was, like a coupl'a goddamn deef dumbies.

"One night I was settin' lis'nin' to the radio an' laughin' my can off at Amos n' Andy, an' she snuck up behind me an' grabbed me by the hair an' snatched my head back, an' said, 'I ought to cut your dirty th'oat!' Talk about a niggah prayin'! Man, I sent up a prayer that was a killer-diller. I didn' know if she had a knife or not, an' I didn' look. My eyes was closed, 'cause I figgered if she was goin'a cut my th'oat, I didn' wanta see her do it. She kep' snatchin' my head back an' shovin' it front ag'in. Then, after a while, I felt something drop on my face, an' looked up an' 'at crazy broad had busted out cryin'. Yeah, man. Cryin'! A long time after I had done gone to bed, man, I heard her still cryin' in her room."

"You mean you didn' sleep wid dat woman, man?" one of the men said, incredulously. "What was de matter wid you?"

The short one whistled in amazement. The barber stopped snipping at my hair. His stentorian breathing was the loudest sound in the room. His comb raked aimlessly at my neck.

Chris took off his hat, adjusted the feather, then tilted it back over his eyes again. His head, I had seen, was a tangled mass of black, crisp curls.

"I lived wid that cat two years an' never slep' wid her once. That was the thing about it," Chris said. "I thought I was goin'a be her easy rider too. She gim'me a room to myself, but I thought that was some'a her jive. I figgered to break 'at broad down.

"I tol' you 'bout her poundin' me that night we lef' outa Les's. Well, when we gits to her place, soon's I'd et, she starts slappin' me, beatin' me all up in the face an' all. It didn' hurt me none, an' I tried to think she was jes' a playful cat an' all, but I didn' know what to make'a no broad like that, an' I wasn' goin'a hit her back. But she kep' darin' me to hit her, an' she kep' callin' me names, an' after a while she hawled off an' scratched hell outa me, right on my cheek. Then I let'er have it. She didn' holler nor nothin', but she got that funny look aroun' the eyes, an' she cussed me like A'nt Hagah, cussin' soft like she had something in her th'oat an' couldn' talk no louder. Then pretty soon, she lit into me agin, an' I jes' plain knocked her down, man. Jes' knocked her down.

"She didn' git up good. She crawled on her han's an' knees an' went in her bedroom, whimp'rin' like a baby. Then I was skeered! I made sure she was goin' for a gun. I was skeered to stay an' I was skeered to leave. But I stood there an' nothin' happened. She wasn' makin' no noise much, jes' whimp'rin', an' 'fore long I creeps up to the bedroom do'. An' what you think, man? There 'at broad was takin' off her clo'es, gittin' naked. She seen me 'bout the same time I seen her, an' she rushed me, an' I knocked her down agin. An' ever' time she got up, I knocked her down, an' ever' time she'd jes' call me names an' beg me to hit her agin, an' then she'd jes' shiver. But, hell, I wasn' all that mad, an' it was crazy-actin' stuff to me, an' I stopped beatin' her."

"What kinda woman was that!"

"Well, that's the kinda broad she was. I had to beat her a coupl'a times a week. She got so she gim'me things to beat her wid. I never was real mad wid her. She wanted me to beat her across her back an' over her butt. Sometimes, man, the whelps would stan' out on her like railroad ties. Then she'd kinda git up in a corner o' the bed, naked as a snake, an' whimper whilst I soothed her down wid lemon juice an' warm water. Sometimes I'd lay her, but I always had to beat her firs', an' then she never would cry—jes' git stiff an' beady-eyed, an' when I soothed her down wid lemon juice she'd whimper like a runned-over pup.

"The damndes' broad in the worl', man!"

No one spoke while he lit his cigar. I could not see now, for the barber had my chin against my chest. But I heard the scratch of the match, and later, before Chris spoke again, I smelled the smoke of the cigar.

"But I got tarred' that ol' stuff. I like a easy livin', but she jes' wasn' my kind'a broad. I stached away mos' o' the money she gim'me. Didn' have nothin' to spen' it for noway. Sometimes I bought me a quart o' lush, but she raised hell 'bout that. Said she didn' want no drunk'n whisky-head disgracin' her house. Man, I got a bellyful'a that broad. So one day las' spring, I copped the dough she had 'roun' the house, packed my duds, an' lef' on out."

The short one got up. I could see him now. He was excessively neat. He strutted to the mirror between the chair where I sat and the next chair and picked at a pimple on his chin.

"Man, I never woulda lef'!" he said.

"You'd'a got tarred of it," Chris said, getting up and stretching, like one who is bored with his experiences. He strolled to the window and back again. "I'm glad I come back. Nothin' beats a reg'lar broad makin' a few bucks she don' mind puttin' out. I hadn' been back a week 'fore I jived one of the fact'ry gals. Man, I didn' know this town was bloomin', or I'd'a been back here. Me an' her's got a little camp—nice little place—an' sometimes I runs a little game, jes' for the sport. Hell, ain't no sense in a man workin' in no town fulla clock-punchin' broads like this if he's got any stuff a-tall."

The barber lathered my temples and the back of my neck in cold lather. Then he smeared the lather with his fingers and stropped the razor on the palm of his hand. He bent close.

"Chris, you ain't no credit to the race," the barber said.

"Well, I be goddamn!" Chris said in amazement. "Who? Me? I ain't never said nothin' 'bout bein' a credick to the race. I'm a credick to Chris. Yes, sur, man. I'm goin'a always be a credick to Chris. What is you a credick to?" Then he burst into laughter.

The barber only breathed stentoriously against my neck. He finished with me and I paid him. As I knotted my tie, I saw the doctor going by in the street and tapped on the window. He stood waiting for me in the street. Chris was talking again. He had sat down again and thrust out his softly draped legs.

"I got a nice little camp now. Run a little game ever' once 'n a while. You boys come up an' see me sometimes. Ain't no sense in givin' it all back to the white man. Me an' my broad . . ."

He was still talking when I went out to join the doctor.

4

The trip up through the Blue Ridge began in dreary monotony. In the early morning the mountains were shrouded in flannelly gray clouds, which lay like heavy fluffs of dirty wool in the dripping valley. Now and then a bald mountain top, with a dribble of sun upon it, rose above the mist and floated there like the escarpment of some fantastic aerial city hidden in the clouds. I drove close to the shoulder of the mountain. Occasionally through the fog I saw on my left the ragged fall of the mountain dropping sharply to the edge of the valley stream below. There was sun down there. I saw it putting a sheen on the water. Then abruptly the road dipped and the narrow valley, liquidly shining with the sun on the water, stretched out before me. In the mountains once more, the sun was beginning to lick up the mist.

I had said good-by to the doctor the night before, but in the morning he had come down in his pajamas and a velvet-silk robe that reached to his ankles. He sat at table with me while I ate fruit and drank coffee. His teeth were out and his jaws and lips were collapsed in spongy weakness. He looked much older. Speech came grotesquely from his rubbery lips.

"Don't be too hard on me when you write about me," he said. "After all, I'm not a good terrible example." His laughter was thick, jovial, patronizing.

"Aren't you giving yourself away?"

"No, no," he said, laughing.

"Now that you mention it," I said.

"Good Lord! There's no use everybody being full of passion and despair."

The houseboy stowed my things in the car and the doctor and I stood on the porch and shook hands. He looked very old.

"Don't be hard on me, remember."

"I'll try to tell the truth."

He laughed. "That's it," he said. "No one understands the truth, and no one believes it."

After Bluefield the mountains were better. They were bright with sun and soft and cool with green and blue colors. In the foothills were lush meadows with herds of goats in them, and sometimes one saw a mountaineer working a crop in the flat places. The road ran along a narrow shelf which sometimes climbed above the valley but always followed the course of the twisting, swift river. There was no sign of human dwelling for mile after mile. High tension wires strode on long steel legs across the mountains, and the path that had been cleared for them through the timber was growing up in pine.

But the mines of Hooten County begin at Tazeman. From this point the mining towns, which are owned and operated by the mining companies, litter the length of the Kanawha Valley to Charleston. They follow each other in a dismal succession of grim squalor. Complete with the company schools, the company stores, the company hospitals, the towns differ from each other only in the degree of ugliness and whether the grime-smeared miners' shacks hang precariously from the sides of the mountains or squat drearily on the low banks of the river that flows in a black jet through the valley. The light and air are damp, dim, murky, as if a weak sun shone through a depth of gray water. The townspeople show the effects of this polluted air and this niggardly light. Their faces are startlingly white or damply gray, thin and drawn. The faces of even very dark Negroes have a grayish or yellow tinge. There is no patch of pleasant color anywhere. Dominating all are the black mine tipples, the black slack heaps, the gray slag piles, the dark, yawning mouths of the slope mines, the weathered adits of the shaft mines, and the coke ovens that smoke day and night. Through all this bitter scenery the broken, tortuous road runs to Belcher and beyond.

I reached the town by dark, just as it started to rain. After many inquiries I found the hotel hidden away in one of the steep, cramped streets above the river. I was lucky to find a Negro hotel at all. This one smelled of damp. The narrow lobby, into which the staircase entered, was insufficiently lighted by a single bulb high in the damp-stained ceiling. The stairs went up into inky darkness.

I found a bell on a chair in the lobby and rang it. The inflexible sound ricocheted from the walls. Pretty soon I heard steps, and then I saw a dim light up the stairwell. The light did not dispel the darkness. It seemed to solidify it. A thin tuberculous-looking man came down. He did not greet me. He stood three steps above the landing and swallowed me with his enormous eyes.

"Single or double?"

"Single," I said.

He led me up the stairs and down a hall, and then, still in the dark (he put out the dim light in the stairwell as we came up) up more stairs to the third floor. There he threw open a door and switched on the light. The room jumped at me, its details blurred and out of focus. The damp crawl of the man's breath on my neck made me recover. The brass was peeling from the bed. A washstand in the corner was fastened upright to the wall with wire. The shattered mirror in the bureau cast a thousand twisting images. At the window a dirty rag of lace, yellow from rain, served for curtain.

"Two dollars," the man said, and held out his hand. The palm was waxen.

"And for a week?" I asked.

"A week?" He hesitated. "Two dollars a night just the same."

"Is this all you have?"

The man shrugged. "They're all the same. If you want anything, just stomp the floor. We ain't got bellboys neither," he finished sarcastically.

I brought the last of my things in from the car and disposed them very carefully on the bare space between the baseboard and the edge of the raveled carpet. The bed crawled. I threw the bolster in the corner by the window and stripped the bed. The mattress was as thin as a biscuit and spotted with stains that looked like mildew. Over the mattress I laid newspapers, folding them over the edge and tucking them between the mattress and the springs. After carefully inspecting and shaking the sheets, I spread one over the newspaper and the other I folded to cushion the back of the chair which I had placed back down and legs up on the bed to sleep against. I took my belt and suspended my bag from the pipe that ran across the ceiling, and the clothes I took off I also suspended from the pipe.

I lay in the bed with my back and shoulders against the slanting back of the chair and my feet drawn up. My topcoat was tucked carefully around me. Bed vermin are afraid of the light, I had heard, so I kept the light on. I read for a while, and then I dozed. I do not think I had been sound asleep when I heard the knocking. It came with a peculiar, soft insistence, as if it had been going on patiently for a long time.

"Who is it?" I called.

"It's me," a woman's voice answered in undertone.

"Well, what do you want?"

"Mister, have you got a match?"

"No. I'm in bed. I'm undressed," I said.

"That's all right. I've seen naked men before." It sounded as if she were talking through some aperture that I could not see. Her voice was low, but very distinct. "I just want a match, Mister."

"Go 'way."

"Aw, give us a match."

"For Pete's sake!" I said. Cursing myself, I got up and slipped into my topcoat. There was not space between the bottom of the door and the floor to push the paper of matches through.

"Open the door, Mister. I ain't goin'a bite you."

When I opened the door she was standing there apparently perfectly at ease. She looked tall. Only a little light fell over my shoulder and the hall was dark and I could not see her very well. I gave her the matches and told her she could keep them, but she stood there. When she struck the match and held it to the cigarette butt in her lips, I saw her face. It was a long, wide-eyed, oval face.

"I want to close the door," I said.

"Close it. I've had doors closed in my face before too. Say, what's all that up in the ceiling?" She took a step nearer and peered in the room. She smelled strongly of yeasty body odor drenched in perfume. "That's a good one," she said, laughing, "but you won't beat 'em. They'll crawl along the ceiling and drop down on you."

Leaning toward me, she looked all around the room. Then, suddenly, she turned her eyes on me and smiled with her lips.

"You ain't fooling me, are you?"

"Fooling you?" Then I understood her. "No. I'm not fooling."

"Okie dokie, Mister. Don't forget I live here. Thanks for the light."

I was there a week and I saw her at different times sitting cross-kneed in the lobby or the evil-smelling hotel restaurant with various men, but I had no opportunity to talk with her again. Though I used to hear women's voices and their heels in the halls in the night, she was the only woman I ever saw in the hotel, and she seemed busy. But she smiled whenever she saw me, and when it was not a professional smile, her eyes smiled too. I mention this because the morning I was leaving town someone had found her wrist watch and a note on the bank under the bridge where the water suddenly deepens below the railroad yards, and the police were dragging the river for her body. Her name was Sabrah Keys.

The mountains hang over the town like a threat, and Coe Harvis, who is a lawyer in the town, will tell you how those threatening mountains darken the lives of the ten thousand people in the town—darken them, dominate them. He will tell you that there is "God's great difference between living among mountains whose bowels are coal and mountains that are merely high hills." He will speak of violence. He will speak of murder and mayhem and rape, saying that the hatreds of Alabama and Mississippi pent up in black boys almost from the day of their birth explode in the freer community of the town when those boys follow their fathers and uncles and cousins and become young men in the coal fields of West Virginia. He will tell you that seventy-three per cent of the court docket is violence and almost all the rest of it vice. And because he reads a good deal, Coe Harvis will say that more than cities like Chicago and Philadelphia and Pittsburgh, the coal camps of Hooten County nurture Bigger Thomases.

Sitting in his bare little office overlooking the long tin shed that is the railroad station, you will look down on the plaza while you listen to him. If it is late afternoon there will be white and black miners sitting on the plaza rail waiting for the night-shift dinky. If it is still enough, you will hear them discussing red-checks, script day, and fire bosses, things in fear or in anticipation of which they live. But dark comes quickly. The sun drops behind the mountains and the shadow of them plops like a great black cat in the plaza, and it is dark. Then the whores

walk from their homes in the sides of the hills over the narrow
bridges across the See River and stroll among the men who have
come in for the night from Maidlen camp and Pryco and Verco
and Wayburn. The whores wear a badge of perfume. They go
in and out of the hole-in-the-wall beneath Coe's office. Down
there there is a huge red, white, and brown banner over the bar.
It says: WORKERS OF AMERICA YOU ARE FREE! and
following the exclamation mark there is a drawing of a horse's
hindquarters dropping dung. CONTRI . . . The rest of the
banner is hidden by stacked crates of wine. Down there white
and black consort in the rather hysterical camaraderie of liquor
and vice and the United Mine Workers of America. Coe Harvis
says, "Anything goes here that you can pay for."

He will begin to tell you stories. Somehow they will all be
stories compelled by the mountains and damning the coal companies. They will all tend to show that behind the stern compulsion of men's deeds stand the coal companies and the mountains, like the Fates behind the shoulder of Aeneas. He tells you
of Jim Bold who killed Officer Dermot and fed his butchered
body to the dogs. He tells you how the companies issue script—
"just as good as cash in the company stores"—but allow only
eighty cents on a dollar's worth. He tells you . . .

But then Coe Harvis soon begins to lie. He reads a good deal
and he drinks heavily. He says that to live beneath the threatening mountains without reading and drinking and lying is impossible to him. "It would be like living in hell without inventing a
heaven," he says. From the stories he tells, part truth, part lie,
before the liquor thickens his tongue and blunts his mind, it
seems to me that if it is hell in which he lives, he dreams of an
even deeper, more violent hell.

The liquor is green-tasting, bitter, bringing tears to the eyes
and a poisonous taste to the mouth. He drinks it from a chipped
inkwell. He gets very drunk very suddenly, it seems. His face
thickens, then collapses. He mumbles, and after a while you do
not listen any more. You look across the valley to the opposite
mountain, where the only mine tipple that can be seen from

the town now has a light on it. Other lights are moving about up there in the velvet darkness. They are lamps on the caps of miners. You think how this Coe Harvis, who was a barber until he was thirty-five, came to this place from somewhere in Arkansas and started the practice of law. He sits mumbling in a drunken doze in the big chair behind his little desk, his khaki face all fallen in, his head lolling. Above the bookcase behind him are framed degrees from Walden University, 1920, and Howard University School of Law, 1931. Coe Harvis's life does not make sense to you, or it makes the kind of sense a desert makes, or a dismal swamp—a sense too deep and cogent for you to know.

A man came in while I was there. He saw me first, for Coe's desk was behind the door and the electric bulb dangled just above my head. The man stuck his head in, and I recognized him as one of the men who had directed me to the hotel two nights before. Though it was not cold, he was dressed in a heavy woolen jumper and a felt hat that was torn and finger-bitten at the brim. A large wen bundled at his throat.

"Is Coe in?" he asked, opening the door wide to see. "Drunk again." He pushed his hat back from his forehead and stood there with the back of his hands held lightly on his hips and looked at Coe. "I'll wait till he comes out of it," he said. He came in, closed the door, and took the other chair. He looked at me.

"Say, ain't you the young feller what ast me the way to the hotel?" he inquired, making hotel sound like two words.

"Yes," I answered.

"An' you come up to see Coe an' foun' him drunk." He was a black man with big, dull eyes and a ragged, gray mustache. "Danged shame. Coe's a good lawyer, 'bout the best they is. They's five colored lawyers in Hooten County an' Coe's the best. He don't ast nothin' from none of them, black nor white. I got to see him tonight. Was he very drunk?"

"He got drunk suddenly," I said.

"You can't tell 'less he's been hittin' it hard all day." He laughed. Either phlegm twanged in his throat or the wen gave a stringy resonance to his voice. "He can hol' more likker than any man I mos' ever did see."

"Have you known him long?"

"Ever since he come here in thirty-two," he said with satisfaction. "I hawled this furniture an' them books up here for him. I brung him his firs' case, near 'bout. I hawled his wife's trunk when she come out here from Arkansas. I been knowin' him. You ain't in no trouble, is you, young feller?"

"I just wanted to talk to him. Just wanted . . ."

The lawyer opened his glazed eyes, licked his tongue at the corner of his mouth and mumbled.

"Go'n back to sleep, Coe," the man said gently. "Git good an' sober."

Harvis's eyes closed again, his chin dropped to his chest. He had neither seen nor heard.

"He knows more drunk 'en mos' do sober. I been here since eighty-one, an' ain't been nobody like him in my time. I was here when Garfiel' was killed, an' that was September the year eighty-one. I was here when them ol' wood-burnin' engines use to cough down the tracks out there, an' that was 'fore you was borned."

"Is that so?"

"Coe's a smart lawyer. An' he ain't always after the dollar. That's what us ig'rent colored folks likes 'bout him. Go to the others with a little case an' firs' thing they want to know is you got any money. Not Coe. That ain't him. Four months ago, when my son-in-law kilt 'at coon, I come to Coe, an' he ain't said dollar to me yet. 'Course I paid him what I could, an' I'm goin'a keep on payin' him soon's I git my ducks in a row, but he ain't ast for it."

He had laid his hat on the floor and now was rolling a cigarette expertly between fingers stiff and tight-skinned with toil. The one front tooth in his upper gum sank deep into his fleshy underlip.

"But if people don't pay him . . ."

"That ain't what I said," he interrupted sharply. "I said he ain't always after the dollar. Besides, he has white customers."

Then, as if to take the edge off his sharpness, he said, "I'm forgittin' my manners. Name's Will Blount."

Abashed, I told him mine and we shook hands. He smoked a while in silence, alternately watching Coe for signs of recovery and looking out the window.

"I brung Coe his firs' case, near 'bout. I been dealin' in junk and scrap for forty-five years, an' it sure would s'prise you to know how much law there is in paper an' scrap."

"How?" I asked, amused at the thought.

"Well, you see a heap of stuff in somebody's yard or on the gutter. It looks like junk to you, jus' waitin' for the trash man, an' you take an' hawl it off. Maybe there's some ol' metal an' rags an' stuff, but you figger you doin' somebody a favor. Then it comes out that they say you stole it. That's law there. Coe's brung me outa many a little hole like that."

"What did you do before Harvis came?"

"I was more keerful," he said, lifting one patched leg over the other. I laughed.

"I knowed Lawyer Cartwright when he was goin' 'round here with a little satchel sellin' don't-rain-on-me suits, but he's got so airish I wouldn't take none of my lawin' to him. Oh, I had lots a little things to come up."

"Even before Harvis came?"

"I went to Cartwright the firs' time. I 'bout took him his firs' case too. But he's a switch nigger. All of them here is switch niggers 'cept Coe. An' you can't never tell. Coe might be a switch nigger too if it wasn't for his drinking. In a way o' speakin', likker keeps him down here with us, where he can he'p us. If it wasn't for that, he might git up an' git airish.

"Coe he'ps us mighty much with our lawin' an' with votin' sometimes too, only he don't have no money for votin', like Seaby Cunniman. Now there's a nigger leads a pretty good bunch of coons. But he don't lead 'em for theyselves. And he gits his'n. He leads 'em for the mayor, an' people like that. They vote the way he say. But he's a switch nigger too. Take him an' Lawyer Cartwright an' ol' man Taylor. They can't do nothin' for nobody 'cept theyselves. They got prop'ty, an' they know soon's they show their hand for niggers white folks'll be down on 'em."

He stopped and scratched his head with all ten fingers. He screwed up his face into a frown of pleasure. His scratching fingers made a sound on his head like toast being buttered.

"Funny thing, but if you ain't got nothin' seems like there ain't nothin' you can do, an' if you got something, you's 'fraid to do anything. It ain't nobody's fault, I don't guess, but it sure looks like we'se in a poke. I heard Coe say that if Lawyer Cartwright would live twenty-five years more, he might be worth a half a millyun dollars. Now what can a nigger with that much money do for anybody but hisself? But, pshaw, he ain't goin'a live that long, an' what he's got now's goin' back to the white folks."

The lawyer did not stir when a train of empty coal cars sped through the station. The train gathered up the world and rushed away with it. The office filled with the acrid odor of coal smoke and gas. Long after the train had passed, we could hear it screaming down the valley, and there seemed to be nothing in the universe but the sound of that yelling train. We kept a long silence.

"But I got along pretty good. I ain't got no kick. I come here from Decatur when I was a boy eight years old. Never went to school a day in my life. Got me a han' cart an' picked junk. Then I got me a horse. I made a livin' for me an' my wife an' my daughter. Had time to play ball, too, an' after my uncle, who I'd come out here with, got kilt in the mine, I looked after his ol' woman. Pretty soon I got me a truck. I was the only coon in Hooten County what had a truck. They didn't need n'er a one. They was miners, an' miners ain't got no use for trucks."

"It's a wonder you didn't go in the mines too," I said.

"No it ain't no wonder," he said, shaking his head. "I've stood to drif' mouths an' seen 'em bring up dead men piled in them cars like coal. In 1912, when they had that big 'plosion to Pryco, I seen 'em dig for 'leven days 'fore they got the firs' body. It ain't no wonder. I'd ruther a truck any time.

"I'd take my truck an' ride 'round an' out to the camps an' colleck what I could find. Shipped scrap way from here by the carload. I used to have a big business. I sol' my scrap mostly in Lynchburg an' Charleston. War time I use to git sixty-five dollars a ton for scrap metal, an' they'd pay the freight. Scrap's goin' up now too. I got a carload o' scrap an' paper, lackin' 'bout a ton or two. Want me a truck now to hawl it to Charleston with. Went to a man las' week to git a truck. Tol' him what I wanted to do, an' he said he'd loan me a truck if I'd go half. I tol' him I'd give him thirty dollars for twenty in thirty days, but I wouldn't go nobody's half. Cardboard paper's sellin' for fifteen dollars a ton, an' I got 'bout ten ton of it. I wouldn't go nobody's half."

Suddenly, fumbling at his fly, Coe Harvis lurched up. His eyes were glassy, and he looked stupidly around, then reeled for the door. We heard him stumble down the hall, and after a moment we heard water flushing through bad plumbing. When he returned, he slouched again in his chair and closed his eyes.

"He'll be all right in a little while," Will Blount said. "He can hol' more likker'n any man I mos' ever seen, an' he can sober up quicker. Drunk or sober, he don't take nothin' off none of 'em."

Again a silence, for Harvis now showed definite signs of coming around. The lids lifted heavily from his eyes; his tongue fumbled at the corners of his mouth. He was like some torpid, obscene animal fumbling out of slimy hibernation. He groped in the pocket of his grimy shirt and brought out a crushed package of cigarettes. But in the very act of fingering for the opening in the package, his head dropped forward on his chest and he collapsed into an inert, uncouth lump.

"I got nearly a carload a cardboard paper now, if I can git me a truck to hawl it with."

"What happened to the truck you had?"

"I had to let it go," he said. "My son-in-law, Pearl, he kilt a man 'bout four months ago, an' I had to let it go tryin' to git him clear. He's doin' time now.

"You know, it's kinda like Coe says. Something in the mines makes people weakid. This feller picked on Pearl 'bout a year. Then one day he heeled Pearl home from the mine, pickin' on him. Pearl's kids was playin' in the road. Pearl said when he seen them kids an' 'membered how this feller been pickin' on him, something jus' flip-flopped in him, an' he kilt the coon.

"He got nine years, but I'm in hopes to git him out in 'nother year. I was talkin' to the jedge this mornin'. Coe ain't said dollar to me yet, but when you take a case like that to a lawyer, it ain't no church social. So I sol' my truck. I didn't git much for it, but it was something."

Harvis was now looking at us heavily from behind thickened lids. He shook out several cigarettes from the package in his hand and picked up one and lighted it.

"Hello, Coe," Will Blount said. "How you hittin' 'em?"

"Go to hell," Coe said.

"How's everything?"

The lawyer looked from one to the other. His eyes already seemed remarkably clear for one just rousing from a drunken sleep.

"What were we talking about?"

"A little bit of everything," I said.

"You said something about passion and despair. Great subject, passion and despair."

"I was quoting," I said.

"Then I passed out. If I couldn't— Say, the phone didn't ring, did it?"

"No. It didn't ring."

"Not since I been here," Will Blount said.

"That's good," Harvis said. He jerked at his tie, ran his tongue around the inside of his mouth and went to the window and spit. He seemed to be quite sober now. From the window, he suddenly yelled at Will Blount.

"What do you want, Will Blount?"

"Coe, that man's goin'a rent that place out from under me," Will said.

"Here's a sly darky who makes a sucker out of me," Coe said, coming back to his desk. His voice had a somewhat high, discordant twang, and it broke frequently, like a changing adolescent's.

"I can't put my paper out in the weather. You know that, Coe."

"I don't give a damn what you do with it. I told you to sell it."

"I can't hawl it without no truck," Will Blount said.

"Freight it, damn it!"

"You know what 'at'll be," Will Blount said patiently. "The dealer'll say all my profit's went for freight."

"I can't stop the man from putting your paper out on the street if you haven't paid your rent," Coe said.

"There's something you can do."

"Oh, go to hell!"

"I know there's boun' to be something," Will said.

"What? Just tell me what?" Coe shouted. "I'm no miracle man! What the hell can I do?"

"You always have did something," Blount grinned, showing the blackened tooth in his upper gum. "I don't know what you can do, but you can do something."

"You black bugger!" Coe said. "All right, you sly, flattering, two-timing, no-good black bugger. All right, all right. See me tomorrow. Now get the hell out! Get out, damn you!"

"See you tomorrow, Coe," Will Blount said, unperturbed. And then he left.

Coe's eyes were quite clear now, but he kept running his tongue between his lips and his gums and wiping his lips hard against his hand. He was trembling pathetically. For a long time he stared in morose silence out of the window. Finally he wrapped his handkerchief over his forefinger and wiped his gums. Then he took a drink. He was better after the drink.

"It's people like Will Blount that may be our salvation. Who's the guy you were saying spouts about passion and despair? Well, he's no good compared to Will Blount. I'm one of your men full of passion and despair. All right. Outrage is passionate and violence is desperation, and at best we live in outrage and violence. It's the history of us. It's the history of the world. Violence, violence, violence! It's the fundamental thesis.

"But there are kinds of violence. There's a violence so damned furious, so damned direct that it's instinct. That's the violence like Pearl Slade's. That's the kind of fury he knew. Then there's the violence that's as cold and calculated as a market report, as devious as a whore's alibi. That isn't the kind of violence we're born to. That isn't the kind of violence Will Blount or Pearl Slade would know anything about unless they were taught. We're not psychical killers. We're going to kill right now, on slight or intense provocation, or we're not going to kill. There's something clean about that. A nigger might whip out a gun and shoot you dead for stepping on his toes or calling him a son-of-a-bitch, and that would be a clean killing, a sign of health. But he's not going to hunt you down for a year afterward, or even six months after, or even six days after, if you spit in his sister's face. And that would be a diseased killing, a sign of sickness."

I did not know what he was driving at. He seemed to be haranguing me, and I thought perhaps he was less sober than he seemed. His features had sharpened a little under the stimulus of the whisky and his trembling had stopped. His eyes glowed. His fingers were locked behind his head and his protruding elbows made jerky gestures as he talked.

"Now, what's happening? What's happening to men like Will Blount? They're learning. They're human and they're learning things. They're learning that they're not always oppressed simply because they're jigs. They're learning now, some of them, that oppression is part of the system, and they're beginning to find out that when they come together with other people, white people, who are oppressed, their collective security is no longer liable to be disrupted by some bastard's whim. They're learning, by God.

"And they're learning calculated violence. They're learning to scheme about it. And that's bad. It's not human. It's twisted and depraved out of God's own notion of what man is. We're brutal. All right. We're brutal enough to kill instantly, in a flash, without a thought between the emotion and the deed. But machines, deliberately reckoning on a day of vengeance, no. But look here. That's what the coal companies are, machines, deliberately cruel. And that's what we've got to fight. They're creating men in their own image, those companies. Say, did you read *Grapes of Wrath*? Remember when they're made to get off the land and the fellow looks around for something to fight? What the hell's he going to fight? There's no man to fight. You can't fight a damned bank. And you can't fight a company. So you begin to scheme. You get depraved with scheming against the company."

He let his hands down from behind his head and swiveled his chair until he faced the open window. But even as he turned, he saw the bottle on the floor beside his desk, and he looked at it a long moment before he took a drink.

"That's what these poor bastards are up against," he said, speaking more calmly. Looking out the window, he held the broken inkwell filled with whisky. "They're up against it with nothing but their guts and their changing instincts. The union's no good to them. They get hurt in the mines and they go to the company hospitals, and the company doctor says they're not badly hurt, and then the compensation commission, which is put in by the company, upholds the doctor. All right. I leave it to you. What can a bastard do but scheme?" Then he threw the whisky down his throat and set the inkwell on the desk.

"Then they go to the courts, and when they go to the courts, they're already becoming depraved. It's not justice they're looking for. They don't expect justice in the courts. They're after making somebody pay. They're after vengeance. My God, I hate it!"

But that was not all he hated, and he spilled his hatred as a tipped bucket spills water. (He was drinking with a peculiar and serious absorption.) He hated the hypocrisy of the unions. He hated the stupid errors of the Communist cell that was having growing influence among the miners. He hated the professional race leaders, "many Judases," he called them, who made their living from the exploitation of the race problem. He warned me not to be fooled by the apparent gains in civil life, gains which he said were made necessary by a campaign for national unity. Did not the same thing happen last time? And when it was all over, did not they go on lynching?

"Sure, certainly we'll get jobs; but we won't be allowed to keep 'em, unless— Look here. I'm not drunk a little bit. Just listen to me a moment. The only way we'll keep jobs is that by the time the war is over we will have welded ourselves into an industrial-economic caste so necessary to American life that no one will dare break it up. It's got to be a system as thorough-going as the cotton South thought slavery was after the cotton gin. But it's got to be voluntary, and there'll be no escape from it, no war to free us, no new Abe Lincoln."

After a while his voice grew blubbery. When the phone rang, I could tell from the tone of his voice that he was talking with his wife. He called her Hattie. I wondered what kind of a woman Hattie was. I did not think very much, for a man is not always thinking, even when his mind is most active. A man's mind can be a sort of squirrel turning a spit, even the spit of another's hate, passion, and despair.

Coe Harvis may have talked an hour after the phone rang. Or perhaps his voice thickened in less time than that. But I sat there staring out the window at the dimly lighted plaza a long time after he was silent. Harvis stared at me with blear-eyed concentration. I got up and went to the window. There was no one on the plaza. The Union News stand was folded up and dark. From the window in the hole-in-the-wall a yellow square of light shimmered across the pavement. Way up, there was the lighted tipple. Looking up at it one got the impression of seeing also the encircling, frowning mountains, whose shadow in the plaza was more than the darkness of night.

When I turned at last to go, the lawyer did not rise, but made a blurred gesture with his hand and licked his lips. His eyes were like old bird eggs, bleary and opaque. Even as I closed the door, the phone rang, and it was still ringing when I had stumbled down the dark stairs into the street.

5

It rained most of the week I lingered in the mountains. The narrow mountain roads through the coal camps were slippery with the rain and dangerous with sudden landslides. I traveled them frequently on foot, but twice with Coe Harvis, who seemed to know the very least person in the very last shack in the farthest camp.

The camps were unbelievably squalid. The atmosphere seemed tense, lairlike. Harvis told me that this was because of the long spell of wet weather. Wet weather multiplied dangers. Mines sometimes became flooded, causing shoring to collapse and trap workers in the mines. Sometimes wet weather caused the air in the mines to become so heavy and saturated with damp that the ventilators could not pull it out. In the poorer, independent mines, where safety measures were most lax and not enough fire bosses were kept on, sometimes the ventilators stopped altogether. Men suffocated unknowingly, or were blown into chunks of meat and rags.

All that week the rain was a constant threat. It rippled darkly down the sides of mountains into drift mouths. It fell straight into shafts. It set under-surface springs bubbling through veins of coal. We saw a great many pumps going, and the ventilators had been stepped up.

The miners' shacks were mere boxes, painted yellow and black or red and brown outside and divided inside into four rooms of equal size by two beaverboard partitions. No matter how large the family, it lived in one of these shacks. White and colored lived side by side. Harvis said that the common bond of work was cemented by this proximity as well as by a certain raw, green idealism springing from the roots of oppression. He said that this was salutary. He believed that any non-violent association of people was wholesome, and he laughed with triumphant pleasure when Virgle Mitchell, a thin, unattractive miner's wife, told us;

"I've learned some sense 'bout havin' kids too. I got three, but I ain't goin' a have no more. I know what to do now. The white girl who comes through here every two weeks an' leaves 'em papers told me what to do."

She pointed to a shallow pile of tabloid-size papers on the table in the center of the room. I picked up one of them. It was called with rugged simplicity *Pit*. Beneath the ragged masthead a headline proclaimed, "John L. Fights F. D."

"Commanism means more to me now than settin' 'round drinkin' Red Top ale script days an' Sundays," Virgle Mitchell went on. "In the meetin' the other night, the man said this war in Yurip was just what the minority people needed to get a break. What you think?"

Coe Harvis laughed happily at this, and at the snapshots she showed us of white and colored men and women apparently enjoying themselves on an outing together. The white people had the massive-boned heads and faces and the blond, stringy hair of eastern Europeans.

"I tell you, it's good for them," Harvis said, when we were once again walking through the camp. It was a small camp, belonging to one of the independent companies. For every two shacks there was an outdoor toilet which was reached by a plank walk from the back stoop. These walks were now under water. Water also stood in black puddles in most of the little squares of bare front yards. Nothing grew in the soil, for the soil was covered with slag.

"It's really good for them."

"How?"

"How! How!" he said with high-pitched exasperation. Then he was silent so long that I looked at him—the good features coarsened by alcohol, the eyes clear but streaked with fine brown lines radiating from the pupils.

"I don't know," he said doubtfully. "It looks like it ought to be good for them. It ought to broaden their sympathies, and that's good for them."

And within limits it was good for them. Perhaps, as Harvis argued, it was teaching them that they were not the only victims of greed and exploitation, and that this had a bolstering effect upon their sense of common humanity. Perhaps, as he said, the class struggle in which they were involved was less vicious than the myth of the race struggle in which, under other conditions of oppression, their brothers believed themselves involved. Perhaps deep down was beginning to stir and simmer here that sense of the inherent dignity of man, that hatred of oppression, that "desire for the sun, which from time to time had yeasted" in the masses and widened the limits of social advance.

But these were moot questions, and I could not share Harvis's certainty and enthusiasm, which bubbled again as we moved on. Besides, I was tired of so much unalleviated misery, of the utter absorption in a struggle against a system. It seemed a blind struggle, unlighted by aspiration. Even the alcoholic brilliance of the polemics of Harvis could not argue convincingly an idealistic basis for the communism I found in the coal fields. What I had seen of it did not convince me that it was interested in broadening the basis of human relationships, but rather that it aimed only to transpose them, so that those at the top—the rich and mighty—would come to the mud in the bottom. It seemed not to be interested in leveling barriers of caste and class and race, but only in scaling them. Surely this imbruting struggle was not all. Surely, even here in the coal fields . . .

"Even here in the coal fields," Harvis said, "men have souls that dream of heaven."

As proof of this, he proposed to take me to a church in the mountains. I thought at first that he was playing some sardonic joke, but he was not. When he came for me two evenings later, he was cold sober. It was raining in hard, swift squalls. Twice we had to stop on the narrow road to let the squalls blow themselves out, but after a while the wind died and the rain came slow and steady.

The camp lay in a kind of pocket in the hills, and we approached it over a road that did not reach the camp, but was blocked by a spur of the mountain. We climbed the worn path over the spur and into the camp. It seemed a big camp, and there must have been a road straight through it, but I did not see it in the dark. A few lights showed through the windows of the shacks, but we saw no one as we crossed the camp and started up the mountain.

"Is this all the path there is?" I asked.

"There's another where the chute was, but that's down at the end," Harvis said.

Water dripped on us from the thick bushes and trees that hemmed the path in. Higher up we came to a slag heap and an abandoned heading on a shelflike clearing. Here Harvis pulled out a bottle of whisky and took a drink. The mine shaft rose dark and massive and rather frightening in the blackness, but from here the ascent was easier, for a broad path—the chute way —cut through the dead trees from another direction and curled up the mountainside. Soon we saw several distinct glimmers of light above us, and then, very low, we heard the tinny clash of cymbals and the pulse of a heavy drum. I stopped to listen.

"Is that the church?" I asked, whispering.

"Come on. Come on," Coe said. But we both waited, listening.

The cymbals stopped, but the drum continued to give off a monotonous, almost inaudible, but living sound. Its rhythm reverberated from the trees: it seemed the very pulse of the ground. Everything was caught up in it and had life by reason of its relentless will. Relentless. That was it. It was like the heartbeat of the night.

"You go in," Harvis said.

"Aren't you going?"

"I think not," he whispered.

The light streamed through a dozen cracks in a small, low

building above us. The front half of the building was on the shelf facing the next rise, but the back half rested on heavy pilings sunk into the slope where we were. We climbed. The cymbals started again.

"Why?"

"I've been. I'll stay out here," Harvis answered.

"You'll get soaked, man."

"Just sit down and don't say anything in there. Don't say a thing." He pulled out the bottle and took a long drink.

"All right," I said. "I'm going in." I certainly had not come all this way simply to stand out in the rain, and I was annoyed by Coe's refusal to go in.

"Don't speak to anyone," Coe said, as I walked toward the door.

Indeed, I could not have spoken had I wished. I had to squat near the door. Set two feet from the walls, a row of benches made a hollow square of the small central space. I faced an almost solid wall of backs. In order to get a seat, one had to walk behind the benches to a break in the side on the left and go into the square in full view of everyone.

There was nothing in the square. Suspended by a strand of wire from the ceiling above it, a lantern cast a damp light. No one seemed aware of my presence. The backs in front of me were curved in rigid lines. The faces I saw on the side benches were set and empty, the eyes wide and staring blankly into the empty square. No one moved except the young white woman beating the cymbals and the Negro woman beating the drum. The white woman had dank hair which wormed in long strings down her thin cheeks. I counted nine white people, four men and five women. Most of them were broad-headed, massive-boned, thin. There were perhaps forty people in all. The room smelled of damp clothing and kerosene.

Antiphonally to the throb of the drum and the clank of the cymbals, a pair of hands began to beat with the sucking sound of cupped hands. I could not see the clapper, but another pair of hands joined, and soon a dozen, and then all hands were beating.

Almost imperceptibly the heads in front of me began to bob. The sound and the bobbing heads made a definite pattern and the pattern had an indefinable power which flowed like a tide from beat to beat. Not a vocal sound was uttered. Stooped there behind the curved and now flexing backs, I grew tense with expectation of a shout, a moan. The blood ran heavy to my stomach. The throbbing sound went on for ten minutes, then gradually died. Still no word was spoken, no vocal sound made, and the silence had the same inexorable quality as the rhythmic sound.

After an interval, during which faces again became set and drained and no one moved, a short, dark woman rose and began to speak in a voice so low that I could distinguish no words. The voice came unhurriedly and with apparent calm and she seemed to be repeating something in a series. She looked at no one and no one seemed to look at her. All eyes stared into the square. The woman wiped her face clumsily with a rag balled in her fingers and talked in a low, unhurried voice. Another woman, one of those on the bench in front of me, arose and began to speak. She was less than three feet from me, but I could not make out her words either. They seemed to come in a strange tongue. A man arose later, and then another person and another, until a dozen people, among them two of the white women, were talking all at once in low voices and with strange words. All this was done in apparent calm, the same dead calm as in a state of hypnosis.

When half the room was standing and speaking, the pounding rhythm broke in again. The cymbals clanked first, then the drum pulsed. As I listened, something began to happen as irresistibly as a tide happens. Voices fell into the cadence of the drum beat; eyes which had been merely staring, like the eyes of hypnotics, now gleamed fanatically, with a kind of lustful ecstasy. Still none of the sound was loud, but it was steady, compelling, implacable. I got up, for everyone was standing now, and I could not see from my stooping position. The square was still empty. Like a great force, the primitive rhythm slowly broke down restraint, beat aside the decorous cloak of humanity, drew from out dark depths the forces that civilization had leashed.

A sickened, heavy feeling in my stomach, I watched over the shoulders of those in front of me. A slim, brown man, with a bulging deformity of the shoulder, began to dance. Sweat rolled down his face and purpled his shirt. Then a woman, and a second woman danced. And yet, it could not be called dancing, for their feet did not move—only their heads, shoulders, and arms—and there was a terrible compulsion about it. Others joined the first three. Then a woman's thick, Slavic voice rose in an incomprehensible gibberish. It was not cadenced like the others. It broke through the rhythm without destroying it. I got a glimpse of the woman beating the cymbals. She held the cymbals at arm's length above her head, and her lips were drawn back over her clenched teeth in an ecstatic snarl. Her eyes were closed. A man in front of me thrust out his powerful arms. The spastic movements of head, shoulders, and arms were beginning to possess them all.

I cannot describe that orgy, nor put into words the pulse of the strange, compelling rhythm. It went on and on inexhaustibly. It seemed to strip one, tear one apart. No prayer had been offered, no hymn had been sung, but a great and red-eyed god had been invoked out of the dark forests of humanity's beginnings. Somehow it sickened me and shriveled me with shame. And out of shame grew my anger at Coe Harvis.

I slipped out. I pumped the air of the place from my lungs. It had stopped raining, and a piece of moon guarded a flock of sheep in the sky. A little wind was up, soughing gently through the mountain pines.

I did not see Coe until his voice, quite near, said, " 'S'at you?" He was sitting on the ground against a tree. He steadied himself against the tree and got up. He was drunk.

"Well?" he said, twisting close to my face.

"Oh, go to hell," I said.

"Dish make you feel funny? Watch out! Watch out!" he said, curving a warning finger under my nose.

"Give me the light. Come on," I said.

"Lishen, lishen," he said, grabbing my arm. Holding me with one hand, he pointed toward the church with the other. "In there they ash'ly forgetch. Look. Lishen," he said, clawing drunkenly at me. "Univershal brotherhood. See? It ain't goin'a come with brains. T'hell wits 'at stuff. No ph'losophy. Lishen. When it comesh, it'll come from 'moshion, from 'at stuff in 'er 'peated over n' over." He slashed the air drunkenly with his free hand. He made drunken gestures and he talked drunkenly, but he was in dead-sober earnest.

"Lishen. Shutch forch all the di'tators in the whole wide worl' won't stop. All the laws n' all the thinkin' in whole worl'. Makes you feelsh funny, don' it? In'ellecksuals—you know what I mean?—on their arses. Shocked!" He tittered drunkenly, but almost immediately became drunkenly serious again. "Absho-lutely shocked what you saw. You saw it, didn' cha? Lishen. Thatsh way it's goin'a be, so help me. People who don' think. People wi'out tradishun, noshing but pashion n' 'spair. Lishen. They'll do it, by God!"

Pushing against me, he straightened himself upright and shook himself. He handed me the flashlight. "Gim'me cigarette. Waitin' f'you bring me smoke," he said.

We started down. I went ahead with the flashlight, but Harvis stumbled after a few paces and I took him by the arm. The water from the foliage dropped on us. The pulsing was in the woods again, flowing through them like an unstoppable tide. I hurried, dragging Coe with me.

"Lishen."

"Forget it. It's not going to happen. Baloney," I said.

"Don' 'gree, don' 'gree. Objec', objec', objec'!" he fairly screamed.

"All right, all right," I said. "Then it will happen."

When we started down the slope below the abandoned mine, Harvis broke into high-pitched, raucous song, and I could not make him stop.

Way up in-a dat valley,
Prayin' on my knees;
Tellin' God about my troubles,
An'to he'p me ef-a He please.

Way up on-a dat mountain,
Prayin' . . .

6

Within the borders of the traditional South I was free to go wherever I chose and to talk with whoever would talk. The only real limits were my resources in making contacts. I found Negroes generally easy to approach. Most of them would not have understood me had I explained my mission. They would have been suspicious and resentful. But they made it unnecessary even to mention my connections or to use the flattering letters of introduction given me by various friends and influential acquaintances.

Occasionally my letters and connections did come in handy. I used them only after the embarrassing experience of having a letter to the president of a Negro college in West Virginia go unanswered. I asked permission to visit the campus and the privilege of talking with him. I offered myself in no special capacity, and it may be that the letter did not reach his desk. But after that, whenever I wished to visit a Negro college, I first revealed my connections. Indeed, I was forced to acknowledge a fact I had avoided. Negro schoolmen are terrific snobs, the true bourgeoisie. Grasping eagerly for straws of recognition, a great many of them proclaim loudly their race-faith and avow social radicalism. Some let it be known discreetly that they are Communists. But theirs is a puerile profession of faith, a smart-alecky, show-off kind of radicalism. In reality they look to the upper-middle-class whites for their social philosophy and in actual practice ape that class's indifference to social and political matters and reforms. They are a bulwark against positive action, liberal or even independent thought, and spiritual and economic freedom. Though as a schoolman myself I had had experience of the utmost extremes of reactionary fatuity, I was constantly shocked and baffled by the prevalence of certain paradoxical attitudes and the dominance of certain characteristics.

There was a shocking indecency in their intellectual pretensions. One listened to unnumbered recitals of excellence in scholarly fields. All talked the language of pedants. Nearly everyone was "writing a dissertation," or "gathering data," or "fixing to study," usually at Columbia. Too many of them were mere manipulators of knowledge. Only the exceptional few were true to themselves. Few of them seemed to realize that there were great issues abroad in the world, or even that there was a war being fought to settle them. Nearly everyone professed an interest in some recondite and esoteric metaphysical problem, or in some discovery that once and for all would clinch proof of a vanished Negro and African civilization older and better than anything the whites had ever known. The other extreme of this was the way in which some of them played down their Negroness and with traitorous scorn belittled everything Negro from Booker Washington to Joe Louis.

They were an intensely race-conscious lot, these schoolmen, but lacking any real pride in it and any real faith in its future. Most of them saw the Negro's position in America as growing worse every year. They cited items from the less responsible Negro papers. They seemed to take the attitude that passive pessimism was the smart thing, a really brilliant and saving grace for them. And yet they were angered by the passivism of others. They had attained that elevated state of mind in which everything becomes absolute. They were bold in their assumption that no one else knew or had read anything. I heard one professor argue arrogantly, straight from William James, he said, "that the degree of a people's advancement could be estimated by its acquisition of three wills—the will to live, the will to power, the will to immortality. The trouble with the nigrah race," he said, using that polite southern white compromise between nigger and Negro, "is that it's got nothing but the will to live."

Of the brilliant, down-to-earth race scholars in the humanities—Frazier, Reid, Davis, Johnson—they knew nothing but the newspaper write-ups. Obviously the schoolmen's leanings toward things esoteric was a puerile flight from reality. This was especially true of the teachers of humanities in the private institutions. The teachers of science and the teachers of the trades in the state institutions were usually better. They were generally closer to life. But the teachers of the trades were considered a lower class, and they were the sensitive victims of the snobbery of the teachers of the humanities.

Even the work of the better teachers, especially in the state colleges, was too often vitiated by the testy captiousness of the administration and the death-dealing attitude of paternalism. Administrators spoke of *my* institution, *my* faculty, *my* students. This attitude was almost universal and went altogether unchallenged. Even teachers in unguarded moments spoke of the *president's* faculty and the *president's* campus.

One Sunday in October I sat in a college chapel at the vespers hour and listened to the president address the audience.

"I feel sorry for you, my students," he said. "I don't see how you learn anything. I don't see how you can develop to your highest and best. Oh, it isn't your fault," he said, shaking a hand at them and smiling piteously. Then in a voice still low, still compassionate, but grown suddenly exhortatory, he went on.

"Do you know how our blessed Lord-'n-Saviour Jesus Christ taught his disciples? He taught by example! That's why the disciples developed to their highest and best. They had the example of Christ. But you've got no examples in your teachers, and you can't develop to your highest and best, because even though your teachers think they're high-powered and smart, they're not teaching by example, and therefore you can't develop to your highest and best."

He had been leaning forward, talking intimately to his audience. Now he straightened up and walked to the other side of the pulpit.

"I hear my teachers are running 'round at night, married ones the same as those not married, young ones and those so old they ought to spend all their spare time praying. Yes indeed. Drinking liquor an' smoking cigarettes an' dancing in beer parlors out yonder on the road. That's why I feel sorry for my lambs this evening."

Really uncertain for a moment of where I was, I looked about. But there above the rostrum a wide fringe of velvet valance bore the letters of the college in scripted gold. The college choir, which a few minutes before had sung so beautifully, was banked on the rostrum behind the president. There was the unmistakably student audience, more than five hundred of them, the young women in the center, the young men farther over on the right. And there were the faculty, immediately in front of me on the left. They were obviously cowed. No one looked at another. A few squirmed, grew tense, lowered their heads. Some others tried to look nonchalant, protected, self-righteous.

"You know, my students, gratitude is a wonderful thing. I wake up every morning feeling grateful to God—and telling Him so too!—for sparing me through another dark night that we know not what the end will be. Don't you feel grateful to whoever befriends you? Don't you? I have no respect for that man or woman who does not feel gratitude. So if you haven't got it, don't let me know it, because I don't care if you've been here a hundred years, I won't let you graduate.

"I'm going to tell you something a lot of you didn't know. Some of my teachers came to me as poor students, like you. I won't call any names, because I don't want to embarrass anybody. But some of them . . ."

The faculty was looking up now from lowered heads, interested, resentful, but not daring to show resentment too plainly.

". . . didn't have anything but the clothes they had on their backs. Their folks couldn't hardly spare them out of the cotton patch, but they were making a sacrifice. These teachers, who were poor students then, poor's dirt, poor's a farm full of gullies, they came to me and threw themselves on my charity and mercy. I gave them work. I let them register in this fine institution here without one penny to rub against the other one. I went into the city and begged my friends for clothes to cover up their nakedness. I put them on the pay roll in the summers. . . ."

The faculty was whispering as school children dare to whisper under the eyes of a stern teacher. Neither their heads nor their lips moved. Their words made a low, sibilant sound.

". . . I was a father to them. And when they graduated, I made them teachers."

There was a long pause now, a period of gestation. Then, almost whispering, eyes a-glitter behind his glasses, the president leaned forward.

"Wouldn't you feel grateful if someone did all that for you? Wouldn't you? Wouldn't you do all you could to develop to your highest and best? Of course you would, my students. You'd do all you could to show your appreciation." Then his voice roared out in disconsolate anguish, "Oh, if only I could awaken in my teachers a sense of gratitude tonight! Oh, if only I could make them see how fortunate they are to have jobs! If I could only open their hearts to the humble feelings of the blessed Martha when she took down her hair and wiped the feet of Jesus!

"Let the choir sing 'Live Humble.'" Then he sat down.

Surely these were not teachers who had just been lashed! Surely this was not an institution of learning, of higher learning! No wonder, then, that a terrible apathy, cloaked in job-saving dilettantism, had replaced the enthusiasms of the earliest days of Negro education. While the choir sang, memories flowed back on me in a turgid flood, and I wondered how I could have forgotten the snobbery and the moral weakness, the paternalism, the downright administrative bullying, and the almost psychopathic hurly-burly of much that passed for education.

When the singing was over, I walked toward the domestic

science practice cottage where I had been assigned a room. I walked slowly, hoping that one of the teachers would overtake me. I looked back. They were in a tight, animated group under the light outside the chapel. I could tell they were the faculty because most of them wore hats. They had gathered in impotent, fearful discussion before. They would gather again. There was a pattern to their conclave. The bolder—that is to say, the younger, newer—among them were probably protesting vehemently. They would protest a second and perhaps a fifth time. But eventually someone would warn them. The wording of the warning had long since become standard. . . . "Nothing goes on here that the president doesn't know about. You can't even go to the toilet. . . . Blacklist. These presidents have a blacklist. . . ." And the bolder ones would become cautious, and later they would begin to compensate, to grow snobbish and effete. By the next fall, they would listen to the new, brave people and shake their heads and murmur weakly, "That's right. That sure is right." But in their hearts they would know that the fight in them was gone, the game had exhausted them and murdered their morale.

Now the students had streamed out and down the gravel path, the young women in ragged formation, two and two, matrons bringing up the rear. The young men straggled away. There was the decorous sound of low voices, a light, trilling, fancy whistling of "Live Humble," and then, as the young women disappeared through the door of their dormitory and the young men vanished in the darkness, everything was quiet again. A smaller group of teachers was under the light in front of the chapel now. In another moment the light went out.

My mind was busy with its memories, and I did not see her until she cleared her throat nervously and stepped into the walk from the shadow of a tree. I recognized her instantly, for she and the official who welcomed me were the only persons I had met. I did not know her name.

"I was waiting," she said, and laughed in confusion.

"Were you?" I said. I was as confused as she.

"It was disgusting, wasn't it?" she blurted out impulsively.

"I didn't see you," I said.

"Oh, I was in the balcony," and again she laughed.

She was a big, young woman. I remembered from the afternoon that she was clean-limbed, undecorated, with a wiry thatch of unpressed hair. Her voice was toothy and edged with excitement.

"I shouldn't be here," she said. "I should have waited out on the road. But I never think of these things until afterwards." She stopped, listening. "Oh, Lord! They're beginning to come. Quick! Let's get out on the road."

I gathered that she was talking about the members of the faculty, who had broken their group outside the chapel and now were beginning to appear dimly as jerking, lengthening shadows through the trees. We could hear their soft talking. Though it was just after nine, except for them the campus was quiet, full of shadows made the more black by lights that shone in the doorways of a few buildings.

"We'll walk up and down the road," she said. "See? There's a little light here. Nobody can say we're doing anything bad. Everybody can see us. It's important that you make yourself seeable around here at night. Oh, Lord!" She laughed nervously, without amusement. "Gee! How close behind us are they? Do you think they see us?"

"I think so," I said.

Where the light from the suddenly opened door of a cottage streamed across the road, I stopped and pretended to be studying the stars.

"They'll be sure to see us now," I said, amused at my own sympathetic reaction to her.

She looked up too. I stole glances at her uptilted face. It was dark and structural-looking, and neither soft nor beautiful as women's faces usually are in the night.

"Gee! This is a good idea," she whispered.

The voices approached, and we could tell by the sound of them the moment we were seen. The patch of light in which we stood ate up the approaching shadows. Then suddenly the people were there, going by us, peering at us, speaking to us in simpering tones with peculiar emphasis. When they had gone, we turned and started in the opposite direction.

"I had to take a chance," she said. "I didn't think you'd have time to see me later. Isn't this a killer!" She turned her head to look at me and gave a low, astonished whistle. Then she laughed. But in the middle of her laughter, she caught herself and exclaimed, "We mustn't walk too fast, like we're going somewhere, or either too slow, like—like sweethearts."

I laughed then, and she turned, almost stopped.

"What's funny?" she demanded.

"This," I said, throwing out my hands. But she continued to stare at me until my laughter went hollow. Then she strode on in silence beside me.

"I want to get away from this place," she said tensely. "It's not funny. It's really not."

"No. I guess maybe it isn't."

"My Lord! I'm going on three years here, and it's anything but funny. Oh, Lord!" She made a sound in her throat, like the beginning of weeping. All her impulses seemed right at the surface, as if she had been stripped of all but raw nerve tissue.

"Maybe you can help me, or either give me some advice," she said. "Do you know anything about these scholarships?"

"A little," I said.

"Seems like everybody but me can get one. How do you get them? If I could get one, it would sure fix me right up."

"Getting one seems to be quite complicated," I said.

"Oh, Lord! You have to know somebody, I guess."

"But first you have to apply."

"You can't tell me anything about applying," she said. "I've applied to three different things twice. And that's all you know? Or either you don't want to tell me," she added accusingly.

"That's all I know," I said. "Some people get them, some don't."

"I'm not the type," she broke out, in a sudden, hot passion of self-pity. "I'm too black to get one! All I have to do is send my picture and they don't bother to look into my record. I send my picture, and they don't even bother to write any more."

She was strange, frustrated, and full of troubles. Some of these troubles were imaginary, little devils of a growing persecution complex perhaps; but others were real, the burgeons of awareness of a situation against which the sound part of her mind fought. I think she was the only one of many college teachers with whom I talked who told me the truth.

I answered nothing to her outburst.

"Don't pay me any mind," she said later. "Those things just come out. So you can't help me after all? Would you endorse me for one?"

"I'm afraid my endorsement wouldn't mean anything," I said.

"I guess I'll be a lost chicken this time next year," she said quietly. "I think he's going to fire me."

"Why do you think that?"

"Because he doesn't like me sitting in the balcony. There I am up in the balcony all by my lonesome every time we have vespers. He doesn't like it. I know he doesn't. I think he halfway suspicions something, and he's going to fire me, or either make a rule."

"But what's the good of sitting up in the balcony all by your lonesome?" I asked her.

"It's funny," she said. "It's really a killer, and I know it's crazy of me. But when I was a little girl, the preacher came to our house and tried to run his hand up my clothes. I was afraid to tell my mamma, but every time I went to church I always sat up in front and made faces at him. Now I sit up in the balcony. . . ."

"And makes faces?" I laughed.

"No. I don't make faces, but I look straight at the old boy. That gets his goat."

"Did he try . . . ?"

"Oh, no," she said quickly. "I'm too black for his speed. I'm not saying what he does to others. I'm not saying."

She had not answered the question I was going to ask, but now it did not matter. I said nothing.

"You don't know," she said. "I'm halfway sorry I got an education, my poor mamma working herself half to death and all. Lord, how she worked! And for what?"

"Listen. Aren't you taking a chance, talking to me this way? Suppose . . ."

But she had halted in her tracks and was looking at me searchingly in the dark. "Oh, Lord!" she said, and I thought for a moment she was really going to cry. "Oh, you wouldn't!"

"No. I wouldn't," I said, "but . . ."

"I didn't think you would. I thought I got your number right," she said, not at all intending flattery. "I felt like I halfway could trust you. Everything's bad enough as it is. The highest and best. Humph!"

"That's an awful phrase," I said.

"Everybody's always mocking the old boy with it around here. Anything you get here is an awful get."

We reached the curve opposite the boys' dormitory. The road went over a fill, and farther down a row of faculty cottages faced on it. The farmland stretched beyond. We went down the road to the farmland, and then we turned back.

The cottages sat far back from the road, separated from it by a wide stretch of grass. The dark shapes of grazing cows moved over the grass, and we could hear pigs snuffling hoarsely in the ditches. It was a beautiful night, very still and quiet and warm. The stars were packed in the sky like sequins in a tub, and their glittering was a kind of song. Our footfalls clacked on the hard clay. The fall rains had held off, and the dry odor of parched vegetation lay in the air.

But what tension and anxiety, what turmoil and guile lay

beneath this soft cloak of peace! I felt suddenly overwhelmed by past experiences which filled me with a sense of dismal futility. What was there about the getting of knowledge that so perverted and robbed us? What was it that made us rotten before we ripened? What process of cultivation necessary to a slow, firm fruiting had we missed in that swift harrowing of the immeasurable field from slavery to higher education? We seemed to rot at the touch of ripeness, as the night-blooming cereus rots and grows fetid with the coming of dawn. Like it, we too, perhaps, stemmed from the leaf rather than from root and branch.

I had heard it argued by wise men. In Atlanta in 1931, I think, among a little group of white and colored men, I had heard Toyohiko Kagawa. The Japanese, half-mystic, half-pragmatist, was on a lecture tour, and this was at a reception following a platform address. It was one of those stand-up social affairs where people gather to gape and hear the lion of the moment roar. Only Kagawa was not a lion. Very human and very shy, I thought, he stood in a corner surrounded by a group of important men. His eyes were very sick and he kept wiping them with a wad of absorbent cotton soaked in something that smelled of almond oil. He held his glasses in his hand.

When I edged up to the group, the men were discussing the race problem and underprivileged peoples generally—the peasants of Spain and Poland, the muzhiks of Czarist Russia, the Negro in America. They were really not discussing, but uttering platitudinous half-truths conversationally, and Kagawa kept bobbing his head and smiling politely. John Hope was in that group, and Ivy Lee, a publicist who was in Atlanta in some connection with raising money for Negro education, and I think also one of the grandsons of John D. Rockefeller.

Breathlessly, in a pause before anyone could stop me (my voice sounded loud in my ears, for at the moment a dead silence had fallen), I said, "Then the problem, sir, if it is a problem, looks hopeless?"

Mr. Hope looked at me irritably, his gray eyes almost white behind his spectacles.

"Of course it's a problem," he said.

"Yes, yes," Mr. Kagawa said, with a courteous softness of speech. "You are a teacher, yes. To some educated underprivileged the problems of the underprivileged always seem hopeless. It is the same everywhere. It is a penalty they pay for being educated, and it is also, if I may say, gentlemen, an absence of Christ. They breathe an atmosphere of poison. Once education lifts them above the level of their people, there is no longer any direction for them to go. Forgive me, gentlemen, but I am a religious man," he said, smiling deferentially. "I say go in the direction of Christ. What else is there for the time? If education has proved one brilliant, he can never go to the level of his capacity, for the world he strives to attain is walled higher than the old wall of China. In Poland and Spain it is the wall of the aristocracy. And yes, in Spain, I must say, the wall of the established church. Among the black people in America it is the wall of the white race. For these people no great scientific laboratories, no skyscrapers to build, no high government spot. Such a one in his career soon reaches the limit to which he can go. He reaches it early, at forty or forty-five, the prime. Then in the fullness of his strength there is the wall, a wall so high. And there in the shadow of that wall he begins to rot, to go to pieces morally first, then spiritually, then intellectually. At fifty he is no better than a shadow of his promise at thirty. Surely it seems hopeless to him. But is there not Christ?"

No one answered him. Kagawa daubed his inflamed, thick-lidded eyes with the wad of soaked cotton and put on his glasses. His lids quivered painfully. A shining, beautiful black girl in a maid's cap came with blocks of ice cream in saucers. She gave me one first, and I passed it on to the Japanese. He smiled shyly, thanking me. Then the talk went to other things and I moved away.

All this came back to me now as I walked in the quiet-seeming night with this young woman by my side. Even the smell from the cotton sponge, the feeling of the cold sweat in my hands, the looks on the faces of the people came back to me. And then I realized that my companion had been talking some time.

"And she won't stop," she said. "She just keeps on teaching and farming and doing day work for white folks besides. She could come here and live with me. I make eighty dollars a month. But she wants me to save, to go on and on studying. Oh, Lord! for what? She might's well come, 'cause I can't save enough out of seven-twenty a year. And I can't get a scholarship, seems like. Lord, but my mamma's got faith in education! But she don't know. She don't half know!"

She left me at the path to the practice cottage, because for some reason which she thought good she did not wish me to walk with her to the dormitory.

7

I went in to see the president the next morning. He was having his shoes shined. A young man was kneeling before him. The president's foot rested on the boy's raised knee and the boy was coating the leather with polish. Leaning back in his chair, the president talked to me of inconsequential things the while he kept his eyes on the job the boy was doing, cautioning him in the midst of the brushwork not to get the dressing on his socks. The gray socks matched the soft gray shirt and the design in the blue breast-pocket handkerchief and the tie.

"Want you to tell me what you think of our place here after you have a chance to look around," the president said. "Did they fix you up nice and comf'table?"

"Fine, thanks," I said.

"That's good. That's good. Glad to hear it. Be careful, son!" He withdrew his foot suddenly and then replaced it gingerly. "Hits my pet corn every time," he said, snuffling with cautious laughter.

The office was beautiful. The chairs were upholstered in soft green leather. The president's desk had everything, and everything looked shiny and new. Large portrait photographs of important and formerly important white men in the state looked down from the cool green walls. An oil portrait of the president slanted cautiously against the wall from the top of the bookcase. The shelves of the bookcase were empty of books, but they held an old iron bell, a bulbous-welled oil lamp with a broken chimney, and a metal water dipper. The president told me that the site on which the college stood had once been a plantation and that the bell had been used to call slaves from the fields. The lamp, he said, was the one he had learned to read by. The water dipper was the last thing his mother had touched. He said that there was a great deal of "symbolical significance" in these things, but he did not bother to explain.

The boy finished and got up and stood uncertainly waiting while the president examined the polish job.

"That'll do, son," the president said. "Put those things away neat."

Gathering the shoeshine things, the boy went to a door in the corner of the room, and in a moment we heard water running.

"What you doing, son?" the president called. There was more than a trace of steel in his voice.

"Suh?" the boy said, coming to the door, his hands dripping soapy water.

"You know I don't allow you to wash up in my closet. You know better than that, son."

"Yes, suh," the boy said darkly, wiping one hand down his thigh. He kept his eyes lowered as he went out.

"Well, well," the president said, rubbing his soft hands together. "And is this the first institution you've visited?"

"No, it isn't, Mr. President," I said.

"Well, what do you think of us here?"

"You said you'd give me a chance to look around," I reminded him. "I got in only last night."

He snuffled with appreciative laughter. Each time he laughed his hand flew to the knot of his tie, as if he were afraid the action of his gullet would untie it. He was a man in his late middle years, with a dark and very dry skin. Skin and hair looked as if they had been bleached.

"What do you think of the campaign? Who's going to win?" It was obvious that he was just making talk.

"I don't know."

"It's a hot one," he said. "Willkie's liable to root Roosevelt out on this third-term business. And then there're a lot of people who don't like this W.P.A. W.P.A. and relief and things like that are ruining our people. Never were but so anxious to work, but relief is making them too shiftless now. Sort of subsidizing shiftlessness. It's no good for Negroes. There's no substitute for hard work.

"And what's their argument? The W.P.A. people, I mean. Their argument is that the big trouble in the South is poverty and ignorance. Then if that's the case, make 'em work. Put 'em out in the fields and let 'em chop cotton, even if it's only ten-cent cotton. Give 'em a sense of responsibility for earning their bread. Don't feed 'em! Let them work for it. All this idle farm-land. I can take you a few miles back country here and show you place after place where a furrow hasn't been turned in five years. Negroes living on 'em too. Hoeing a little garden, some way or another, maybe, but living mostly on relief. There's no sense to it."

He had very strong convictions on this point, but either it had never occurred to him or he had ignored completely that the general poverty of the Negro in the South was only one phase of a problem rooted in economic causes of great magnitude. Indeed, by inference he denied this. He believed that the plight of the Negro was altogether due to certain traits in the racial character, and in general held to a large portion of the South's conception of the Negro as improvident, immoral, and generally no good. I do not know whether any feelings of propriety kept him from revealing his ideas on this score to his professional underlings. Probably not. He was a voluble talker, though not a harem-scarem one. If he knew the destructive force of his ideas, how they vitiated the already weakened idealism of his profession, and if he had some ulterior motive for talk-ing to me in this fashion, I could not discover it.

I did not argue. He was not the sort with whom one can hold a conversation. He talked at me, spouting like a geyser, and holding the upper hand completely. Even my questions fell on deaf ears.

His ideas on politics baffled me. He had once let a teacher go for trying to vote. "A man like that can tie a knot in five minutes it'd take another man a lifetime to undo. A lot o' north-ern men are lacking common sense. I don't want 'em on my faculty," he said. For some reason the whole idea seemed amus-ing to him, for he snuffled with laughter. Voting in local elec-tions was a waste of time anyway, and he could not understand why people ever bothered to vote in them, "voting for patronage over little ol' two-cent jobs." On the other hand, he said, he could not see that it made any difference to Negroes what party was in power in Washington. "The issues raised in national pol-itics," he said, "are foreign to the mass interests of Negroes. What do Negroes know or care about isolationism, or the na-tional debt, or breaking the third-term tradition? Or even anti-lynching bills? They just aren't real issues, except maybe anti-lynching, and I'm inclined to agree with my friend up there," he said, tossing his head in the general direction of the photographs on the wall. "I think the South can take care of that business."

"Then your belief is . . ." I tried to break in headlong, but he interrupted me, and I heard a buzzer going in the outer office.

"Let me show you something."

The secretary appeared, and he asked her to bring him his "race material" scrapbook. "I been following this thing a long time," he went on. "You might say it's a hobby with me. I've been collecting material on it for a long time, and you can fol-low it through the papers, you can see the changing attitude. I've got friends scattered all over the South who clip things and send 'em to me. One of these days, I'm going to write a book about it. White and that N.A.A.C.P. crowd—they're all right, you understand. Doing a good work. But they'd swallow twice if they could follow the thing like I been following it. I've spent money on this thing. Photostatic copies and such cost money. I've paid as much as twenty-five dollars to have newspaper files searched for something I'd heard about. I wouldn't sell this for anything. Look."

The scrapbook was a huge affair. Its hard, paperboard back, much patched, covered the desk. It was really quite a remarkable collection of newspaper clippings, photostat copies of clippings, political tracts, and broadsides printed on slick, greasy-looking paper.

"Look," the president said, eagerly turning and re-turning the huge sheets. "Read any one of these first ones. Wait. Read this, and then . . ." holding one hand in the place, he turned toward the back ". . . read this. If these things don't open your eyes to the way things are changing in the South . . ."

I bent over and read in almost microscopic print from the *Louisville Daily Commercial*, August 26, 1870:

Maysville, Ky: August 25. Intelligence has just been received from Flemingsburg of the hanging of a Negro last night by a party of citizens in disguise. The brute was taken from the jail, wherein he had been placed for a brutal ravishment of a lady of respectability. The circumstances were of an unusually aggravating nature, and the summary course of punishment meets with general approval. The lady is in a somewhat dangerous condition. . . .

I raised up and he let the pages fall to the other item near the back of the book. I stooped again and read, this time from the *Commercial Appeal* of Memphis, Tennessee, under a Jackson, Mississippi, dateline, October 10, 1940, less than a week before:

Governor Johnson Thursday night was reported on good authority to have ordered out a detachment of National Guardsmen to prevent violence at Friday morning's hanging of Hilton Fortenberry at Prentiss. . . .

I skipped the next paragraph.

. . . Use of troops was believed necessary because of the enraged attitude of Jeff Davis Countians over . . .

My eyes wandered over the clippings on the double page. The clippings were all about race-relations and generally mob violence. I wondered what they proved, or what the president thought they proved. I raised my head.

"A world of difference, eh?" the president said.

What was there to argue about? I believed also that at the very top and perhaps at the very bottom attitudes were changing, but I could not help noticing that the president's scrapbook as proof of this was valueless, a deliberate self-deception.

"Mob violence, of course, isn't the only problem," I ventured.

"Of course not. Of course not," he agreed. "But it's the only one the white man is duty bound to do something about, because he makes that problem, you see. The rest of it is mostly ignorance and shiftlessness on the Negro's part. If the Negro would get rid of some of those problems—if he'd just get some of that shiftlessness and laziness out of him, then the white people would be more disposed to do something about their end. They're already doing something about it as it is. I've just shown you," he said, laying his hand on the scrapbook.

"Then in your opinion, the reason the race problem is not solved is because of the Negro's irresponsibility and . . . ?"

"That's about the size of it," he answered, his hand slipping to his tie.

"But if education's any good at all," I began. But he interrupted me quickly, almost angrily, to reveal one of those inconsistencies of thought and character that made him so puzzling to me.

"Education! Who said anything about education?" Leaning forward confidentially, he went on. "You don't call this education, do you? T. and A. or A. and M. colleges. You don't call that education, do you? My institution doesn't pretend to do anything but train. A.B. degrees," he said, scornfully, breaking into his snuffling laughter.

"Did you ever hear that story about the two old colored men and the A.B. degree?"

"No," I said.

"These two old boys speculating what A.B. meant after a man's name, and one of them said it meant 'also black' and the other said it meant 'arse backwards'? You've never heard that?"

"Oh, yes. I've heard that," I said.

"Well, that about gets it," he said, his hand flying to the knot of his tie to hold it in place while he laughed.

It was difficult not to speculate about him, especially since he would tell me nothing of his life except that he was a graduate of one of those Reconstruction period schools in the deep South. He said he never talked about himself. He had never even written an autobiographical sketch for *Who's Who in Colored America*. That worthy volume had got nearly everything about him wrong. "My parentage in that thing," he said, "is just fifty per cent wrong. They invented that father."

So there was everything about the man to arouse speculation. The general impression I had of him from his vespers speech was not materially altered by closer contact. He was paternalistic, but he was also aware that paternalism was frowned upon. He believed in what he was doing, and he also believed only in his way of doing it.

"I don't want to turn out gentlemen here," he said. "What good is a Negro gentleman? What good is a gentleman with a manure fork? You know what my job is? My job is to train these black boys and girls to do their prescribed work with a singleness of purpose. That's my job. To train men, you've got to tough out of 'em certain crazy notions. That's different from educating them. You don't talk about educating men for farming and road-making. You don't hear the government talking about educating men, do you? Ever notice what these N.Y.A. signs say? They say, 'N.Y.A. work training center.' You don't talk about educating men for war. That's nonsense. You know what soldiers have to do and you train 'em to do just that. Well, I know what Negroes have to do and I train 'em to do just that."

I did not bat an eye. "You've got to be very sure," I said.

"I'm sure."

I changed the subject. "Speaking of war," I said, "what do you think of this one?"

"It looks like all Hitler to me," he answered. "There's a man! If he's wrong, he's wrong in a big way."

"But suppose he wins?"

"It's about time for England's number to be up. He may win."

I got up, wishing now to get out quickly so that I could put down the things he had said.

"There's a lot of propaganda about this totalitarian business," he said. "All the Italians and eighty-five million Germans can't be all that wrong. Well," he said, getting up now also, "make yourself at home here. Make yourself at home. How long you staying?"

"I'm not certain," I said.

"Glad to have you. Like to have you to dinner 'fore you leave us. Make yourself at home."

(About a month later I mailed him a political ballad which I found outside the general store and Post Office in a town in Mississippi. Apparently the ballad was from a sheaf that had been nailed to a board just outside the store. The top margin was torn in the way one finds the top margins of handbills advertising railroad excursions in southern railroad stations torn. The ballad said:

> All good white men listen to me say,
> It's a fine life here in the U. S. A.
> With Fords and Chevvies and coffee with cream,
> Eating what we like and talking what we mean.
> That's the American dream.
>
> Across the water this Hitler guy
> Ain't no better than a pig in a sty.
> We got him figgered right enough.

When he starts raring we'll do our stuff.
When he gets tight we'll get tough.

Our great statesmen will bring us through,
Roosevelt and Harrison and Cord Hull too.
So white men be you good or wicked,
Keep the nigger in his place
And DAMN the Willkie ticket.

I do not know whether he put it in his scrapbook.)

8

Neither letters nor connections would have meant anything
to most of the people with whom I talked, in whose homes I
visited, whose bed and board I often shared. Occasionally I
found suspicion and silence, a great deal of it among the tenants in the lower Mississippi Delta and the inhospitable flats of
Arkansas. But generally I found simple folk, eager to talk, and
hospitable to the point of embarrassment. One profane, frosty-
headed man, who lived in a one-room cabin ("But unbehol'in'
to ne'r a cracker, by Jesis!") smack in the center of a Louisiana
cane field, invited me to share his moss mattress with him and
his lanky young third wife. It was a cold night, and the wind
in the cane sounded eerily like the wailing of lost souls. But I
slept in my car in the brake, and at intervals all through the
night Jake Ancram came out with a lantern to bring me first
an extra quilt, then a moss cushion for my head, and finally a
hot stone wrapped in burlap.

There was something heartening about these people. There
was strength in their utter lack of sophistication, and a kind of
fulfillment in their terrigenous dependence upon a will which
they called God. Not that they were all Christians. I hitch hiked
across half a county in Arkansas one rag and scrap of an old
woman who said she was a sin-eater. She looked it indeed. She
had been driven out of Pine Bluff at the turn of the century,
and now she followed a route, like a circuit preacher, eating

sin. It was a good calling, she said, and perhaps by "good" she meant Christian.

I cannot imagine my letters doing other than arousing a mild sense of derision in the Beans. Mrs. Bean would have been polite and said, "Ain't that nice!" But Mr. Bean would have read them through solemnly and solemnly handed them to me again, and his stiff, high shoes would have creaked as he walked away. He would have felt but not said that the tongue of the serpent had at last entered his peaceful bit of the Tennessee Valley between Halls Cross Road and New Market, where there are still white Republicans, and where from the Beans' front porch on still nights one can hear the oozing sound the marsh makes from the action of the Holston River that runs close by. Later he would have made a "parable," by which he meant merely a story with a point. But "made" is also the wrong word, for out of his forty-seven years he would have found an experience to tell to make the point of my having letters of introduction as sharp as a lancet.

For seventeen years the Beans had been in the valley. They had stumbled there in a blind and driven search for refuge. In South Carolina, down around Denmark, John Bean had been a cotton farmer and had prospered. But he had had a brother, and that brother "they say, forced a white woman." They let John Bean come and cut the blackened, mutilated body down.

"I thought I stood in right good around there, but the nex' Satterdee night they come again. There was only six of them, and I knew them all. They were pretty much jacked up. They had something in a sack. They emptied the sack on the kitchen table, and Callie, she screamed. But I couldn't tell what it was at first. Looked like little sweet pataters that had got black in the sun.

" 'Well, Johnnie,' Mr. Exum says, 'I guess you gotta go.'

" 'Yes, suh, I guess I better,' I said.

" ' 'Morrow night, Johnnie, you be gone,' Mr. Exum says.

" 'Yes, suh, Mr. Exum,' I says.

" 'An' don't come back never no more,' he says. An' I nodded my head an' he turned to the other mens and says, 'Come on, boys. Johnnie'll go. I can swear by Johnnie.'

"If it wasn't for Mr. Exum, they'da killed me," John Bean said.

After the men had gone, he realized what the things were that looked like sweet potatoes that had blackened in the sun. They were human fingers.

That was how the Beans happened to be in this little cup in the valley.

John Bean had an eighth-grade schooling, so he taught the one-room county school, filling in, he said. The young woman from the city who had been the teacher fourteen years ago just went back to the city one night and never returned. He had been filling in ever since. He had always intended to go down to Knoxville to the summer school, but that was the "main garden and canning time," and five acres of mean ground was too much for Callie with her bad knee. Besides, she could not preach for him. So he had never got around to going. And his sixth-grade pupils always did all right at the county school. Not many of them had been going the past four or five years though. The girls always seemed to go further in school than the boys—one or two girls even went to college in Knoxville. But the boys, who were always late finishing up, "near about men when they get through," because they had to stay out two or three of the six school months, seemed to get discouraged. Now they "mostly followed up" the T.V.A. all through the valley. Some of them had worked on the dams at Wheeler, Pickwick, and Gunawald, and were now way down in Kentucky working on the dam at Gilbertsville. But those that went to county school, and especially the girls, always did all right. All of them did all right, "excusing Alec Hill's young 'uns."

John Bean happened to tell me the story of Alec Hill because one evening Alec came down the road and sat within touching distance of us on the edge of the porch. He was a small, dried-up, yellow man, with the startling, alert, blue-gray eyes of a young child. He was dressed in washed-out blue denim jumper and overalls. On the porch stood three blackened smudge pots, converted from half-gallon syrup tins.

"Goin'a burn 'em out, huh, Fess?" Alec asked in a voice entirely lacking tonal quality. He looked among the dampened leaves and straw in each of the pots, and then he swung down from the porch and went to the cart track that ran by the side of the house and picked up two handfuls of dung. He broke the dung, spit in it until it was soft, hashed it thoroughly, and put some in each pot. He was smiling blandly.

"That stuff stinks, Alec," Mr. Bean said.

But Alec did not hear him. He was as deaf as a stone. He had sat down again on the edge of the porch, his back to us, one leg on the step, the other swinging free. And while he sat there, John Bean told his parable in the same tones of bemused sympathy with which he seemed to tell everything.

"Everybody 'round here tells it, an' if you was going to be here a couple more days and got to talking to people right good, you'd hear it a dozen times or more. Even some of them that don't really know it tell it. So besides what I know of it by seeing it an' being with it—an' that's more then most—I know what people tell.

"To tell you the truth, it ain't really remarkable, I guess. But it's a parable in a way of speaking. Even those folks who ain't no better than Alec, there, tells his story. I ain't talking about the kind of better of being good. The real old folks tells his father's story, or his uncle's story. They all 'mount to 'bout the same thing. An' telling gives the folks who tell it something. I been here seventeen years, an' I can't figger out what it is."

Even though I knew Alec Hill was deaf, I felt a flutter of embarrassment when John Bean started talking. The man sat right in front of us, and so long as it was light I could see the side of his face. Every now and then he turned and said something, smiling that bland, light-eyed smile. But as the story went on, I lost my feeling of embarrassment altogether.

"It didn't seem like nothing at all when I first heard it," Mr. Bean said. "But this is the thing like a parable about it: You study it over in your mind, an' after a while you begin to see something in it.

"Take for instance when I first got ahold to this place. The road ran back of the house and where the house sets now was marsh. My piece o' garden was the other side of the road, an' the house that was here wasn't no better then a terbacca shed. But I bought it, house, land, and all for three hundred dollars. Out front, there, the land had to be filled in first. I'd get up soon in the morning an' hawl stuff to fill it in with. My mules drug many a wrecked ottimobile from the Cross Road an' dumped in there. I worked on it morning and evening. But more'n once I started to give her up, an' then I'd get to thinking 'bout Alec, there. It wasn't strength thinking about him gave me, an' it wasn't ambition. I be dog if I know what it was, but it was something. I filled her in an' built me this house, an' then the county come along an' built the road out there an' finished fillin' in as much as it is.

"The thing about it, it's hard to tell a story about a man that's still living. It ain't got no end yet, an' it's all in little stray pieces which you can't make fit sometimes 'til you know the end. Ends of things are funny things, an' sometimes powerful important from a understanding point of view. I'd give a heap to know what Lazarus done after Jesus raised him from the dead, an' a heap to know what happened to the lef'-over fish after He got done feeding the multitude. I'd have a more better understanding if I could know.

"Well, Alec's story ain't got no end. It won't have no end 'til he's dead. An' then it's going to begin all over again in one of his childring, just like it begun all over again from his father in him.

"Some folks mighty li'ble to say Alec should a been dead, with all the things that's done happened to him. But you see him setting there, an' he ain't full of misery. I bet a heap if Alec ain't freer in his mind than you or me or anybody.

"When I come here, Alec was a man on the sunny side of thirty. 'Bout thirty-two or three, I figger, just a piece older then me. His first wife had been dead a year or two. She had broke down in health when her seventh child come, just completely broke down. She'd been flat on her back more'n a year 'fore she died. A couple of their childring was in school, an' I use to see them trotting by here. Pretty little gals. They put me something in mind of yeller windfall apples before the sun and damp specks 'em. They wasn't taken proper care of, but they was pretty.

"The gals dropped out of school along in November. This ain't no cotton-growing country here, but in them days it use to be if a man was able, he'd take his whole family an' move 'cross the mountains 'bout the last of October an' they'd pick cotton til Chris'mus time, an' then come home just in time for hawg-killing an' Chris'mus cheer. But Alec was a cropper on a right sizable place further down, an' he wasn't able. He couldn'ta moved nohow himself till late November an' accounts was all straight. 'Course Alec had right much freedom. It was just about the meanest, poorest land there is that he was working, an' Mr. McSmathers figgered he couldn't lose, no matter what Alec raised. So when the gals stopped trotting by here to school, I thought Alec was having some new trouble, an' I went on down there.

"I never had seen Alec before, though I'd heard a heap about him, 'cause folks was beginning to talk about him like they talked about his daddy. He hadn't been struck with lightning then, neither, so he wasn't deef. But I wasn't paying no mind much to what folks was saying. It wasn't nothing real bad then, you understand. I don't just mean sin bad. Folks was doing a lot of guesswork, or they was talking mostly 'bout his daddy an' where the Hill blood come from in the first place. You can look at him and see he's all a mixture. But who ain't? I am myself, I guess, way back somewheres. Over in South Ca'lina you can pretty much tell about folks, but here 'mongst these knobs an' hollers you just bound to guess at what your eyes don't see.

"I went on over there because I thought he was having a trouble. A man with a sick wife an' then a dead wife an' seven childring is kinda handicapped. An' I knew something about being handicapped myself.

"I went on over there an' found him an' four of his childring, even the little-bitty one, who wasn't more'n six, picking a two-acre field of the meanest cotton you ever saw. I was so surprised that I didn't think nothing 'bout the two big gals an' the oldest boy at first. I'd heard them say Alec had a cotton crop, but I didn't give much credick to it. When folks start saying you're peculiar, they begin to add on to it, 'cause even a peculiar man ain't so peculiar you can't think up things to make him look more that way. I thought this cotton crop Alec was supposed to have was something like that. This ain't no cotton section here, an' I never had heard of nobody trying to make a crop. This stuff Alec had had come up all right, but it wasn't no more'n eight inches an' the bolls was 'bout the size of runt radishes. If he'da had a hundred acres of that kind of cotton it wouldn't a brought him ten dollars. But I was so surprised when I seen it that I disremembered what I'd went for.

" 'Mr. Hill,' I said, 'this ain't no cotton-growing section. How come you plant cotton?'

"He looked hurt, like somebody had beat him. He kept working his nose with his upper lip. Put me in mind of a man with a nose fulla snot berries an' both hands full so he can't pick 'em. Then he says what I found out later he always says. 'I guess I took a wrong turning,' he says. 'I figgered I might could grow a crop of cotton an' surprise folks an' have a money crop too. I guess I took a wrong turning.'

"He was like a little yeller whupped dog, only it was worse. He had whupped himself, but didn't blame himself an' wasn't mad nor disgusted about it. He kept turning his hat 'round on his head an' turning it till it provoked me.

"Then I remembered what I'd come for, an' asked him 'bout the gals.

" 'I think I got that right,' he said, kinda smiling. 'I sent them 'cross the mountains with Laurie to pick cotton. They'll be back nex' month.'

"I said, 'What, Mr. Hill?' 'cause I couldn't take it in. An' he told me all over again. I didn't say nothing. Here he'd done sent his daughters with his boy, who wasn't more'n 'leven or twelve at the most, an' both of them was older then him. Clear 'cross the mountains, over 'round Sparta. The oldest gal was only around fourteen.

"Well, the boy didn't come back at all. He ain't come back to this day. The youngest gal come back with some valley folks who was over there picking too. It was spring 'fore the nex' one come back home, an' she come pregnant. She birthed a snow-drift baby that summer."

Just before it grew dark, Alec lit the smudge pots and set them in a smoking row to windward. He stood watching them for a while. The smoke seethed around the tops of the pots, then broke and drifted heavily toward us. It stank. Alec came back smiling to the porch. Watching the smudge pots complacently, he pulled out a plug of tobacco, champed it off in a corner of his mouth, and sat down again. Mrs. Bean came out and joined us. She brought one of the front room chairs, because there was only the rough bench upon which John Bean and I sat on the porch.

"To look at Alec," Mr. Bean said, "you wouldn't think he could be the daddy to all the childring he is. How many you think he's got?"

"I don't know," I said.

"Fourteen," John Bean said, leaning forward so that his large-knuckled hands hung loosely between his knees. "Fourteen, an' all but five of them living at home, helping him sharecrop on halves. Living in two rooms and a loft an' no doors between the rooms.

"An' Alec ain't what you'd call a plain ign'rent man. I heard him tell me with his own mouth that he went to school till he was twenty, an' got to the fifth grade. I guess it weren't his fault that he didn't get no further. He had to stay out right much, I reckon. His daddy share-cropped too. His daddy had twenty-two childring an' three wives, an' he lived to bury every last one of his wives.

"Alec himself got married again in 1928. He didn't marry nobody from this valley. Didn't nobody know he was going to do it. He just went away one day an' stayed about a week, an' when he come back he was dragging this woman with him. Folks say he didn't marry nobody from 'round here 'cause everybody knew about him an' none wouldn't marry him. But I don't think Alec tried to fool nobody, the woman he married nor nobody else. I guess he was just able to get her 'cause she figgered no matter who she married she couldn't be no worse off than she was, I guess. Anyway, he brought his second wife on back here. I was preaching some an' filling in at the school, so when I heard Alec had him another wife, I felt like it was my duty to go on down there. I just felt like things like that was my business. Still feel that way. I wanted to have a look at his woman too.

"Alec's been share-cropping them sixteen acres of mean land for fifteen years anyhow. He ain't a bad farmer when it comes to raising stuff that can be raised on the land he's got. He'll work a crop a mighty heap better'n most. Mr. McSmathers used to give him his head, 'cause he knew it was mean land an' anything he got out of it was better'n nothing an' more then he would of got with anybody else on it. But the place changed hands, an' old man Billy Davenport wanted them sixteen acres all planted to terbacca, 'cept a little-bitty strip, 'bout half a acre, for Alec's garden. The garden was right up to the door. Old man Billy Davenport was a hard man.

"Sometimes it's pretty chilly down here in April. I've seen the ground so hard the first of April you just couldn't get a plow blade in her. An' it was right airish that day. But when I went on down there, Alec's new wife was outside washing. I was glad to see that, 'cause the Hills had been going dirty.

The oldest gals didn't seem to be much good at housework somehow.

"But I seen right away that Alec's wife was pregnant, an' I knew she musta been pregnant when he married her. This didn't surprise me none. Folks 'round here do things like that. Seems like they don't care 'bout who nor what. But they're getting a heap better now. I guess I been preaching about it so much that it's took hold some kinda way. I got a good look at Alec's wife when I was coming up through the low ground, an' she was pregnant all right. But what seemed peculiar to me, she had some kind of wire rigged up from the tub to the boiling pot, an' every time she went to the pot she'd hold on to this wire till she came to the starb that the wire was rigged to. Then she'd feel out with her hands an' drop whatever she had in the pot. Coming back to the tub was the same way. An' then I figgered it out, Alec's new woman was blind.

"When I come up. I spoke to her, an' she looked like she was looking to see where my voice was coming from. Her eyeballs looked like they was painted white with 'namel paint. Kinda raised the pity hair on my back.

" 'Ha do,' she said. 'Who are you?' She had a mighty soft way of speaking. To look at her throat you'd think she would of whistled her words. Her throat wasn't much bigger 'round then that pipe stem, an' a great big vein ran down it an' inside her dress. Otherwise she wasn't no big woman an' she wasn't no small woman.

"I told her who I was, an' she said, 'I'll learn you after a while. It don't take me long to learn folks.' An' she reached down in the tub an' picked up a piece, like she wanted to show me being blind was no handicap to her.

"I had seen Alec. He was setting on the toilet. The toilet didn't have no door, but it had a potato sack stretched 'cross, an' I could see Alec's legs setting there. I went over an' stood outside an' called him.

" 'That you, Fess?' he wanted to know.

" 'Well, Alec, so you got you another wife,' I said.

" 'That ain't all I got, Fess,' he says.

"I started looking 'round then, but I was still on the wife question. I wanted it to be a proper, legal marriage, 'cause I was trying to teach 'em about that. So thinking about that, I didn't see nothing new. I said, 'Did her preacher marry you up, Alec?'

"'Yes, suh, Fess,' he says. 'It's a good, legal marriage. But go look the other side of the house an' you'll see what else I got new 'sides a woman. I'll be out in a minute.'

"I didn't know what I expected, but I walked on 'round the other side of the house, an' when I seen what it was I thought I'd have a stroke of fit. It was a old piece of car. Looked like it was older'n me. It didn't have nothing like a car ought to have. There wasn't no lights on it, and the steering wheel was broke, an' the roof was stove in. Some of Alec's childring was playing 'round in it, an' on the inside it looked a heap worse then on the outside. Well, when Alec come out, I asked him where in the world he got that thing.

"'Mr. Billy Davenport give it to me,' he says.

"'Give it to you?' I says.

"'Well, it won't hardly cost me nothing,' he says. 'I'm going to tear the body off it an' build me a bus body. I'm going to make a bus out of it. A heap o' childrings' folks that goes to the County says they'd be mighty happy to pay me fifty cents a week to take 'em back an' forth. Mr. Billy says if I do that, it won't hardly cost me nothing. A whole heap a folks wants me to take their childring,' he says. 'I think I took a right turning when I got it,' he says.

"There wasn't no use arg'ing. I knew what had happened how come he had it. Mr. Davenport's a hard man. He was expecting a good crop, an' he'd about took a mortgage on Alec's half for that old piece a car. It was done, an' there wasn't nothing to do but wait for the outcome. Alec's a pitiful, stubborn man sometimes, an' just naturally wrong-headed. There wasn't no use arg'ing with him."

Alec Hill got up. It was quite dark now, and I could just make out the blur of his face as he turned to us. He had said nothing since lighting the pots, apparently content just to sit there and look out across the marsh and turn occasionally to look at the smoking, stinking smudge pots, and then back at us, smiling his light-eyed smile.

"I guess I'll be slippin' on down, Fess," he said, in that hollow, toneless voice.

Before he left, he went to each of the pots and shook it vigorously, making the smoke pour out in great volume. He said something afterwards, but we did not catch it, and then he glided away into the darkness of the road. After he had gone, John Bean was silent.

"I wonder that Alec didn't go away from here when he was a young man," I said.

"You ain't from 'round here," Mr. Bean said, "so you wouldn't hardly have the right understanding. You wouldn't hardly have the understanding of valley people like Alec. The young ones are different. But the older ones, they're like trees. They're rooted to the land where they're planted. A tree don't think whether the soil it's in is mean or fat. It just thrives and blossoms, or withers up an' dies. Alec didn't get married the first time till he was twenty-five an' a little more. He lived with his daddy till he got married. But marriage wasn't no plant food for him. He ain't throve a bit better than he did when he was living with his daddy.

"Well, I guess you know I wanted to ask him how come he married up with a handicapped woman like that. I'd give a heap to know whether he was sorry for her 'cause she was blind, or just what. That baby she birthed wasn't none a Alec's. I know that. I don't believe he'd seen her till he went out there a piece from Mountain City an' married up with her. No. I think maybe he just sort a saw her standing on the road some place. Maybe she had a bundle. Maybe she didn't have no place to go. He could of been over in another valley somewhere saying he wanted to get married an' nobody'd have him when he come across Pinkie.

There ain't no telling why Alec does things. He don't seem to have no reason like other men. I'd sure give a heap to know.

"Alec never did get that old piece a car to run but once, an' then it jumped about twenty yards an' busted into the corner of his house an' knocked the post down. Never did hear no more 'bout the bus, 'cept from the school childring kidding Alec's young'uns, which I made them cut it out. I guess Alec forgot what he had a mind to do. He wouldn't of done it no way, an' if he would of done it, he couldn't have done it that year, 'cause terbacca is a slave crop. With his wife handicapped an' the youngest childring in school, he had only the boy to help him. Alec had to do it all, near 'bout. The debt old man Billy got him into with that car got a strangle holt on him. He's in a square box, an' two sides is debt, an' two sides is work, an' two sides is just plain wrong-headedness. What provokes me about Alec is that he never finds fault an' he never gets mad. I'd like to see him get mad once.

"He should of got mad that time the medicine man come through here. He always come 'bout settling time every year. If he was coming, he'd come in a few weeks now. Didn't come last year. I guess his business fell off. I preached 'bout him a heap, an' I guess it's took some effect.

"But he come through here one time an' sold Alec a whole gallon jug of some stuff that was supposed to fatten hawgs. You was supposed to feed 'em a little bit of this stuff every day. Alec only had three hawgs, an' them hawgs mighta died anyhow, but I be dog if two of them hawgs didn't turn up an' die about a week 'fore Chris'mus. There wasn't no hawg disease going 'round, an' Alec's hawgs was the only ones that died. Nobody else hadn't bought none of that stuff. But Alec didn't get mad. Next settling time, the medicine man come around just as big, an' Alec bought him some more kind a stuff, for himself this time. I guess if that would of killed him, like the hawg stuff killed the hawgs, I guess he'd a been satisfied. But I don't guess Alec even had remembrance of it, how he had to go 'round begging hawg-meat for him an' his'n that Chris'mus.

"He had a right nice Chris'mus that year, better'n ne'r a one he's had since, an' before, too, I guess. The church had a basket collection for him. Give him everything—can goods an' meal an' dress goods. That was the year he didn't raise nothin' to eat for himself at all, nothing but the hawgs that died an' terbacca, an' he owed old man Billy his part of that.

"It raised pity hair that night in church with his wife. Alec set there just smiling, like you seen him do this evening, like nothing had happened, an' he was just as good off as the next one. He don't never smile no other way. But his wife, she was blind, an' I be dog if she didn't shed tears that night after I commenced reading off the names of the givers and what they'd gave. I never knew blind people could cry until that night. She was pregnant again, an' her dress was hitched up over her stomick like a tent with the wind under it, an' she stood there crying an' picking at her cheeks, an' Alec was smiling like it was a pleasure to see her cry. A heap a women cried to look at her. They had so much stuff, I had to hitch up my cart to tote it for 'em. Pinkie cried all the way home to her place."

He paused to listen to something, and then I heard it too. It was the rain, coming in swift, heavy drops, like droppings of warm lead. It ran swiftly down the road and then suddenly on the porch roof. There was no wind at all.

"I don't know whether this here's the fall rains—it's overdue —or just a little rainblow," Mr. Bean said. "I guess this is the last time I'll set comfortable on the gallery till spring though."

It did not seem to rain very hard, but in a few minutes it had made puddles and we could hear it dropping in the puddles from the eaves of the porch. The air became saturated with damp. Mrs. Bean went in, and after a while I began to feel chilled.

John Bean got up and went to the smudge pots, which were going out in the rain. He was a tall, ungainly man, with a loose way of moving, as if he were strung together. He brought the smudge pots back and put them on the porch against the house. Then he sat down again, and I could hear him shaving raw

tobacco from his twist and stuffing his pipe. His square, dark
face jumped out in the flare of the match.

"If a man's story can end before he dies," Mr. Bean said, "then
Alec's story ended with a storm. It ended year before last. An'
maybe it is ended, 'cause things won't ever be any different with
him. He turns about on himself, never learning nothing from
the last time, an' never getting mad. He talks about his wrong
turnings, but he don't never stop taking them. He talks about
what he'd do if he could live over again, or if he had his wishes.
But he wouldn't do any different. He'd still kill his hawgs with
poison medicine. He'd still live in a house without any doors on
the inside of it. He'd still plant cotton against the laws of nature.
He'd still sleep with his wife in the same bed with his half-
growed daughter. He'd still take bad turnings an' not get mad
about nothing.

"People say it's his blood. Folks say that by the time the Hill
mixture of white an' black an' Indian an' I don't know what
all got down to Alec, then the blood started running backwards.
But that ain't it. I think Alec's a living parable that the good
Lord's sent down here in this valley to teach us a lesson of some
kind. I don't know what the lesson is, but it's there, and getting
plainer every day. If I outlive him—an' that's what I'm fixing
to do—I'll know what it is. I'd give a heap to know. When I
know that, I'll be almost ready to die.

"It's pitiful to hear him sometimes. It's a bad kind a pity, 'cause
Alec ain't felt no real misery himself. It may be a sin to wish a
human man felt misery, but I wish Alec did. An' it's a sin in a
way for him to make somebody else feel misery an' he don't feel
none himself. It's 'zactly like one time I seen a cripple man over
in Johnson City. He was begging beside the Post Office an' I gave
him some change in his cap. He was a bad cripple, one leg
twisted up an' turned clear 'round back of him, an' the other
didn't look no more good to walk on than a cornstalk. I gave
him some change, an' then that night I seen him again out to the

fair grounds. He was drunk as a new-born lamb. Alec makes me feel kind a like I felt that time.

" 'Fess,' he says sometimes, 'my greatest trouble I've seen is to accomplish anything an' treat my family like I think they ought to be. I can't charge nobody with that. I've give shelter to my childring, but that ain't mine. I've give 'em clothes, but they was some other body's first. I've just took too many wrong turnings.'

"If anything else happens to him, it'll be the same kind of thing, an' it'll go on in his childring till God sends one stroke and kills them all. He's fifty-one an' a little more now, an' he's got Pinkie pregnant again. The youngest gal from his first wife, they say, is woodsing pretty free. They had to put her out of the county school. The next boy ain't worth the sweat it took to get him. So the thing is repeating itself. I notice this year, too, he's got another stand of corn.

"Year 'fore last, when everything was way down, old man Billy Davenport told Alec he wasn't going to contract for no crop the old way. He said he was going to try him out on money rent that year. 'Course, old man Billy made like he was doing Alec a favor, but all he meant was that he was charging Alec a hundred an' twenty dollars a year for land an' the house an' wasn't going to stand behind no agreement Alec made with the contractor neither. The way they do in this valley is to contract with a company down to Halls for terbacca plants and fertilize, an' then the planter stands behind the cropper. But year 'fore last, with everything way down, an' too much warehouse terbacca anyway, old man Billy wasn't taking no chances. He took a lien on whatever crop Alec growed for his one hundred and twenty dollars. Well, Alec knocked about, going to first this one an' that one till he got his plants an' fertilize.

"Alec had did a little public work that winter, but 'steada paying some of his debts or furnishing himself for the winter, he bought himself some cockerels. He had it in his mind to caponize them. Feed for them things was mighty expensive. But that ain't all. Where was he going a sell 'em? People in this valley raises their own chickens and things. Alec had some notion of doing business with eating places in Johnson City an' Knoxville an' the like, but a trip over there an' back costs a heap a money. Besides, he wasn't stretching himself enough to really do business in Knoxville. But anyhow, Alec guessed he'd save on cockerel feed if he growed some corn. So he went ahead on an' put in four acres of corn an' about six of terbacca. Them's all the terbacca plants they'd let him have.

"Alec's a good farmer. He can get something out a the meanest kind of ground. That's one of the things that makes you study so hard about him. He ain't lazy. He'll work a piece of mean land an' coach something out of it if it ain't no more than runt radishes. If Alec was lazy, I would have a more better understanding. Put me something in mind of something Callie told me once.

"One time Callie went to a circus when she was a bitty-gal, an' there was a rope walker in it. He got 'bout halfway 'cross walking the rope an' all of a sudden he fell. The ringmaster come out, she said, an' explained to the people that he was a good rope walker, but something had went wrong, somebody had messed with the rope or something. That's the way it is with Alec: something's always going wrong, an' the rope's always messing up on him.

"Alec's a good farmer. Along in the last of May his terbacca was as pretty as you please, not high, but leafing out, an' his corn was earing out nice. Looked like Alec had took a right turning.

"Long about that same time, a jobber come through the valley. Jobbers go 'round buying up crops like they stand. They buy right in the field an' don't wait for harvest. They offer you so much for your crop, an' if you agree an' something happens to it, then it's their loss. Alec should of took his offer. He didn't have no terbacca barn, an' he was going to cure in old man Billy's barn, an' he was goin'a charge him for that. He didn't have nothing to transport it to the warehouse with, an' somebody would of charged him for that. He should of took the offer, but he didn't.

"The jobber hadn't been gone out of here two days when we had one of them fast, bad storms. It was a hailstorm, with plenty of wind and lightning. Some of them hailstones was as big as a baby's fist. It broke out winderlights an' tore off roofs. It only lasted 'bout twenty minutes, but it was a mean twenty minutes. Most of the crops 'round here was still in the ground, 'cept terbacca an' early corn. I thought about Alec right away, an' soon's I could, I slipped on down there.

"Well, suh, all Alec's crop was beat down, an' Alec looked like he had been out in the storm, which he had. He had big bruises all over his face an' arms, an' they was swolled up an' turning blue by the minute. He was setting on the stoop just looking at his crop. 'Bout a dozen of the cockerels that couldn't get under the house soon enough was dead there in the yard. I don't know where Pinkie an' the childring was—in the house, I reckon, but I didn't see 'em. Alec was just setting out on the stoop looking at his beat an' ruint crop when I got there.

" 'Well, Fess,' he said, when I come up, 'I should of sold it. I'd be mighty proud now if I would of sold it. I guess I took a wrong turn that time.'

"There wasn't nothing for me to say an' I didn't say nothing. I was feeling sorry for him, an' I said a little prayer to the Lord to myself for his always taking wrong turnings an' never blaming himself or anyone, an' just accepting it, like a tree accepts the weather. It's a stubborn kind a thing, an' I can't get the right understanding of it. But that's just the way he is. That's the way he's always going to be.

"He looked up at me, though, an' I had to say something. He was smiling in his way, but his eyes was like the pictures you see of old-time statchers' eyes, just as blank as eggshells. 'Too bad, Alec,' I said.

" 'What'd you say, Fess?' he wanted to know.

" 'Too bad,' I says again. But I could tell he wasn't hearing me, an' it just come to me all of a sudden that he was deef. But he hadn't found it out himself. I think the lightning must of struck him without him knowing it, or else the hail had busted his ear drums. He didn't know anyhow, an' even when he talked an' couldn't hear himself, he didn't know it. Maybe deef folks can hear themselves. I don't know. He looked at the field an' the dead cockerels laying in the yard again. He looked like he was still smiling, but I couldn't tell so good with his face swelling bigger every minute. Or it could be that he was just getting something out of his teeth with his tongue.

" 'My gal, India, she's took a wrong turning, too, Fess,' he says. 'Sleeping with me an' Pinkie every night, but I be dog if I knowed she was going to have a baby. Did you?' "

John Bean stopped and lit his pipe again and smoked without saying anything for a while. The rain had stopped, but the damp chill in the air was sharper. It was very dark. We could hear the sucking, licking sound that the action of the river made in the marsh.

"I'd sure give a heap to know for certain whose baby that was India birthed," John Bean said, after a while. "I sure would."

9

John Bean did not make a parable of Aunt Julie Lively. I suppose there was really nothing in her life to make a parable of, nothing whose meaning was not plain except perhaps her ancient, unknown age. For this John Bean had a great respect. "I suppose," he said, the day he took me to see her, "God's reserving her for something." In this case, he was willing to let God's hidden purpose reveal itself.

Aunt Julie had been in the valley only four years. She had been brought there from Knoxville by a white man, the same one who had arranged her pension for her and whom she knew only as "Mr. Pete."

"In the city those darkies would have robbed her every whipstitch," Mr. Pete told John Bean. "So I heard about this place and what fine folks you-all were and brought her out here. She gets twelve dollars pension money, and that ought to be enough to keep her. I or my wife'll run out here every little while."

So John Bean had fixed up the one-room shack that had formerly been the school and Aunt Julie was installed. She insisted on living alone, on cooking her own food, on doing everything for herself, " 'Til I drap on my feet."

Her shack was comfortable, but dark, for in the fall and winter she kept the rough wooden blinds drawn shut over the windows. It was furnished with a billowing bed, an old chest with brass fittings, and innumerable odds and ends. Near the center of the room, facing each other across a frayed rag rug, stood a straight chair and a wicker rocker. Between them a polished brass spittoon gleamed in the dim light. Aunt Julie sat in the rocker and I sat in the straight chair. John Bean went on down the valley to have a look in at Alec Hill's.

"I live easy now, son," Aunt Julie said, "mighty easy. I don't have to worry for nothin'. Not a thing in this worl' do I have to worry about. But it ain't always been this way. No, suh, it ain't."

Her voice seemed to originate in her skull and came with a reedy, quavering quality. Her lips would not close over her ill-fitting false teeth, so that she wore a strained and rather fierce grin. There were irregular spots on her face that had lost pigment. Her hands were already dead white.

"Son, I don't know how old I be. There was a woman in Knoxville that was a right young chippy when I lived with my husband in Plaino. That's a right smart time ago. She might could tell you."

"You don't ever remember hearing your age talked about?" I inquired loudly, for she was so old, so desiccated that it seemed only the final trumpet blast could reach her ears.

"No, suh. Only Miss Peggy Rose. She use to git to talkin' 'bout it some. She'd know sooner than anyone else. When she was a right young chippy she lived in Plaino. She's gone from Knoxville now. She use to run a travelers' place there, but she's gone now."

"Do you remember much about slavery, Aunt Julie?"

"Slavery? 'Deed I do," she said, sighing and slowly rubbing her stick with her dead-white hands. " 'Deed, son. I b'longed to ol' Doctor Smith first. He buyed in me an' two boys off the block in Paris. Nigger-buyers had drove us from somewheres, an' I reckon they was taking us South. Heard some o' the ol' folks talkin' 'bout it. I don't know where I come from. I must a had a mammy, but I never laid eyes on her. I might a had some more folks, but I never knowed. I was a right young chippy when ol' Doctor Smith buyed me in."

"And do you remember where he took you?"

"Yes indeedy. Up to Woodburn. That's where he lived at. He didn' live right in the town. He had a farm, an' he buyed in two boys to work on the farm. One a them run away. Never did fin' him neither. I git to studyin' 'bout him now sometimes. When he run away, ol' Doctor Smith chain t'other one to the plow handle. I never seen him, but I heard them talkin' 'bout it, you know. No indeed. Never did lay eyes on him after he buyed us in. Night come, he chain him up. Wasn't no paddyrollers then."

"You never saw the boy who didn't run away?"

She shook her old head. "Never laid eyes on him, I tell you, after we was buyed in. I was raised up in the house. I wasn' 'lowed out in the fiel's. Wasn' 'lowed in the kitchen garden 'dout Mistress bein' there too. They trained me up for house-work, an' that's how close they kep' me."

"And you were the only slave in the house?"

"Yes, suh. Ol' Doctor Smith were a poor man. Poor white trash, that's the stock he come from. Oh, you can tell 'em, son. I didn' have no pride in 'longin' to him, I can tell you that. Poor an' mean with it. He was the meanes' man that ever was. I was kep' to the house all the time to look after the babies. I wasn' s'posed to let them babies cry. Did, I got punishmen's. Kep' to the house all the time. Wasn' 'lowed to talk to no darkies. Darkies pass by goin' to town an' I want to hol' talk with them so bad! But it didn' do me no good. I was a right young chippy, an' I got lonesomey. Sure make me feel humble to see t'other darkies go 'joy theirselves."

"It must have."

"What you say, son?"

"It must have made you feel humble," I said.

"That ain't no stage joke, son. They had one baby when I was firs' took there, then after while Mistress, she had 'nother one. An' pretty soon Mistress still had 'nother one. One day ol' Doctor say to Mistress, 'Damn me, Miss Marg'ret, I'm sick an' tarred seein' you feedin' babies. I'm goin'a fix it.' Use to swear an' carry-on same's any polly parrit.

"I didn' know what he was talkin' 'bout then, but I foun' it out. Yes, son, 'deed I did," she said, peering at me with curdy eyes. "He come to my quarters 'fore long an' made me git out o' my clo'es an' he 'xamin' me. I didn' like him lookin' at my secrets, but I'd git punishmen's if I was to say anything. He were a hateful man. He buckle me down on a board an' beat me 'til blood run once. Yes, I been whupped thataway, an' I ain't shame to tell it. Us darkies had rough times in slav'ry, mighty rough."

She leaned forward, supporting herself on her stick, and wiped her mouth with her hand. She had once been yellow, and once her hair had been fine and black. Now her face was almost green. One or two patches of black hair that stubbornly refused to turn gray or to fall out looked like scabs on her whitish scalp.

"Jus' a few evenin's after the ol' doctor 'xamine me, Mistress tol' me I ain't goin'a sleep in my quarters in the house that night. They was a ol' cabin, where Denver was chained in every night, 'cross the fiel', an' a ol' shed kitchen so give in 'tweren' used for nothin'. I ast her where'bouts I was goin'a sleep at then. 'You goin'a sleep in outside quarters tonight,' Mistress said. I didn' call that ol' cabin no quarters. 'Am I jus' 'bliged to sleep with Denver?' I ast Mistress. I was glad an' sorry too if that was it, 'cause I didn' have no other darkies to have talk with. She say I wasn' goin'a sleep with Denver. She say it was com'table in the quarters. She say they done putt nice beddin' out there an' I could have a fire too.

"I didn' want to sleep in no outside quarters. I weren't use to it. But I know I had it to do. 'Deed, son, I had that thing to do. Then ag'in, it was col' winter time, an' cabins didn' have no wood floors.

"When ol' Doctor Smith come in that evenin', I heard 'em talkin' 'bout me. An' pretty soon, Mistress, she tuck a lightwood torch an' called the ol' hound dog an' 'scorted me down. 'Tweren't for the hound dog, b'lieve I would of runned away that time. But that dog would a hindered me. Then ag'in, I didn' have no place to go to run to. So I went 'long nice. There was a fire in the cabin an' nice an' warm an' I commence to b'lieve I like it better then quarters in the house.

"Long late in the night, I heard somebody comin'. I jumped off the pallet an' squashed me down by the chimbley. I didn' know what. Heard 'em comin' an' couldn' holler to save my soul. 'Deed, I was mighty skeered. After bit the door open an' I hear ol' Doctor Smith say, 'She in there, Bailey. Break her out.' Then somebody come in like they was fallin', an' the door close' an' I heard ol' Doctor Smith chain it. I was skeered to look to see who 'twas."

She wiped her mouth again. Her lips were like puckered seams on a drawstring.

"In course, Bailey seen me. He was a bull darky from t'other side o' Woodburn. I didn' know what he was then. I jus' knowed he was a man, an' it come to me what I was doin' in the cabin, an' I was skeered. He jus' picked me up outa the chimbley corner an' I fit him. Yes, suh. I fit him for a little bit. He had a jug o' hard likker what ol' Doctor Smith had give him, an' he try to make me take some an' I flang it out his hand. He were a shiny black man, tree-top tall, an' a great laughin' man. He commence to laugh at me an' say—he talk like a fiel' darky, right funny. 'Deed, his talk itself would make you laugh. Little bit more, an' I weren't skeered. He was the firs' darky I had opportunity to hol' talk with since I was buyed up. He laugh an' say, 'Now, gel, ain't this some foolishmen' 'twixt us?' That's what he say.

"Held talk for a long time 'fore he got down to business. He done been a heap o' places I didn' know nothin' 'bout, an' he done seen a heap o' things. See, son, he were a bull darky an' his marster was 'blige' to let him go 'round like that. Bailey tol' me plenty things 'bout what he seen. One thing he tol' me I kep' in my min'. Tol' me all darkies tweren't slaves, some was free as white folks. Said he heard it from a travelin' white gen'l'man firs', an' he didn' b'lieve it neither. Then he seen some free darkies. He tol' me so plain I jus' had to b'lieve his word."

"Did you want to be free?" I asked quickly.

"Yes, suh. I did indeed. I had it mighty rough in slav'ry time. 'Deed I did, son."

"Did Bailey tell you that all colored people might be free some day? Did you hear anything like that at all?"

"No, suh. When freedom come, it were a complete surprise to me. That time wi' black Bailey was long 'fore the war. It twere a long bit 'fore I seen bluecoats an' graycoats both a-swarmin' 'roun' an' heard talk about a war. But I didn' know nothin'. 'Cept for that one time, I was made to stay right in the house, an' there weren't nobody to talk sich talk with."

"Did Bailey say he wanted to be free?"

"He didn' seem to keer much for it," she said. "He 'longed to a gen'l'man name o' Cardigan t'other side o' Woodburn. He didn' have it rough as me. Then ag'in, he traveled 'bout lots o' differen' places. Bailey was a proud darky. He laugh too much to keer 'bout freedom.

"He hurt me right bad that night, son, an' all he done was laugh, like my hurt weren't nothin'. He didn' go to hurt me, but he did however. I wasn't nothin' but a chip. They kep' us locked up in 'at ol' cabin three nights. In the mornin's they let me out an' I done my work 'roun' the house, but for three nights ol' Doctor Smith lock' me up with Bailey. By the las' night I were use to it.

"I didn' have no baby under Bailey. Mistress kep' right on tit-nursin' her own. Ol' Doctor Smith raised four on her—an' ne'r a son—an' she nursed 'em all. But I didn' have no peace. Seems like he tuck spite out on me 'cause I couldn' nurse 'em. He giv' me punishmen's like I was a dumb beas'. He tied me up an' whupp me for nothin' sometimes, till I feel real faint. Sometimes I was layin' in my bed an' he come way in the night an' make me git buck nakkid an' tie me to the bed postes an' beat me. Sometimes Mistress'ud come a-runnin'. But you think he stop for that? No, suh! No indeed.

"One time I was standin' to the stairs, holdin' the baby. Mistress had jus' giv' her to me. You know how right young babies be fretful sometimes. The baby started to commence to cry. Ol' Doctor Smith offer' to cut my throat sure 'nough that time. He tuck out a sharp knife like he always carried. Mistress come a'runnin' an' snatch the baby. I don' know why he didn' kill me that time sure 'nough. Believe me, I were ready to go when he made to kill me. I were jus' that weary."

She sighed and rubbed her hands together, and did not hear my question. I did not repeat it, and after a while she went on.

"Lord, son! I done everything. When the young missus was gittin' big, Mistress learn them 'bout the house too. Ol' Doctor Smith, he didn' like it worth two cent, but Mistress learn' 'em. No, suh. He didn' like it, but he had to lump it. Use to say young missus was ladies, but Mistress, she weren't no fool. Ol' Doctor Smith were right nex' to poor white trash hisself. He didn' have no house full o' money, 'n no drove o' slaves neither. Them young missus was learned. They weren't learned no heavy work, but they was learned how to cook an' sew."

"Do you know what happened to the Smiths after slavery, Aunt Julie?"

"Son, I los' track of them people," she answered. "I 'spect they all dead. Ol' Doctor Smith an' Mistress both died 'bout the commencin' o' the war time, an' I was buyed up to Marster Billy Lively. I don' know what come of them Smiths. Marster Billy was a great rich man with a drove o' darkies. It twere 'bout the war time when he buyed me up, 'cause the firs' thing most I 'member 'bout Marster Billy is him standin' on his back gallery devil-blessin' some graycoats who had done been down to his paster an' trussed up some sheep. Went off with 'em too. Graycoats an' bluecoats was all in there then, takin' folks' stock an' feed without no thank-you-suh. Marster Billy devil-bless, but them graycoats don' pay him no 'tention."

"Was your new master good to you, Aunt Julie?"

" 'Deed he were, son. He treated his darkies like human, an' he didn' 'low no person to mistreat 'em neither. He had a drove o' darkies. They was six worked in the house. He let me an' Lias git married an' giv' us a painted cabin—'deed it twere painted, son!—off to ourself. When me an' Lias ask' him, he say to me, 'Julie, you ain't hardly ol' 'nough for no married. You don' know what it mean, do you?' I tol' him 'deed I did. Then he ask me has I ever had a baby, an' I tol' him no, suh, an' I didn' know if I could.

" 'You ain't skeered, is you, Julie?' he ask me nex'. Then I tol' him no, suh, I weren't skeered, an' I tol' him 'bout black Bailey tryin' to have a baby on me for three evenin's an' nothin' come of it. That seem to make him mad-like. 'Damn it, gel,' he say. 'You was too young.' Then he tol' Lias to take me for his wife-mate. Then when he sprinkle the water on us two, he say to Lias, 'Lias, 'member you married to this winch, an' she ain't neither houn' bitch nor yit a cow. See that you treat her accordin'.' "

"And did Lias treat you accordingly?"

"He were the bes' darky ever borned," she said. "We lived wi' Marster Billy 'bout ten years after freedom come, 'most till he died. He put great 'pendence in Lias. One o' Marster Billy's boys were killed in the war, an' t'other one were slow-witted. A bad bull tromped him to death. All Marster Billy's darkies lef' him when freedom come, 'cept me an' Lias an' some few more. We stayed right on with him 'bout ten years. Then we buyed in a place near Plaino."

I looked at her, trying to reach a reasonable approximation of her age. All the signs of ancient flesh were on her: crooked spine, wrinkled, crepy skin, eyes curdy with age. But these helped me not at all, for time itself had wrought on her a quality of timelessness and indestructibility, as if the times that lived in her would perish with her dying.

"Me an' Lias 'joyed our freedom. 'Deed we did. We loved to dance. We dance' an' cut up all night an' walk home jus' 'fore day jus' noddin'. Then we work all day, an' night come ag'in I be so give in I weren't able to milk my cows an' churn the butter. Spoilt many a churnin' sleepin' over it. We carried on that-away 'til my belly commence to git big under Lias, an' then 'twere all I could do to pack that baby. Every mornin' I thought I'd vomick it up."

"You didn't have a baby until you'd been married ten years, Aunt Julie?"

She nodded slowly. "He were borned the year Marster Billy died."

"How do you remember that?"

"That ain't hard to 'member, son. Marster Billy tuck sick. He jus' simply give in. He were to Woodburn an' we were to Plaino, but he sen' for me an' Lias. 'Course, I had to take my baby. Marster Billy was tuck in bed, an' we went right on up the big steers to see him. I s'pected he was goin'a die time I went in. Seems like I can smell death, an' the bedroom was full o' death smell. I think Marster Billy 'spected to die right soon too.

"Lias an' me went in. Marster Billy were in his high bed, wi' a step all 'roun' it, an' he tol' me an' Lias to git up on the step. He wants to see the baby, so I holded him down for to see. He tol' me, 'Julie, I didn' know darkies could have no baby pretty as that one.' An' 'deed, he were a pretty baby! He ask me for his name. Me an' Lias ain't thought 'bout no name, we jus' was callin' him Honey or Sugar, an' baby names like that. I don' know what tuck it to my min'. I tol' Marster Billy, 'We name him after you, Marster Billy.' He smile an' say, 'I'm right proud, Julie.' Yes, suh, he did, son. He smile an' tol' me he were right proud.

"He didn' want us to leave him. He say he were goin'a die an' he wants some o' his own folks 'round him. He say we was loyal darkies an' he want us to be with him till the end of the road. Lias weep' when he tol' us that. Lias 'longed to Marster Billy 'fore he were ol' 'nough to know hisself.

"We stayed there. I disremember how long, but it were some days. Then Marster Billy died. He died same like he were goin'a sleep. He sen' for me an' Lias to his room, an' death smell was everywheres. He give Lias his key-winder an' he give me a pin. He look' at me an' Lias in our face for a long time, an' I know it ain't right for me to say, but I loved that man like Jesus. 'Deed.

" 'I'm goin'a close my eyes,' he say, an' he close 'em. Then with his eyes close' an' the color dreenin' out his face, he say, 'May the great God be my witness that I done live' as good as I know how to.' Lias was weepin' 'cross the bed. ' 'Deed so, Marster Billy,' Lias say. But Marster Billy's voice weren't no dyin' voice. I didn' hear no death rattle. But I kep' lookin' at Marster Billy, an' after bit I knowed he were dead."

She sighed and leaned forward again, crossing her dead-white hands over the head of her stick.

"Tweren't that a pretty way to die, son?" she asked, peering at me and nodding her head. "Tweren't many white folks coulda die' that easy back then. Ol' Doctor Smith, he died fightin' the devil. But Marster Billy—'deed, son, it were the pretties' dyin' I ever seen.

"Lias didn' live long neither. I disremember when he die an' how long a bit he were my husbin' after we buyed in the place. But he died an' lef' me an' my boy. I scraped an' raked. Miss Peggy Rose' folks help me, but I were a widder-woman, an' the white folks tuck advantage o' me. They tuck my place. I had a nice place, with a nice brick house, but they tuck it. Then I tuck my boy an' move' 'way from there."

It was as if she had come to the end of something as simple and conclusive as the folding of an ironed shirt. After a long silence, I asked where her boy was now.

"Dead, son," she answered simply. "He died with a brain fever a long time ago."

"Do you know how long you were in Knoxville?"

"I disremember," she said, shaking her head. "I worked hard all my life. I worked hard in slav'ry time an' I worked hard whilst I was free. But I didn' min', son. I worked day work in the city. I worked for Mr. Pete an' Miss Clary an' they was right nice to me. They got me my pension money, an' say I got to res' my ol' bones, an' in a little bit I give in."

"You deserve a rest," I said.

"I worked hard all my life, son. But I'm livin' easy now, mighty easy."

There was really nothing in Aunt Julie's life for John Bean to make a parable of; really nothing that had a meaning hidden to anyone.

CHAPTER THREE

Poor Wayfarin' Stranger

I

OF COURSE there is no typical southern white man, just as there is no typical southern Negro. There are niggers, darkies, and colored folks or nigrahs, terms which during slavery were based on differences in status in the social order, but which now imply only a nice discrimination on the part of the whites in such intangibles as attitudes and dispositions. Of course, to the vast majority of southern whites all Negroes are niggers. "All niggers look alike to me" is an axiom of great force, and the majority admit no exception to it. For them there is no mobility in social status and no elevating accomplishment among Negroes.

But also there are poor whites, plain crackers, and the good white folk. These distinctions were founded originally in economics, but they are less valid now than they were twenty years ago. Perhaps when the economy of the South progresses farther in the direction in which it seems to be going, these distinctions will be wiped out entirely. The plantation system is dying. The plantations themselves are passing into the ownership of companies and banks, and the *good white folk* who formerly lived on them (or off them, if you are opposed to a feudalistic society) are moving into the cities, where the crackers and landless poor whites have already been driven in great numbers by competition with progressively cheapened labor on impoverished soil. But though the distinctions were based in economics, they carried all the implications of the social pattern of relations between the races—a pattern that is breaking up also. The Negro can no longer tell his white friend from his white foe, the crackers from the good white folk on the basis of occupation or lack of it, economic position, or even on the basis of the constantly thinning personal relations between himself and somebody white. So complex have relations become in comparison with their earlier simplicity that in order to safeguard himself the Negro typifies all southern whites in gross, and when he comes across a deviation from this type he exaggerates the deviation as much as his concept of the norm is exaggerated. He does this in order to bring a more favorable balance into the picture, and not through either shock or surprise, for he knows that there are some good white people.

What is the southern white man? From childhood I had carried about in my heart and brain one picture of him. My grandmother's stories of Caleb Wrightson, her master; the Negro papers my father took; the cold fury of the editorials of DuBois; the immature but gripping stories in the *Crisis* and *Opportunity*; bastardy, peonage, and lynching tales; and finally a little book of obscene cartoons, which came from heaven knows where, but which circulated surreptitiously through our school for weeks, all shaped my picture of the typical southern white. He was a soulless creature of the devil, drooling blood and venom, ignorant beyond belief, but also cunning beyond belief; filthy, lecherous, murderous; cowardly, superstitious, and by God accursed. He was gangling, raw-boned, pot-bellied, sandy-haired. He went about barefoot, in an undershirt and dirt-crusted blue denim breeches, without which he never slept and within which he concealed a bottle of red whisky, a horse pistol, and other lethal weapons. He was the bogey-man with which a great many Negro mothers in the North frightened their children into obedience. In short, he was the Negro version of what (I discovered through Thomas Dixon and Fairfax Craven) the Negro who was not a buffoon was to the white man.

I knew my picture was exaggerated and false, as composites are always false, but experience and cold knowledge in the head seem to have little power over images that well up from the vivid memories of childhood fears. Six uninterrupted years in the South had not blotted out that image of the southern white man. It lurked deep within me, a gnawing, subconscious fear. On this journey through the South I was constantly expecting to meet him, for now less than ever was I protected against chance contacts with him.

Indeed, I sought no protection, and often against my better judgment I picked up hitchhikers, who were generally harmlessly and defensively voluble on such subjects as their colored friends (all of whom nearly all of them expected me to know), Hitler, hitchhiking, animal husbandry, fornication, money, and getting where they were going. Many of them were looking for work, or merely going to the next town to see a girl. One faded-eyed fellow, who was easily forty, was going to Texas because he had "haid a eachin'" to go there since he was a boy, and he had just seen Tom Mix and his wonder horse in a "stage show," and so he was going. I did not mention to him that he was sitting on a newspaper which carried an item relating Mix's accidental death in an automobile wreck in Michigan. I think it might have killed him. Unlike most of them, he called me neither "Preacher," "Perfesser," nor "Docter."

Twice I thought I had met my typical southern white man.

Once when a bridge was out and a little three-car ferry was pressed into service across the swollen St. Francis River in southeastern Missouri, I thought I had met him. My car was the third in line in the narrow, improvised slipway. The other two drivers were white men, one a young man driving an ancient, high-wheeled Dodge and the other in his middle years, apparently prosperous and apparently on the return end of a motor trip with his wife. His car, which bore a Kentucky license tag, was piled high with luggage and gaudy souvenirs, and the windows were all stuck up with guest stickers.

I was standing looking at the swollen river when the older man came up and then the young man. We fell into pleasant conversation about cars, roads, and the little ferry, which we could see bobbing and dancing frantically in mid-river. It was late afternoon, growing dark, and the young man was worried that his old generator would not give him sufficient power to run his lights in the night. We all went over and looked at the generator. None of us knew anything about it, but the young man felt better for our looking.

"She's getting old," he said. "Anything's li'ble to happen. I sure hope she gets me where I'm goin'. She always has."

"She will," I said.

"Lotta life in her yet," the older man said. "Them old Dodges was good cars when Dodge made 'em."

"Mine's a Dodge," I said.

" 'Tis, ain't it? What kinda car is it now?"

"Pretty good," I said.

"This here's been a durn good car," the young man said, putting the hood down. It had been painted recently and the brush strokes were pretty bad, but it had a certain dignity still.

"They made 'em to last when they built that'n. I knowed a feller in Versailles drove one twenty-some years."

"Versailles? Where's that at?" the young man asked.

"That's my home. That's in good old Kentuck."

"It's a funny thing, but your home state always looks good to you when you ain't in it," the young man said.

Just then we saw the boiling dust. The road off the highway where the damaged bridge was to the ferry slip was a bad dirt and gravel road. My own dust had not settled on it. We could not see what was coming, but we could see the dust whorling up and rolling thickly across the scraggly cotton fields.

"Here comes another car," I said.

"Yeah. I see it. He's got a hour to wait. Can't but three cars get on this ferry," the young man said, looking up the road. He was a good-looking young man, somewhat short and stocky, but with handsome eyes and a fine, mobile mouth.

"How you been finding the roads?" the older man asked me. "Good."

"That's one thing. We got a system o' roads in this country, best in the world. All the way to California they're good. They tell me the army's going to build all the new roads. Gittin' ready for war, I reckon. Gittin' ready to fight that damn fool Hitler. War ain't no credit to nobody, but we can lick any nation on earth. Think we're ready?"

"I had to register," the young man said. "I'd's soon be in the damn army as doing what I'm doing."

"I never was in the army. I've come up between every war," the older man said.

Now we heard the rattling, metallic, machine-gun sound of gravel flying into fenders: We still could not see what was coming, but it sounded like more than one car, or a car traveling at high speed.

"Somebody sure is helling," the young man said.

"Goin'a bust a spring, too."

"Some guys is crazy." The young man hitched his thumbs in his belt.

The car poured out of the dust and in another second yelled to a stop just behind my car. It was a new car, one of the fast, light machines, but the left fender was smashed and the radiator grill and headlight entirely gone. A big, sloppy man got out, looked at my car, then across the river to the ferry, then at the other two cars and at us. He was dressed in khaki trousers and shirt, and just above the top of his trousers his shirt was open, exposing a mat of hair around his creased and startlingly white navel.

"Which one o' y-all does this yere car 'long to?" he asked, pointing to my car and walking toward us.

"Him. You sure was helling," the young man said.

"Big boy, yere?" the sloppy man said. "Big boy, you're goin'a hafter back up an' let me in 'er."

"Why?" I asked.

"Why? What the hell! Whare you from, boy?"

"None of your damned business," I said, hoping I was saying it quietly and without my voice trembling.

He turned his big bulk as if he were coming for me. His face, at first red with astonishment, was now white with anger. He looked at me and he also looked at the others. The young man and the older man looked at him impassively. The older man's wife was leaning across the seat under the wheel looking at us. The sloppy man licked his lips. I had made up my mind what I was going to do if I had to do it. I meant to send my foot plunging into his white belly.

"I ain't in no hurry," the older man said. "You can have my place."

"I'm goin' a have this yere niggah's place. Lis'en, you black . . ."

"For Christ's sake! Wallace Beery comes up an' wants to make trouble," the young man said.

The older man stopped going toward his car. Something passed out of me. It was as if stitches which had been tight and festering for a long time were being drawn. The something gathered in the top of my head and in the tips of my fingers and then ran up my arms and down through my chest and stomach and legs and into the ground. It was a sensation as real as pain. It left me feeling very light and free and no longer holding myself with that terrible, galvanizing concentration. I saw everything clearly, the lady watching us through the car window, the old man who had stopped in the middle of the road, the young man, and the white, hairy belly. I was not afraid.

"Damn'f I'd move for him," the young man said.

"I don't b'lieve I will now," the older man said, standing in the road. "No, sir. I don't b'lieve I will!"

The way he said it, suddenly flexing his arms in decision, seemed indescribably comic. The young man laughed. Then I laughed. The sloppy man licked his white lips. The lady got out of the car.

"What the hell is this?" the big man said.

"Wasn't nothin' but three cars waitin' for the ferry 'til you come," the young man said.

"Y-all side with a niggah 'gainst a white man?"

"What you wanta make trouble for?" The young man kept his thumbs hitched in his belt. He had not once raised his voice.

"Y-all mus' be niggah-lovers. This black bas . . ."

"Dick Eberle, you ain't a-goin'a move," the old lady said, "an' I ain't a-goin'a stand here an' listen to his swearing."

"If it wasn' for the ol' woman," the sloppy man said, threatening now also the young man.

"Yeah! You're Wallace Beery. You're Humphrey Bogart."

"Shut up, you!" And standing three feet away, the sloppy man drew back his hand.

"You stink!" the young man said, not moving.

Without another word, the big man went to his car, backed it furiously, and drove off in a great cloud of dust.

"He-hee," the older man said. After that there was an embarrassed silence.

Suddenly I was very tired and weak, and an almost psychopathic awareness multiplied my sensations to the point of pain. It seemed to me that a moment before, the young man, the older man, and I had been close together. Now we were apart. I did not try to think of a reason for this. I simply felt it like a vast, steely emptiness in my stomach. The young man, his thumbs hitched in his brass-studded belt, stood looking at the ground. The old man had stooped and was intently studying a tire. He rubbed the dust off a space and looked, and then he rubbed the dust off another space and looked at the new tire. Still stooping, he duck-walked to another wheel and did the same thing. The lady stood in the road watching the approaching ferry. The young man turned and looked at the river.

"Dick, I reckon we better get in. It's about here," the lady said.

"I'm afraid it'll be dark by the time we get across. If you follow me, you won't have any trouble about your lights," I said to the young man.

"My car don't go so fast," the young man said, looking at the river and the sidling ferry. "I'm only goin' ten miles."

"I'd be glad to help you," I said.

"She'll kick up enough juice."

The ferry came in and a car bumped off, and then we drove

on to the ferry. It was a dinky, flat-bottomed, homemade ferry, with an old automobile motor coughing under a piece of chicken wire in the stern. It had no superstructure except a railing made of water piping along each side. We all sat in our cars on the trip over. Darkness came. When we reached the other side, I pretended to have trouble starting, and they pulled off. Then I pulled off very slowly, and they were gone.

2

The second time I thought I had met my typical southern white man was in Memphis, Tennessee. I arrived in the city on December 6, the very day the *Sun-Observer* carried a statement by a Negro minister in answer to one made the day before by the commissioner of police. The Reverend Mr. Decatur Absalom's statement read:

I have been respectful to white and black, obeyed the law, have not taught or sought social equality nor race hatred. I am a Republican and I believe in political, economical, industrial and civic equality. Since my life has been threatened, I guess it is not worth a dime, but I shall continue as I have and leave the results in the hands of God.

I went to see the Reverend Mr. Absalom. He lived on the second floor of a two-family dwelling that did not look quite up to the dignity of the pastor of the St. John's Baptist Church, an institution which the *Sun-Observer* had described as a "77 year-old landmark." The minister was very cautious. Standing outside his door, I told him who I was and what I wanted.

"I'm not talking," he said shortly. "What I have to say, I'll say in the pulpit or to the newspapers, open and aboveboard."

He studied me carefully, peering around the edge of the door, while I explained that I did not know what it was all about. I had seen only the one newspaper article.

"How do I know that you're not a stooge and a stool pigeon for some of those men downtown?"

I handed him a packet of letters of introduction. Holding the door with his foot, he read through the letters. In spite of his bald, dome-shaped head, he looked quite young and not at all ministerial. He wore a red dressing robe and matching slippers.

"I declare, I'm so upset I don't know whether I'm coming or going," he said, handing the letters to me again. "For three weeks, day and night, every few minutes they've been riding by here. A carload of them in plain clothes. Every time I go out, they follow me. Every time I come home, they're riding."

"Who?" I asked.

"The cops. The cops!"

"Why?"

"Who knows! Trying to scare me, I guess. But I ain't the scaring kind. See, brother. I can take it."

He cocked his head at me and broke into a sudden, white-toothed smile. "Say, listen. You're interested . . ."

"In you," I said.

"Then why don't you go down to Timothy Hanagan and see what he says? They tell me he's got a mess of dirt on Gurley and some more. Might have some dirt on me. But my record can stand," he said quickly. "But just the same, I'd like to know what they're up to down there, what they're fixing to do."

"Who's Hanagan?"

"The commissioner. Bible Tim, they call him. He won't talk to me. He won't talk to any of us what he calls radical Negroes."

In his eagerness he had opened the door a little more, and over his shoulder I could see into a bare, dim hall. At the back of the hall some steps led up to the living quarters above.

"Have you tried to talk to him?"

"Sure. Sure I have."

"Well, what's it all about?"

"All I know's what I see in the papers," he answered.

"And you won't talk to me yourself?"

"You scared?" he challenged.

"No, but . . ."

Here I was in Memphis, where Beale Street, which, incidentally, is called Avenue, was a distinct disappointment; where

Handy Park, of which I had heard so much, was a few trees in a crummy neighborhood of Jews' stores, foul-smelling restaurants, and cluttered pawnshops; where everyone was so frightened that no one would talk to me. Where were the bold, bad river men, the flaming sporting-women, the hot-fish vendors, the railroaders, the tough guys from the gyp joints? Where were the rollicking blues, the low-down blues, the wailing blues? And where the earthborn dignity of these? The John Henrys, the Steamboat Bills, the Ironmen Holy Smiths,

> . . . Allus fightin' fer a fr'en an'
> Buil'in' bridges from noon to hell an'
> Clean on back ag'in.

I looked at the Reverend Mr. Absalom and surprised his face in worried lines.

"All right," I said.

Afterwards I learned the state of affairs in snatches from people who were principally involved—the editor of a Negro weekly, a dentist, another minister—and the newspapers. What had happened was that the Memphis United Race Relations Group, in a resolution adopted by it and presented to the mayor of the city, had charged the Memphis police with intimidation and persecution of Negro suspects. This resolution provided the police commissioner an opportunity to "speak openly and to the point." In the commissioner's opinion the point was that the Negroes of the city were becoming "insolent," "disrespectful," and "forgetful of their place," and it was his job to restrain them. His methods of restraint were constant police surveillance of Negroes suspected of insolence, having every customer entering and leaving certain Negro places of business searched, and by direct threats.

When I was in Memphis, the two places of business where the police were on twenty-four-hour search duty were still open, but one of them closed later—before wide publicity to this Hitlerian method of repression forced the mayor to call off the police. But under this treatment, the Negroes were silent, sullen, cowed. There was no one to speak out for them, no single voice in all that city during that pre-Christmas season that uttered one word of good will. Mr. Emanuel Tyree, chairman of the Race Relations Group, resigned. The other members, white and colored, remained silent.

Though I did not know it then, this was the way matters stood when I met for the second time my typical southern white man.

I went unsuspecting. The Christmas season was approaching, and Market Street was gay with bunting and warm with crowds. It had been ten years since I had seen window displays on so grand a scale, and I pressed with the crowds to watch a marionette Barber of Seville and to hear an animated doll orchestra squeak through the last strains of the last movement of the Nutcracker Suite. Santa Claus had a home on Market Street. He sat on the porch of it and talked through a microphone to crowds of delighted children. Everything was gay, in movement. Salvation Army ladies clinked their bells. Traffic jammed, crawled, jammed again. Police whistles blew. At the mile-o-dimes, where I laid a coin, the microphone said, "And thanks to that colored boy there." Every few minutes chimes rang out snatches of Christmas carols.

I turned off the main street and came to the building where I had been told I would find the commissioner. It was a big building, rather frightening now that I had come to it, and apparently with few people about. The foolhardiness of the whole adventure had not occurred to me before. What did I have to do with this business, this mouthy brawl between the police commissioner and some Negroes about whom I knew nothing? I was curious, of course, but could I present myself on the grounds of curiosity alone? Could I explain the bigger thing I was after to the police commissioner, and would he listen? I was not even a newspaper man who had to get a story. I could not play the champion against oppression. Indeed, I did not know then that there had been oppression. My impression of the Reverend Mr. Absalom had not been a favorable one. Yet, here I was. Fool! and again, Fool! I called myself.

Thus I stood thinking and vaguely wondering where the building directory was when I got a glimpse of a uniform going down the hall. My next action was purely reflexive, taken at the instant I realized that this could not be the building, for the offices of the police would be open all the time. I stepped up and called, "Officer!" I had done it, and now I faced it. The uniform turned and the eyes above the braided collar watched me with cold insolence as I approached.

"What you want, boy?"

"Is Commissioner Hanagan's office in this building?"

"What'cha want with the commissioner? Did he send for you? I seen you some place before, ain't I? Ain't you one of them coons that peddles mary warner sticks for Ormsby down on Florida? You hear me, boy?" His voice rattled and echoed down the empty corridor.

"Answer me," he said. He had small, close-set eyes rimmed with pink.

"Ormsby? Mary Warner?" I said, puzzled.

"Yeah. Dope sticks. That yeller sonofabitch sells 'em. You know it!"

"Oh, marijuana."

"I don't give a damn what y'call 'em. You know what they are all right." He advanced a half-step. "Yeah. That's where I seen you, hangin' 'round Ormsby's joint. Well, we're goin'a crack it wide open, see? We ain't goin'a leave you black rats a hole to hide in, see? We're goin'a clean this goddamn town of all you black bastards. Chase you in the river. Reds, huh? Well, goddamn it! we'll make you red all right."

He stopped, and an instant later a gleam of cunning came into his eyes. His face was highly colored. His chin was blue.

"Didn'cha know this ain't the commissioner's building?" he asked, insinuatingly. "Didn'cha? Did Ormsby sen' you up here to see the commissioner?" His eyes darted from my face and over my shoulder, and then I heard someone approaching over the stone floor.

"I don't know Ormsby," I said.

"Then you come in here to do some breakin' an' enterin', didn'cha? You knew it wasn't likely to be nobody 'round much, didn'cha?"

"What you got, Chub?" a voice behind me asked. I did not look around.

"A thief, or one o' Ormsby's rats."

"Do you think I'd have called you if I'd come to steal?"

"Shut up! I'll . . ." He raised his hand.

"Better search him, Chub," the man behind me said.

"I ought to lock him up."

"Lock him up if he's got anything on him," the man said.

The officer was not content with frisking me. He made me empty my pockets, turn them inside out. He made me unbutton my topcoat, my suit coat, my vest, my shirt. I had felt nothing but amazement before, but now I felt a sense of shame, of sickening humiliation, of terrible impotence. As I thought the thing through, I knew where wisdom lay: it lay in the recognition of my impotence. A move from me, a gesture of stubbornness, a hint of refusal, and I might have had a bullet through the heart, or at the least a battered head and a spell in jail. I did as I was told. Who was it who said that this sort of thing cannot hurt the inner man? Whoever, he was a fool. And years and years of it, ages and ages, back to the beginnings of ancestral memory!

The officer looked in my wallet and counted the bills there. He looked at my automobile papers. He looked at my letters, sneered, and handed them to the man behind me, who also read them. He tore open the packet of cigarettes and broke each cigarette in half and sniffed it. All these things he tossed to the floor. I picked up everything but the broken cigarettes.

"Pick 'em up!" he said. I picked them up.

"All right. Now, scram! An' if I ever see you again, I'm goin'a lock you up."

I brushed by the man who all this time had been standing behind me and left the building. I did not even see his face. The crowds I could see on the main street a block and a half away surprised me, for I had forgotten the crowds in that lonely quarter-hour. I did not go that way. I walked toward the river. There was a little park there on the bluff overlooking the river, and I walked in it. The park was a war memorial. Civil, I think, and I walked from cannon to cannon down the concrete path along the stone wall. The sharp wind from the river blew in my face. Two thick-coated squirrels skittered before me. The street up from the river was jammed with cars, but I was alone in the park. They came, the tears, without my knowing that they would come. They just swam in my eyes and one or two dropped on my cheek before I could dig my fingers into my eyes and stop them. Then I could not stop them. I turned toward the wall and pressed my knees against it and looked out over the river. From somewhere east of me came the sound of chimes making a Christmas melody.

On December 12, after I had left Memphis, I read in the *Sun-Observer* a two-column statement by Commissioner Hanagan in which he said:

I say again this is a white man's country, and always will be, and any Negro who doesn't agree to this better move on.

3

Perhaps what was happening in Memphis was fundamental and necessary to social evolution! There are those, Negro and white, who believe with philosophic imperturbability that bi-racial adjustments must begin in violence and steer their hap-hazard course through meetings and mediations to compromises that are usually unsatisfactory. They are like the old-fashioned people, Grandmother Conway among them, who believed not only that the only relief for a boil was to have it ripen and burst, but that every boil was a further purification of blood. They cite famous riots as cases in point. They cite the Arab-

Jewish troubles in Palestine, and, more recently, the Jewish purge in Germany! Actually!

"But we don't have democracy!" these Negroes say. They are already ripe for fascism. They have no love of freedom. Without knowing it, they have already accepted the attitude of resignation so necessary under fascism, and the coming of a dictator would give them sadistic, pleasurable, I-told-you-so relief. For they are certain they would not be purged! Their techniques of survival, as a class, are wonderfully adaptable, and they would serve them in no matter what situation.

But whatever else it was, the affair in Memphis was certainly a victory for the forces of reaction. And in the South reaction employs odorous methods: propagandic agitation first, enslavement of the press, accusations, intimidation, threats, and finally the blow—swift, inevitable, decisive. Over a period of two weeks, beginning December 3, statements by Police Commissioner Hanagan were headlined in the *Sun-Observer*.

A great many cities in the North and South have had serious race riots with tremendous bloodshed. If careful and stern preparations for the defense of peace will prevent it, it will be prevented in Memphis.

In an open letter to Mr. Emanuel Tyree, chairman of the United Race Relations Group, he declared:

I observe that Zion Wormsley, Clifford Smith, True Gurley, Roscoe Parker are members of your committee. These men run Negro newspapers here in Memphis. For many months these papers have been carrying on a campaign with inflammatory articles calculated to disrupt the present friendly relations between the white and Negro races in this community.

For your information True Gurley lost his job at the Post Office for failing to account for some money. Do you think for one moment that I would meet with Gurley to advise about law enforcement in Memphis? Nor would I meet with the others named above on account of their activities in endeavoring to create race trouble here with their papers. And right now I must tell you that for the good of the community unless they stop these articles, I expect to show them the way out of the city. I am very positive on this. . . .

We have never had it before, and we will never have it. For after all this is a white man's country. . . .

I will deal with them if they continue their present activities. . . .

Of course you are not informed and it would be a careless assumption for you to acquit anyone until you know all the facts.

Dr. Booker Ormsby and his wife went out to Barnum and Bailey Circus and being of light color bought tickets and sat in the seats reserved for white people. He gloated over this social equality.

It is utterly beyond my understanding how you white ministers can get in on a proposition of this kind when you are so poorly informed on what is actually going on. You cannot realize the character of the Negro you are defending. Dr. Booker Ormsby is running a hideout for thieves on Florida Street and is just a common thief.

But apparently all through southeastern Tennessee certain malignant forces were a-prowl. These forces, of course, were new only in that they were aroused by a new circumstance: the slowly widening application of the principles of democracy. The less secure element in the white South looked with suspicion upon certain activities in Washington, even when those activities were designed to help them, for they helped the Negro too. To those who were secure enough not to need the various relief agencies, the relief agencies were poison, for they saw them as an evil that threatened to bring about equality in some mysterious way known only to the radicals in Washington. As I overheard one reedy farmer at a country gas station say, "Yeah. Roosevelt's all right, I reckon, but he's got niggers in this yere C.C. an' W.P.A., an' I wouldn't be a goddamn bit su'prised if he don't have 'em votin' 'fore he's done. Preety soon you an' me an' ever'body else might be votin' side a niggers."

In a little town on my route an incident had occurred, and I wanted to find out about it.

Beyond the highway sign that proclaims it a "good place to live," the town first clusters round the Confederate memorial square and then sprawls east to the bottoms, where the Negroes live in a ghetto of mud and frame. I was told that in former times the square was a pleasant place, with the stores fronting on it, and the white townspeople, outnumbered two to one by the black, congregating there and indulging in such pleasantries as spitting in the gutter, discussing box scores, and arguing about hunting dogs. They even passed some of their raillery with the Negroes, who, in the evenings and on Saturdays, lined the curbing on the north side of the square.

But all this was changed when I reached the town a few days before the national election. The square was brittle with tension. People went about with bowed heads and strained faces. There was little business in the square, and even the low buildings seemed to shrink in on themselves. "All they need to do now is hang a crepe," Flap Conroy said. "Yes, sir. A big, black crepe."

Conroy said this bitterly in a husky whisper from the side of his mouth. He leaned over the chest-high partition before his cash register and cut his eyes down the dim length of the poolroom, where three men were shooting pool in a frozen glare of yellow light. Flap was a short, rotund, coffee-brown man whose trousers sagged beneath his protuberant belly and whose eyes were like nicked marbles. He was a gambler of sorts and he had been a ladies' man. He still seemed to smell faintly of women. His name, Flipflap (Flap for short), derived from the peculiar action of his lips. They were the most immense lips I had ever seen, purple and red-splotched, like thick folds of raw liver. His upper teeth were entirely of gold, and crumby with tobacco. He jabbed ruthlessly at his teeth with a shaved matchstick.

"So they told you I wasn't scared an' you come to me?"

"Well," I said hesitantly.

"Well, I ain't," he said huskily, as if he were angry with me. This I found to be his usual manner of speaking.

"The biggest majority of 'em's scared. I seen you goin' to Doc Pogue's, an' about five minutes later I seen you leaving there an' goin' like you was goin' to the school, an' I wondered who you was. Then a little while ago Scotty Grace come in here an' told me you was some feller goin' round finding out about people. 'Aw, aw,' I said to myself. 'I know good an' damn well he ain't goin'a find out nothing 'bout them guys.' Them fellers think that every stranger comes to town is trying to stuff 'em some way or another, sticking his nose in the mobbing. Well, I ain't scared. It takes me to tell you."

He narrowed his eyes and rested his elbows on the partition.

"Them niggers was scared, wasn't they?" he insisted.

When I again hesitated, Flap drew back and said, "I know they was scared! An' what the hell they scared of now? I'll tell you," he said, again hiking his elbows on the partition. "They're scared that 'lection day some nigger'll make a little break an' there'll be another mobbing. The nearer 'lection day comes, the scareder they git. What'd they say 'bout me, hunh?"

"Nothing," I said. "Mr. Huett asked to see my credentials."

"Oh, that sonofa . . . An' he didn't say nothing 'bout me? Hunh?" He was like some gross and excited bird sitting on a fence. His head becked in and out as he looked alternately at me and at the players down the room. His eyes gleamed.

"Nothing," I said.

"Nobody else didn't ask for credentials? Didn't none o' them say if you go to Flap, he'll talk? Aw, I know them skates like a book! Don't matter what wagon it's in, it's the same old load of stuff."

"How do you mean?" I asked.

"Listen, old man," he said with unaccustomed slowness. "I seen them so-n'-soes, Huett, Pogue, an' a lot more, gitting ready to leave town. The crackers had sent some of them warning. Some left. Niggers boarded up their houses. Scrammed! Scared! It takes me to tell you."

"Was this before . . ."

"The mobbing? Yeah! That's what I'm trying to tell you. Crackers had done sent some warnin' letters or something. Git a stool. Let me tell you something."

I got a stool from against the wall and placed it at the partition. For almost two full days I had met fear, suspicion, silence.

The townspeople watched me with open mistrust. I felt that I was the subject of discussion among the whites on the square.

"I ain't scared," Flap said. "Just remember that. I was bred an' born an' raised here. My home place is only 'bout five miles east o' here. The boy I rent it to just come in Friday an' handed me my compress receipts. I rent it for three bales. It's just short of seventy acres, but by the time we 'vide up three bales nine ways we ain't got nothing. Yeah. Nine brothers an' sisters I got. But it's our place. That's one reason I ain't scared. I know I got some place to scram when scramming time comes. The high sheriff, Top Zuber, come in here this fall an' started hinting round 'bout the 'lection coming up. But I got some place to go. That stuff don't scare me. I ain't saying I wouldn't go if the turf got too tight; but I got a home place to go to. Ain't no cracker so-n'-so goin'a run me off my own home place! What the hell's the good of a man having a home place if he can't protect himself on it? He might's well lay out in the road somewheres.

"That's what I tell my brother. Yeah. He was scared too. Scared now. He started to scram. But he's got a home bought an' paid for here, and that's home place for his kids, an' damn it! he ought to protect himself on it. Here in town, I live with my mother-in-law. But my home place, that's diff'ent.

"I was raised up on that farm. I had the same raisin' as any other average nigger boy. I was the oldest an' I had to look out for the others. My old man was tough titty 'bout that thing. If any of them done something they wasn't s'posed to do, I got the blame for it. I wasn't s'posed to let 'em do it. They look to me thataway now. C. A., when they come an' told him they had found the boy's body in the river an' wanted him to go an' git it, he asked me what must he do. He didn't want no parts of it! I told him to go ahead on an' git the body. Jesus Christ, C. A. wouldn't hardly breathe without me.

"But that's the way my old man raised us. He told us he wanted us to stick together, 'cause a lone nigger didn't have a chance in the world. White folks got the world in a jug an' the stopper in their hand. That's what they think! An' that's what my old man thought too. But I've seen crackers eat dirt, I mean low dirt, in Shy an' Saint Louis an' K.C. But my old man hadn't never been to none of them places. He didn't know no better. All he seen was how the white folks done the nigger in Northrup County, an' he b'lieved it was the same all over the world.

"That's the way I was raised up to think. We wasn't s'posed to let white folks kick us around, or nothing like that, but we wasn't s'posed to be in the way of gitting kicked 'round neither. An' if we was in the way of it, it was just too bad. With my old man, if we got involved with white folks, it was always, 'What devilment you been up to now?' an' never no 'What devilment the crackers been up to?'

"Never will forget, one time a cracker nicked me on the chin with a field clump. Cut me right bad too. See that scar? I'm satisfied had it been a rock that so-n'-so throwed, I wouldn't had no chin at all. He was a got-nothing cropper. That's all in this God's world he was, the sorries' white man in Tennessee. But he was right friendly with us. His cotton patch ended to our lane, an' him an' my old man use to squat in our lane and talk sometimes in the evenin's. Him an' my old man would see who could tell the biggest lies. He had my old man by some percentage on lying, an' my old man wasn't no slouch.

"Anyway, this cracker planted him a whole double-team of cotton. We always picked our cotton clean. My old man didn't like no trashy cotton. But this cracker pulled his. Yeah! Pulled it in the shucks. I was the first one who seen him doing it. I happened to look across the lane one morning and seen him going like hell down a row. I knew he couldn't be picking cotton that fast. Natcherly, I stopped to look. I watched him go down one and come up one, going like hell. I yelled over to him and asked him what he was doing. I wasn't thinking, you know. Just curious. I had heard of people pulling cotton, but I hadn't never seen nobody do it. But when I yelled, the bastard didn't answer, an' I went on over to see what he was doing.

"When I got over there, I seen that sucker was pullin' his

cotton, bolls an' all. I wasn't thinking, you know. When I seen what he was doin', I said, 'Jesus Christ!' Just like that. 'Jesus Christ! That ain't no way to pick cotton,' I said. I made an admiration over it, you know. What did I do that for! The goddamn peck blew up. He called me every kind a nigger he could think of. Then he picked up this field clump an' clipped me on the chin. I went home bleedin' like a woman with her flag up.

"But 'stead of my old man being hot with him, he was hot with me. Yeah! Beat my tail. Yeah! Said I had no business tryin' to tell that white man what to do. Didn't do me no good to tell my old man I wasn't trying to tell that old peck nothing, that I was just making admiration. He wouldn't collar no jive like that. He beat my black can. That's the way my old man was. Nigger was always wrong. White man was always right.

"An' I didn't git over that up-raising for a long time neither. Sligo an' C. A. ain't over it yet. 'Course, my brothers in Shy an' K.C., an' my two sisters in Saint Louis been over it. Never did 'fect my sisters none much noway. Women ain't like men in that respect. When I went out to Shy, pecks wasn't no more to my brothers than niggers, an' my crazy brother, Alley, was buying up all the white tail he could find. But it took me a long time, a munt' or more, to git use to even them cheap white whores out 'round Fifty-second an' Halstead. Old Alley had got use to 'em when he was in the army. Yeah.

"That's one trick I missed. They didn't take me on account o' my health. Ain't that something! I been in more better health than Alley all my life. I'm close to fifty years old, an' I'm satisfied there ain't nothing wrong with my health yet. I married me a young, twenty-six-year-old frail eighteen munt's ago, an' she ain't complaining none. I ought to be in good health. I bet I'm in good a health as some of these boys registered the other day.

"You know one thing? These niggers don't want to go to no army! No, man. An' I don't blame 'em neither. Damn it, there ain't no point! All right, you go fight for Uncle, an' what does

he give you when the fightin's over? The same old crap, all the
time the same old crap.

"But I ought to be in good health. I did plen'y hard work till
I was way past thirty. All the boys 'cept me an' C. A. went off
first one place an' then another, an' the girls got married. Me
an' C. A. an' my old man ran that bitch of a farm till my old
man died. When he died, C. A. wanted to learn undertaker, so I
ran the farm another year, year an' a half, an' sent C. A. up
to Nashville to Lumpkin-Jones to learn undertaker. When he
finished up, I rented the farm out an' hawled tail to town. Been
here right stedy ever since. You know, taken little side trips to
Shy an' around—gone for two years once—but I call this town
home.

"Yeah, man. I went 'round to all them places. Stayed a good
while in Shy. But I didn't see nothing in them places to make
admiration over. 'Course, maybe I didn't stay long enough. But
fellers out there are just making a living, same's I'm doing here.
They just had more ways of doing it. But some of them wasn't
making it, even at that. When I was in Shy, I paid eight dollars
a week for a room with privileges; you know, you could take a
frail to my room if I wanted to. Here I can rent a whole house
for eight dollars a mun't an' let women run 'round naked in it if
I want to. 'Course, I'm married now. But that's what I could do.

"Out there, you git in a little game of dice or poker, an' the
house man has to have his cut an' the law has to have his'n. Here,
Saddee nights, I can run a game back there on the back table an'
don't nobody git a cut but me.

"I don't see nothing to living in them places. Yeah, you can
vote. But when you come right down to it, what the hell's that?
All you got to do is ask a nigger who votes if he's still working
for his living, an' that shows 'em that voting ain't nothing special.
'Course I'm for voting! I b'lieve if white folks got it, niggers
ought to git it too. This ain't their doggone country exclusive.
But niggers ain't never voted here, not even in the president election, an' they been doin' 'bout as good, when it comes down to

bread an' butter, as niggers most anywheres else. Just the same, I was with them when they started the voting agitation here. I was with 'em because we was all colored together an' we got to stick together regardless.

"But now the pecks has got 'em scared, an' the closer this 'lection comes, the scareder they git. Both sides is scared. White folks scared the niggers' goin'a make a break, an' niggers scared white folks goin'a think they making a break. But I ain't scared, buddy. Anybody round here'll tell you Flipflap ain't scared o' nothing. Did I ask you for credentials? Did I? Like hell I did. I got some place to run to, if I have to run.

"Here's how all this stuff started.

"There was a coupl'a men round here started up some kind of lodge. These men's names were Benny Speed an' Link Cave. I didn't know much what it was all about, but I was in it. It was a secret lodge. We held meetings secret. Benny Speed was president, an' he said we had to do that till we got organized right. We didn't want the pecks to break us up 'fore we got started good. We had about a hundred members. But we had one white-folks' nigger in there—Tilson Huett, that so-n'-soing school principal you went to see an' he asked you for credentials. He ain't nothing but a tail-kissing snake. Knowed him all my life. Knowed his pappy before him, an' his pappy was the same. Tilson was born an' raised here. Went to school here. Been here all his life. He's a so-n'-so snake!

"When we got organized good, we started agitating for voting. We ain't never voted here, in no kind a 'lection, they tell me, since eighty-four. So five of us was picked to go up to the courthouse to see about it. They knew we was coming. Yeah. Tilson Huett had told them. Oh, he's low!

" 'Fore I married, my wife taught out there to his school, an' three times a year Huett made all the teachers chip in fi' dollars. Yeah! Thanksgiving, Christmas, an' school-closing. Them teachers had to give that money for a big dinner for the board an' supertender. Had to do it to hold their jobs. Tail-kissing! I told my wife 'fore I married her if I couldn't hold my job on my merits, I wouldn't want the damn job. I told her she'd give no more fi' dollars. Hell, they fired her in the middle o' the year.

"Tilson had tipped them off that we was coming, an' everything we planned to do. This much come out in the paper. Miss Greenlee, the supertender, asked Tilson why he joined the lodge in the first place. This come out with big headlines in the paper: 'Loyal Principal Prevents Race Trouble.' You know what he said when she asked him that? He said he joined to git the secret so he could tell the white people the danger they was in. Now, if that was a lie, the paper told it!

"When we went on up they was ready for us. Before we could open our mouths to say boo Mr. Reid said, 'You men might's well save your breath. The answer's no. We don't never 'tend to let niggers vote in this county. I'll tell you boys, 'fore we do that, we'll wade in blood.' That's what he told us.

"We told him we didn't want to vote for mayor an' sheriff, just president, an' he said colored couldn't even vote for that, not in this county. 'Smoke this in your pipe,' he said. 'I know niggers. I been knowing niggers all my life, an' if we give you a inch you want a mile. If we let you vote in the president election you'd want to vote in every other kind election. Well, let me tell you boys something: President Roosevelt ain't running Northrup County.'

"There was a gang of men round in his office, an' more come in. Such signifyin' you never saw! Top Zuber was one of them. He hadn't been long voted high sheriff, but he wasn't in yet. Yet an' still he was packing a rod. I seen it. He meant for us to see it an' git scared. Benny Speed was doing the talking, an' if Top Zuber thought he was scaring him, he had another thought coming. Benny wasn't built like a gorilla for nothing. An' Link Cave, he was a preacher, an' he wasn't scared o' nothing but God. Top Zuber was trying to put a scare in the wrong set o' niggers.

"Anyway, he puts in his mouth. 'You-all darkies better git on back to the bottom, 'fore you stir up something,' he said. He's a slow-talking white man. Take him all day to say good morning. Right away, soon's he opened his mouth, Benny stepped in it. Benny says, 'Mr. Zuber, you ain't got a dog in this fight. You ain't sheriff yet.' Top said something 'bout giving us fair warning, an' showed his gun again. Then Mr. Reid spoke up an' said he knew what it was all about, knew all about the lodge. Yeah! Knowed its name better'n I did.

" 'You-all boys has let some dangerous northern nigger come in here an' fill you full o' shit,' he says. 'Then he goes on 'bout his business an' leaves you holding the bag. I found out all about it. I found out when he come an' when he left.'

"He was talking 'bout Benny Speed's boy, little Ben. Little Ben had come here from New York on a visit, an' you know how they call on home folks in church who've been away to say something. That's all it was. He gave a little inspiration talk in church one Sunday. Don't know what it was, but it couldn't been nothing special, 'cause I didn't hear nobody talking 'bout it much. Somebody sure made a manure pile out of a rabbit turd, an' it wasn't nobody but Tilson Huett.

"Well, we argid back an' forth an hour or more, an' when we left we wasn't no more scared than we was when we went in. In fact, we wasn't as much. We knew the ropes when we come out of there, an' we didn't know 'em before. But we still didn't know what to do. Link Cave was all for writing to the President. 'He's for ekal rights,' he said. 'He'll do something about it.' An' everybody said first one thing an' then another, but nobody knowed what to do next.

"You know, I kind a b'lieve if that so-n'-so Huett hadn't spilled his guts, we could of got what we went in there for. Took 'em by surprise like, you see. But there's a nigger like him in every bunch. Yeah. If you see two niggers walking down the street together you can bet your mamma's last pair of drawers that one of them runs to the crackers with everything. An' the white man knows it! That's what makes it bad. He knows that if two niggers know something that the white folks ain't s'posed to know, he can git out o' one of them.

"I run this poolroom, see? Guys come in here right frequent an' want to borrow fi' dollars on a suit or a watch, anything they can raise some cash on. I ain't s'posed to run no pawn business, but that's what it comes to. Had a feller git fi' dollars on a suit once. I told him if he didn't git it in thirty days, I was subject to sell it. Friend o' mine, too. Thirty days went by an' he didn't come git his suit. I saw Stud one day up on the Square, an' I says, 'Stud, what 'bout that suit?' 'Aw, I'll git the suit,' he says, just like that. 'Bout two weeks later, I come here one morning an' he had both the laws waiting for me. He had figgered to git his clothes without paying me, so he had went to the law an' told them that I was running a pawnshop business. But I ain't that dumb. He didn't have no tickets. I told the law I'd bought the suit off him, an' I'd sell it back to him. Sure. I'd sell it back to anybody. They didn't do nothing but walk right on out o' here.

"But that's the way one nigger in every two will do. Don't tell me nothing 'bout zigaboos. Tilson Huett f'instance. He told them pecks everything, an' then some! What our plans was, who was officers, where we met at, everything. When he joined up, that nigger knew what he was going to do. We wanted to make him one of the officers. He was s'posed to be intelligent, principal of the school, an' all, an' we thought he'd be a good one to be a officer. But he wouldn't have no parts of it. He made some kind a dog-arse excuse 'bout he had too much other work, an' he'd work with us, but he couldn't accept the responsibility o' leading. But he knowed all the time that if he was a officer he couldn't hardly go to the white folks about it. It would look bad if he was a officer an' he ever had something to tell the crackers.

"It was something like Thursday when we went to see Mr. Reid. We didn't think nothing 'bout any trouble or anything. Friday my brother, C. A., gave a big barbecue for his burial-association members. He gives one every year on the church grounds. Sometimes we have speaking, but this year he didn't have that. People just circulated 'bout on the grounds, eating an' talking. Long in the evening a car come right on up in the yard an' some white men got out. Well, that wasn't nothing to make admiration over. White folks come right frequent to look at us enjoy ourselves. But then we notice that they had been drinking an' that Top Zuber was one of 'em.

"C. A. come running to me, asking me what must he do. 'Do?' I said. 'Don't do nothing.'

" 'Yeah, but they been drinking,' he said.

" 'Well, that's all right,' I said. 'They ain't goin'a do nothing an' we ain't goin'a do nothing.' But all the niggers had heard 'bout the time we had in Mr. Reid's office an' you could see they wasn't particular 'bout having these pecks 'round.

" 'You better say something, Flap,' C. A. said. It was his barbecue, an' yet an' still he wanted me to say something. C. A.'s my brother, but he's got a lot o' chicken in him.

"I got up on a table an' told the niggers there wasn't nothing to git excited about. We just had some friendly visitors. 'Go ahead on an' enjoy yourselves,' I told them. Niggers mumbled a little bit, but they went on eating, an' after while they wasn't paying any 'tention to the crackers. The pecks was standing round their car talking 'mongst themselves an' looking."

"Was Zuber in office as sheriff then?" I broke in.

"No, man! Him an' his little gang was just signifying. I didn't figger they was fixing to do much else but that, 'cause if they had they'da most likely brought more men with 'em. There was a gang of niggers out there that day.

"After a while somebody blowed a police whistle, an' when I looked round, I saw Top Zuber standing on top of the car waving his arms. He was weaving up there, he was just that tight, weaving an' waving. I sent C. A. one way through the crowd an' I went the other, telling folks, 'Don't pay no 'tention. No matter what he says, don't pay no 'tention.' Some few niggers looked at Top, but most didn't, but you could tell they was straining to listen. I was myself. They wanted to hear what he had to say, but they didn't want him to know it. One o' the crackers round the car blowed an' blowed that damn whistle an' the niggers still wouldn't look. An' after while I saw Top reach down an' git the whistle from the guy on the ground an' start blowing it himself. We wasn't ready to start the fire in the other pit, but somebody started it, an' a lot o' niggers walked clean across the grounds an' crowded 'round the fire, way away. Top kept blowing that whistle.

"I don't know what he said or if he said anything. I was way back in the crowd 'round the pit. I think I saw his mouth open, an' then I seen one of the crackers on the ground git up on the running board an' say something to him, an' then Top stopped blowing the whistle an' just stood up on the car with his hands on his hips looking at all the niggers an' thinking God knows what. The man standing on the running board kept talking to him. Then after while old Top Zuber jerked his hands off his hips, like he was mad an' disgusted, an' climbed down, an' they all got in the car an' backed it off the church grounds an' drove away.

"Seems like soon's the car was gone I could hear all the niggers draw one big breath at once. Then one old big-mouth nigger said something funny 'bout crackers going good with Brunswick stew, an' those that heard him laughed, an' those that didn't hear him kept saying, 'What'd he say? What'd he say?' An' 'fore long nobody thought nothing 'bout Top Zuber no more.

"Well, I thought that was the end of it, just like I thought the day before was the end of it. But pecks can't forget like we can. That's their bigges' trouble. They just can't forget! An' this time they had two things to remember. They had the five of us going to Mr. Reid's office to remember, an' they had to remember Top Zuber standing on top of a car blowing a whistle an' trying to say something to a gang o' niggers who wasn't paying him no mind. I can see how them two things would work on the white folks' mind. I can see that they would be insulted 'bout both things, an' shame' too. But white folks' shame ain't the same thing as niggers' shame.

"Anyhow, the next night was Saddee, an' I was home in bed when some jig come an' tried to beat my door in. You know it had to be late, 'cause I closed up here 'bout 'leven, an' then I went to git a beer. It was when I was going down Jefferson that I seen Doc Pogue hurrying toward Jim Covington's house an' I thought somebody was sick. I didn't know what it was till later. It was hot that night too, an' I figgered that that was why I didn't do no business. Yet an' still, I felt something funny in the air. I went on down Jefferson, an' the beer parlor was closed, an' that struck me funny too. Still I didn't think nothing. I went on home.

"I had been in bed when this jig commenced knocking. Been in bed long enough to pay my respects. Yeah. I married a right young frail, an' she calls on me right much. I was just dozin' off when the knocking come. I didn't git up at first. I yelled out, wanting to know who it was.

" 'Flap,' this jig says, whispering it an' yelling too. 'Flap, a mob come an' got Ben Speed an' Link Cave an' some more,' he says. I got up on the side of the bed, an' my wife, she set straight up.

" 'Flap!' my wife says.

" 'Shut up, woman,' I said, just like that. 'Let me git this straight. What they mobbed for?' I asked the nigger. My winder's right on the level with the porch, an' I didn't have to talk loud. I don't know why I just set on the side of the bed talking like that, 'stead o' gitting up an' going to the door. I wasn't scared. Just surprised.

" 'Didn't you go up there with them, Flap?' the nigger wanted to know.

" 'Go where?' I says.

" 'You know. Mr. Reid's office,' he says.

" 'You mean to tell me that's what they mobbing 'em for?' I asked him.

" 'That's what they say,' he says.

" 'Aw, go 'way, nigger,' I said, just like that. 'I don't b'lieve you.'

" 'All right,' this jig says. 'Don't say you wasn't warned.'

"I got up then. My wife, she was already crying, an' my mother-in-law come in the room bringing a lamp. An' she started raising hell about the lodge making trouble. Said she knew a thing like that wasn't nothing but trouble. It was a fair so-n'-so around there for a while. 'Course, the first thing I did was gather up all the artillery I had. Then we all just set there waiting in the front room with the light out, fussin' with each other an' waiting. Set up all night.

"My wife cried so much she commenced to vomiting, an' after while she got 'cross the bed an' fell asleep. She whinnied in her sleep all night long, an' in between spells of whinnying everything was quiet. Wasn't a sound in the road. Not even a car passed. What my wife had vomited smelled bad, but I wasn't 'bout to make no light to clean it up.

" 'Fore day, when my wife had fell 'cross the bed 'sleep an' my mother-in-law had stopped raising hell—I b'lieve she was asleep too, though she swears she wasn't: but once or twice, when I just had to make some kind a noise, I said something to her an' she never answered—'fore day that morning, I sure wished for something to happen, some noise, or something. A coupl'a times I thought I heard something, an' I set just as still waitin' for it to come again, an' then when it didn't come, not hearing nothing was badder than ever. Yeah. I wasn't scared. But just setting knowing that if I did hear a noise it might be them coming to mob me, an' wanting to hear a noise so bad that I almost didn't give a goddamn, well, that was crazy.

"Nobody went to church Sunday. Niggers stayed off the road an' didn't come to town at all. All that day we set in the house. 'Bout dark, Montrose Williams come to our back an' she give us the first news. But she didn't know nothing much. She had been to work. Her white folks had come for her an' brought her back, an' all she knowed was that the law wasn't letting no niggers in town 'less they was with white folks. She said her white folks told her that the mob wasn't goin'a lynch Ben an' Link, just drive 'em out a town. She said Benny an' Link was the onlies' two they was after. She said her white folks said they guess the mob just wanted to make a 'xample. She said things was gitting back to normal in town again. When she went to work that morning, white folks was off the street just like colored, but when she come back in the evening there was some on the street.

"We lit the lamp that night an' when I went to bed I slep' some.

"Monday I come on to town as usual. I didn't leave the house till nine o'clock, an' there was plen'y people on the street. There wasn't nothing to make admiration about, seem like. There was the same people an' the same houses. Them who had always spoke to me, spoke to me, an' nobody looked any different.

"But when I got here, Paul Whitney, the day law, was waiting at the door for me. We been knowing each other all our lives. But I wasn't dealing no cards to no kind a cracker in that damn game that morning. Knowing him didn't matter a damn to me. He was white. That's all I knowed!

" 'Flap,' he says, 'let's go upstairs. I got some talk for you. Better lock your door. I don't want nobody to come in while I'm talking.'

" 'Why can't we talk down here, Paul?' I asked him.

"There's a little attic room upstairs where I keep stuff I make loans on, but I wasn't thinking 'bout that. I was thinking 'bout him trying to play some trick.

" 'I just want it to be secret, Flap,' he said.

"I said, 'You don't mind if I take my gun, do you?'

" ' 'Course not, Flap,' he says. 'I swear to God, Flap, if it wasn't for me knowing you so well, I'd b'lieve you didn't trust me.'

"I didn't say nothing. I come on back behind here an' got my gun an' we went on upstairs, him walking ahead. There was four or five suits hanging up there, an' some shoes on the floor, an' automobile tars, an' batt'ries, an' a set o' suit cases. But he didn't say nothing 'bout them.

" 'Flap,' he said, 'I got a message for you. You knowed they runned some boys out a town Saddee night, didn't you?'

" 'I knowed it,' I said.

" 'Well, they didn't do nothing to 'em. Just took 'em over the county line an' told them to stay out. They wasn't aiming to hurt 'em.'

" 'Well, I'm glad a that,' I said.

"I was waiting an' watching. I was looking him in the face, but I seen him all over. Seem like to me he had shrunk up or something, an' I could see all of him just by looking in his face.

" 'Yeah,' he says. 'I'm glad as I can be, Flap. There ain't no sense in mobbing.'

"I didn't say nothing. He took his stick an' kind a brushed the clothes with it. I was looking in his face, but I seen him soon's he raised his stick. The clothes swang a little bit an' dust fell out a them.

" 'Ben Speed's over in Easter,' Paul said.

" 'Is that where they run him to?' I asked him.

" 'That's where he run to after they put him out 'cross the line,' he said. 'They run him out without a goddamn thing but his underwear, an' I told him I'd come to you an' see wouldn't you go to his house an' git him some clothes. Then you an' me can take 'em to him.'

" 'Why don't you do it yourself?' I asked him.

"He hit the clothes again, an' then kept on hitting them lightly, like he was thinking 'bout what I'd asked him. Then he said:

" 'I wisht I could, Flap. I wisht to Christ I could do it without bothering you, 'cause I know you don't want no parts of it. But s'pose I did go down to Ben Speed's house an' you boys didn't know what I was going for, an' his old woman didn't gi' me the clothes 'cause she figgered it was some kind a trap, like I b'lieve you're thinking maybe this is? Wouldn't his old woman talk about that I was trying to lay a trap? Then you know what would happen, Flap, next time I had to lock a colored boy up? He wouldn't trust me. He wouldn't want to come along nice. He'd want to fight, an' then I might have to shoot him, like Dawson does every time he's got a mind to almost. I don't want to hurt nobody, Flap.

" 'S'pose I had to lock up Wally Spence? You know what

kind a boy he is. 'Member that time he got drunk an' Dawson come along an' said he was going to lock him up, an' Wally said he'd be goddamned if Dawson would lay a hand on him? 'Member he kep' hollerin' he didn't mind going to jail, but the onliest white man who could put him in jail was me? Heard him yelling an' cussing clear over on Main. If you boys hadn't been ten to one, Hal Dawson would a shot him.

"'S'pose I went on down there, like I said, an' maybe to-morrer or next day I had to lock Wally up. He wouldn't trust me no more. He might draw a knife, an' I might have to shoot him. I don't want to hurt nobody, Flap.'

"All he said 'bout Wally Spence was true, 'cause I was there. But I just wasn't playing no poker in a game with a white man that morning.

"'But you was with the mob last night,' I told him.

"'You got me wrong,' he says. 'Didn't know nothing 'bout it till I come from visiting in the country. It was night 'fore last. When I heard 'bout it, I went looking for somebody who was in the mobbing, an' he told me Ben Speed was put out north, toward Easter, an' Cave was put out west. I found Ben.'

"I know Paul Whitney thought I was goddamn doubtful. He slipped that crack in there 'bout me thinking his wanting to talk to me was a trap. But who the hell wouldn't be doubtful? He kept swinging his stick against the clothes, like he was halfway thinking about something else. I'd knowed him all my life, an' it was true that he never had beat nobody up nor shot 'em full o' holes. But that morning he was just another peck to me.

"'How come Ben Speed didn't write me no note?' I asked him.

"'We just didn't think of it, I guess,' he said.

"I studied it a little bit longer, an' then I told him O. K., I'd git Ben's clothes, an' then he asked me to have 'em at three o'clock, when he come off duty, an' he'd come on by here an' git 'em. He asked me was I goin' with him when he took 'em, an' I told him no, but if Ben would write me a note, I'd send him some money. Then we come on downstairs, an' he hung round an' talked while I was taking the covers off the pool tables. Then he left.

"Sure 'nough, I did git a letter from Ben asking me to loan his wife some money so she could git herself together an' git out a town. They went on up to somewhere in Maryland. Link Cave's church members took up a collection for him, an' him an' his wife an' kids moved on over to Kentucky somewheres. Yeah.

" 'Course everybody felt better when they found out they hadn't laid the weight of their hands on 'em to kill 'em. Yet an' still, it was bad stuff just the same.

"Ben an' Link was the onliest ones they chased out, but they wasn't the onliest ones that left. A gang o' folks pulled up an' went. Scared! But them that stayed was on the streets again an' doing their work. 'Course, even then the town wasn't like it use to be, an' up on the Square it was like a so-n'-soin' wake. Yeah. An' now it's thataway again. An' the closer 'lection comes, the more it gits thataway. 'Stead a stretching that sign with Roosevelt's picture on it, they should of hung a crepe.

"That next Saddee things was some better, but colored folks didn't hang round none. Country niggers come to town, bought what they had to buy, an' got on back out. Didn't hang round till dark as usual. I didn't rack up more'n two or three games that whole day. There just wasn't no business. I did have three or four guys to come in an' git their guns. Some of them didn't have the money I'd loaned 'em, but I wasn't holding out in no times like them. Saddee, Sunday, Monday, Tuesday, yet an' still colored folks went on 'bout their business an' white folks went on 'bout theirs. Then on that Wednesday night they had a prayer meeting at that church where Link Cave was the preacher.

"There was a feller round here name of Huett. He wasn't no kin to that so-n'-so Huett that wanted to see your credentials. Clarence Huett his name was. Only way these two Huetts was like each other was they went to the same church an' they both went reg'lar. Clarence Huett was a good boy. I ain't saying it to build him up an' make you think what happened was worse than it was. Most anybody'll tell you Clarence Huett was just a good boy. It would of been bad enough if it was anybody, without going round making it worse by saying it happened to some little black Jesus. Clarence wasn't no Jesus. He was just naturally a good, hard-working boy.

"I wasn't at prayer meeting. I go to church Sundays, but through the week I'm busy down here an' I can't go. But they say it was a warm meeting. You know about testimony meeting. That's what this was. Everybody gits up an' testifies to the Lord an' tells him what they ain't goin'a do no more an' what they plan on doing with His help. They don't mean half what they say, but they git a good feeling saying it, an' they think they mean it.

"I wasn't there, but they tell me Clarence got up an' give testimony. He prayed first. I hadn't never knowed him to pray in meeting nor give testimony neither. But they say he did that night. They say he prayed the Lord to send down a Moses to set his people free. Then he give his testimony, telling how he was trying to buy him a home and live decent in it; how he'd got to studying that if a man like Rev'ren' Cave, who had the real grace o' God in him, could git done like he was done, then there wasn't no sense in him going on like he was going, 'cause he didn't have a chance. The say he preached a reg'lar sermon there that night.

"There was only one thing wrong with that testimony. Tilson Huett was there an' heard it. Yeah! But you see, nobody knew 'bout him then. That stuff hadn't come out in the paper 'bout him giving the lodge secrets to the white folks. Paper hadn't said nothing much 'bout the mobbing of Ben an' Link. I guess the paper thought mobbing wasn't no news 'less it ended in murder, an' it didn't even call the names of the men who was run out. Just said two undesir'ble Negroes. Didn't mention none of the other stuff that come out later. So that night nobody 'spected nothing.

"You wouldn't want to meet a nicer feller than Clarence Huett was. Him an' his wife was trying to buy a little home right next door to my mother-in-law. They both worked in the Snow White laundry. He fired over there, an' his wife ran a presser. They made 'bout eighteen a week between 'em. Clarence was a quiet feller, better-talking nigger than the average, an' he always talked sense. Wasn't no bull with him. His wife had a coupl'a kids 'fore she married him, an' the kids lived with them, an' Clarence took care o' them kids same as if he was their pappy.

"He was in here that next evening. Come in to buy a coupl'a cigarettes. He was telling me how he was cutting down on his smoking by buying two or three cigarettes at a time 'stead of a pack. When he had a pack on him he just smoked every time he thought about it, but when he had only two or three he'd smoke one a little while an' then choke it an' save it. He was telling me how the Snow White had bought out the laundry in Haines too an' that everybody had to work two or three nights week now an' sometimes more. We held a right long conversation 'bout diff'ent things.

"The next time I seen Clarence Huett he was a corpse. Yeah. A dead corpse.

"That same night 'bout ten-thirty, my wife says— I wasn't home, but my wife an' mother-in-law was setting on the porch. Clarence lived right next to us, 'bout as far as that first table. That night a car drove up the road. It was loaded with men, but my women folks didn't pay no 'tention to that. They didn't think nothing 'bout they might be white men. That other trouble had been over near 'bout three weeks, an' nothing hadn't happened to make nobody think something else was coming up. The women folks didn't know they was white men till they seen this mechanic from the laundry git out an' go to the door. They seen him then an' they thought he had come to git Clarence to go to work.

" 'Tell Clarence to come on out here,' my wife heard the peck say. An' Faydella said something, an' then the peck so-n'-so said, 'That's all right. Tell him to slip on some pants an' come like he is.' Then he went on back to the car.

"My women folks seen Clarence walk out to the car, an' then all at once he stopped right short, an' then got in the back seat slow. If he said anything nobody heard him. But when he got in the back seat Faydella ran out with the lamp in her hand an' got there just when the car was pulling off, an' either the car hit her an' knocked her down or somebody in the car reached out an' knocked her down, 'cause she fell an' caught on fire from the lamp, an' my wife an' mother-in-law put the fire out. Faydella kept saying, 'Top Zuber was driving. Top Zuber was driving,' my wife said. My wife said the oil had spilled out the broken lamp an' it was burning in little flames in a dozen places.

"The bottom was buzzing when I got home. Looked like the niggers was coming together on this thing. There was a gang a them at Clarence's house. But they couldn't git straight on nothing. Some was of one way of thinking an' some was another. Some wanted to go out looking for Clarence, an' some said it wasn't no use—he'd be all right, they wasn't goin'a hurt him. Some argid this an' some argid that, an' the outcome was that nobody done nothing but set there. Wasn't nothing but the niggers from right round in that section. I guess the folks over in Hoptown section hadn't heard about it yet. It was a more quiet mobbing than the other.

"The women an' kids was setting out in the kitchen an' us men in the front room. Long 'bout two o'clock folks started drifting off. You'd hear a man git up an' feel his way to the kitchen an' then he'd call his wife an' kids, an' you'd know who it was an' that he'd got tarred an' was going on home. Only me an' Scotty Grace an' Ginnie Oxley, an' Faydella's brother, Russ, stayed till morning. Then I went on 'cross home.

"Nobody heard nothing 'bout Clarence an' nobody done nothing 'bout it Friday an' Saddee. It wasn't the same like it was before, 'cause this time nobody figgered they was goin'a lay the weight of their hands on him. But by Saddee night something of the feeling of the first mobbing come back, 'cause nobody had heard nothing 'bout Clarence. In the poolroom here fellers was talking 'bout it, wondering why nobody hadn't heard. It commence to git on the white folks' nerves too. It wasn't nothing you could say just what, but it was something.

" 'Bout ten o'clock that night, Paul Whitney come in to see me. He had on his cop's pants, but not his coat, 'cause he was off duty an' he was wearing a old gray sweater.

" 'Ain't nobody heard from that boy yet?' he asked me.

" 'Not to my knowing,' I said. 'Where was you this time, Paul?' I asked him, sarcastic-like, but kidding him.

" 'I was here,' he says. 'I didn't know nothing about it. From what I hear, didn't many folks know nothing about it. An' them that was s'posed to be in the car, I hear they ain't come back yet.'

"He was leaning just where you're setting, an' his hands was kind a falling down on this side of the railing. It was a big scar 'cross the back of one of his hands that I hadn't never noticed before. Then I noticed I hadn't never noticed his eyes before nor nothing much about him. I'd knowed him all my life an' that night was the first time I really seen him, an' I seen that all his mush-mouth talk was straight talk coming from him. Yet an' still, I wasn't satisfied.

" ' 'S'cuse me, Paul,' I said, just like that. 'But that sounds like some stuff to me. That was Thursday night, an' here it's almost Sunday morning,' I said.

" 'I don't know, Flap,' he said. Then he looked like he was thinking 'bout something off yonder somewheres. Then he said, like it wasn't no question till the end, 'They tell me Top Zuber was in that car, Flap.'

" 'Is that so?' I asked him.

" 'Well, ain't nobody seen him since Thursday night. He ain't been home. His lady friend, she come over here from Covington yesterday, an' she ain't seen him.'

" 'What's it mean, Paul?' I asked him.

" 'Goddamn if I know, Flap. I be goddamn if I do,' he said, just like that.

"Sunday morning I was setting up in church with my wife an' mother-in-law when a usher come an' whispered in my ear that I was wanted on the outside. I went out, 'course, an' there was my brother, C. A., an' Paul Whitney. Yeah. C. A. said they'd found Clarence's body washed up out the river an' Paul had come to ask him to take it. What must he do? What he said hit me so hard my head swum.

" 'Found his corpse in the river!' I said, just like that. 'How in the hell did it git in the river?'

" 'They must a throwed it in,' C. A. said. 'They must a lynched him.'

" 'Yeah,' Paul said. 'They killed him, Flap. Goddamn if I b'lieved they'd kill that boy.'

" 'Must I git him?' C. A. wanted to know. 'I don't want no parts of it, Flap. Honest to God! Must I git him?'

" 'You're the onliest nigger undertaker in town, ain't you?' I said. 'You damn right you must! Wait a minute. I'll go with you.'

"I went on back in church to tell my wife. But I didn't have to tell her nothing. Soon's I walked in I seen the whole church knowed it. Everybody turned round an' looked at me, an' then everybody seemed to know. I don't know how they found out, but it looked like the minute they turned round they knowed. When I come back out to go with C. A. an' Paul, the whole church come out behind me. They all wanted to go down to the river, but we wouldn't let 'em.

"When we got down to the river with the dead wagon there was a gang o' crackers an' the coroner from the county. C. A. an' me stayed in the wagon till Paul went up an' spoke to the coroner. They made the crowd fall back. Then the coroner come over an' give C. A. a permit to move the body, an' C. A. an' me got out the basket.

"I didn't look at the corpse till we got right on it. Yeah. I looked every place but right at it. Then I seen it. The boy was laying on his stomick, where they had drug him, an' he was beginning to swell up. You could see the tracks where they had drug him through the mud on the bank. Hadn't nobody bothered to cover his nakedness. His pants was all twisted up down around his ankles. A piece of the sleeve of his pajamas was on his wrist, an' the coroner had put a newspaper over his head.

"They had beat him bad. We didn't turn him over. We just layed him in the basket on his stomick, so we didn't know how bad they'd beat him or that he'd been shot till we got him back to town an' took him out a the basket. He had been shot in the back twice, an' there wasn't nothing but two little teeny holes in the back. But where one slug had come out in the front, there was a hole big enough to drive a plow. His insides was sticking out, an' the fish had been nibbling them, looked like. An' he stunk! Yeah. He stunk worse'n a nest o' granddaddies.

"It was the next day that we all found out about Tilson Huett. The paper come out this time giving a history of both mobbings, an' it told how Huett had been to the white folks to try to 'void trouble both times, an' how the white folks had done, an' how when this second trouble started just a few quick-tempered men had 'tended to it quiet. They called Huett a 'loyal Negro' in the paper. Yeah! The cracker so-n'-soes said he had most likely 'voided more serious trouble."

When I moved my feet from the rungs of the stool pain shot through my stiff knees. There was no one in the poolroom now. Some time during the long telling the men had gone. I did not remember their going. Flap went to the back and racked the balls up and spread the gray rubberized cloth over the table. He turned out the light. When he came back again I asked him about Top Zuber.

"He's high sheriff now. Yeah. In office. Been in office."

"And where was he from Thursday to Sunday?"

"You mean Tuesday. Didn't nobody see him in town till the next Tuesday," Flap said.

"Where'd he been?"

"You got to ask somebody better'n me," Flap said.

He got down his hat and put on his street coat over the pullover zipper sweater. He counted the change in the cash drawer and locked the drawer. Then he unlocked the cupboard beneath the register and took out an ugly-mouthed, short-snouted automatic, which he slipped under his belt outside his sweater, handy.

"Other niggers is scared, but I ain't scared," Flap said.

4

There was still no hint of the fall that should have been approaching on crimson feet when I went across Tennessee and over the mountains into Kentucky. It had been my intention to go west through Tennessee into Arkansas, but Bill Perry changed my plans. I picked him up at Rockwood.

"Y'all wanta see Kintucky, man! De rail Kintucky." And he sang unquotable snatches of the Casey Jones ballad. As it turned out, he had never seen the "rail Kintucky" himself, but he wished to go there and "git on the radjo" with his songs and his guitar. He was ambitious to get on the radio in every state in the Union, and for this reason he had left his married daughter's home in Natura, Mississippi, for good.

"You don't look old enough to have a married daughter," I said.

"Don't?" he said, pleased. "Shucks, I got gran'babies. I'm better'n foty years ol'."

Of course he was older than that even, I guessed, though there was an air of jaunty youthfulness about him. He was dressed from head to foot in dingy white—white cotton shirt, white sailor pants, and soiled white canvas shoes. It was already mid-October, and he seemed to have no other clothing but a short, heavy coat, remnant of a uniform I could not identify. This was rolled up and wrapped with twine. He was colored and wrinkled like an old potato, and I realized that the youth that was in him looked out of his eyes. These, like new bright screwheads sunk in old wood, completely dominated his features.

"But how do you make your living?" I asked.

"Livin'?" he repeated, as if it were a strange word.

"Not on the radio? You don't get paid for that, do you?"

"Not n'ar a ten cent," he answered. "But shucks, man, livin's

easy. I comes to a town an' I'se in need o' som'pin to eat, I hauls
my tail to a j'int an' whups my box to a frazzle. Den I passes de
hat. Saddee evenin's an' nights, man!" he said, as if there were no
words to express it. "But I ain't much of a eater myse'f nohow."

He looked as if he were not much of an eater. My shirt cuff
would have done him for a collar. His narrow shoulders fell
away from his neck at so sharp an angle that arms, shoulders,
and neck seemed all of a piece. His thinness amounted to a
deformity.

But he could not have sung for the radio the verses he sang
for me.

> I tuk a gal f'om under Tom McCabe.
> Her name was Essie, high-brown Essie-Babe.
> She knowed John Henry in his primpin' prime.
> She's like a street car, joy ride fer a dime.

Then in the plaintive minors to which both his guitar and his
edgy, unmelodic voice were best suited, patting his foot in an
off beat against the floor of the car, plucking the music out with
brass-ringed fingers (there was a ring on every finger of his
plucking hand) he moaned the chorus.

> Oh, I'd ruther drink muddy water
> An' sleep in a holler log,
> For de way dat high-brown treats me
> Is like a mangy dog.
> Oh, I'd ruther drink muddy water . . .

"Are those the things you sing in the joints on Saturday
nights?" I asked, when he had strummed and moaned his way
through a half-dozen salacious ballads.

"Man, yeah. Dem peckerwoods loves it. Ain't no seaburg
goin', ain't no dancin' when I plays. But de niggahs, now, niggahs is dif'ent."

"How do you mean?"

"Oh, dey likes a lot o' fing'rin', an' dey druther I kinda hum."
And he illustrated. "Dey knows all de words, an' some o' dem

babies kin sing 'em too, what I mean. Niggahs mostly made up de songs.

> Oh, I ain't goin' a give nobody none
>   o' my jelly roll, jelly roll.
> I wouldn' gi' you none . . .

Thus we rode up and across Tennessee into Kentucky. There were mines at Morgan City and Glenmary, but they were idle. The drift mouths were blocked with heavy timbers. In some places coal dollies, tipped over and chained together, barred the adits. The western end of the Cumberland Valley and the whole narrow gorge of the Elk from Huntsville to Jellico lay idly waiting for the tardy autumn. Not a heading worked, not a dolly moved. Mine timbers lay scattered on the mountainside. Here and there coal cars stood frozen with rust. In the villages guards with automatic rifles stood about the company buildings. The guards were about the only men we saw. The villagers seemed to be women and children. Once a guard stood in a narrow village street and waved us down. He wanted to know where we "boys" were going. Before I could answer, Bill Perry broke in.

"Cap'n, we'se goin' to Kintucky. See all dat stuff back dere, Cap'n? Well, dat stuff 'longs ter Mista Rob French, an' he sho' will raise hell ef we don' git it to him," Bill lied convincingly.

"That gittar too?" the guard questioned, already softened to a joke.

Bill grinned. "No, suh, Cap'n. Dis yere box is mine. Dis yere's ma sweetheart! If we-all hed time an' you hed time, I'd beat one out fer you," Bill said.

"G'on. But don' stop nowheres. Don' even breathe hard," the guard said, grinning.

"No, suh, Cap'n. I ain't much of a breever noway. Jus' 'nough ter live on. No, suh. I don' want no mo' o' white folks' air den I jus' got ter have."

We drove on. Bill Perry doubled up with laughter, his narrow, slanting shoulders almost touching his knees.

"I kin lie when I has ter."

"I see you can."

"Man, dat gun was 'bout de mos' uglies' thing I ever seen."

"What do you suppose the trouble is, Bill?"

" 'Deed, I ain't got no notion. But hits white folks' trouble, an' dat's 'nough fer me," Bill said. "Peckerwoods is allus got some trouble. Near 'bout all de trouble dey is is white folks' trouble. Be a reg'lar ol' levee jubilee if som'pin was to blow de white folks all up. Ain't no sense to deir troubles neither. Peckerwoods kin't live less'n dey messed up wid som'pin."

"But you sang a song about trouble a while back," I reminded him.

"Dis'n? Trouble, trouble, I'se hed it all my days. Dat'n?"

"Yes."

"Dat was wrote special for white folks. Else it was wrote back in slav'ry times, when niggahs hed some sho' 'nough trouble of dey own. Dat wasn' de niggahs' fault. What I'm talkin' 'bout, peckerwoods goes 'round makin' a mess. I ain't talkin' 'bout fightin' trouble, like crazy drunk niggahs on saw-mill pay eenin'. I'm talkin' 'bout war trouble, bad-times trouble, tight-money trouble, an' sich as dat. I'm sho' glad I'se a niggah."

He looked eagerly into my face as if he expected a contradiction. Getting none, he settled back and plucked tentatively at his guitar until a broken melody crawled forth. We were deep in the ragged, lonely mountains now. There was much second-growth timber, and here and there the clumsy workings and the slag-crammed narrow mouth of a one-man mine. The mountains looked as if they had been used and thrown away.

"But you know one thing," Bill said later. "Niggahs is gittin' mo' an' mo' like white folks ever' day, 'spec'ly 'long dat line. Dey gittin' ter think jus' like peckerwoods, an' ter look like 'em too. You take notice. I'd ruther be a niggah myse'f. No, suh! I ain't a'ter no change. Niggahs got all de good bottom gravy, ter my way o' thinkin'."

Then with complete disregard for congruity, he struck up the chords of that song especially made for white folks:

> Trouble, trouble, done hed it all my days.

And I thought of Sterling Brown's classic little story of the Negro who listened patiently to the multiple woes of a white acquaintance and then inquired dryly, "What you complainin' 'bout? You still white, ain't you?"

Certainly Bill Perry would have damned and denied the implications in that rejoinder, if he had understood them. And certainly, too, had he heard from Mrs. Hatton the things I heard, had he seen her and come to understand, as I thought I understood the meaning of the dark thing she and her family stood for, he would have damned and denied her. His comment would have been as intolerant and as unerring as a loosed arrow. Bill Perry was no fool. He had the complete assurance and the freedom of a man who understands his environment and has no particular wish to change either it or himself. He was going to Kentucky, and either there or in Patagonia he would have been at home, for he knew without knowing that the 'rail Kintucky,' or the real Maine, or the real Georgia was within him and had nothing to do with geographical or social or economic boundaries.

But Bill Perry did not hear Charity Hatton's dark and simple and often labored recital, for he got out at Richmond, Kentucky. Suspending his guitar by its greasy cord from one side of his neck and his coat by its cord from the other (his shoulders sloped too sharply for a pack), he said, "Dis looks like a good town." I have no doubt he found it so. Perhaps that very night he wandered into a juke joint behind a gas station on the dark edge of town and played and sang for his supper. Besides, there was no necessity for him to hear Mrs. Hatton. He would have been the first to admit that there was nothing for him to learn, no doubts to resolve, no faith to find. As man and as Negro, his values were set immutably, and he knew where to find them.

5

Once in Kentucky, I did not find Mrs. Hatton by accident. There was a tenuous blood kinship between us; there was her long memory of my mother as a school girl. Even as I talked to her over the telephone I could sense that kinship expanding in her mind into something warm and southern and confidential. I tried to remember her children's names. I remembered Rosalie and Tom, who were about my own age, but the names of the other two escaped me. It was just as well, for Clarice had died years ago.

"You must come to dinner, Cousin," the voice said over the telephone. "Doctor is seldom here, and the children . . . But I'll tell you about them when you come. Oh, it is so good to hear you!"

Already I felt like a traitor. Perhaps I should have called my Cousin Charity before I went to see Frissie Barlow. Frissie (she insisted upon my using her first name, though she was nearly sixty) had told me enough and hinted enough about my cousins to set my curiosity ablaze. I had seen none of them for twenty years, and some of them I had never seen at all, and it was difficult for me to feel any family bond. But when I heard that voice, so eagerly persuasive and confiding, I felt traitorous.

"How're Rosalie and Tom?" I called into the phone.

"Oh, Cousin!" And her voice grew suddenly tremulous, "You must come out here." I was a member of the family. I could hear that in her voice.

"I'm going to be perfectly frank with her," I told Frissie.

"Certainly you are," she said.

"I mean it."

Frissie's description of the Hatton house had been so photographic that when I entered it seemed theatrically familiar. It was a large house with large, high-ceilinged rooms, cool in summer and inadequately heated in winter, for it was expensive to heat ten such rooms. In the good times of 1922, when Dr. Hatton was a younger and more popular physician, expense was not an overbearing consideration. Of more weight was the fact that Rosalie Hatton, then a sophomore in college, had to be launched into the fiercely competitive world of marriageable girls (Frissie Barlow told me all this), and in the city the proper setting was a four-figure address on the west side. In the early twenties the substantial whites were moving out (the Supreme Court had just ruled it unlawful to segregate Negroes in residential areas) and the houses sold for twelve to fifteen thousand dollars. Rosalie was brown of face. In the brittle world of college and professional people only a background of somewhat ostentatious affluence could equalize the difference between Rosalie's brown skin and the lighter complexions of most of her rivals. The west side was color-bound.

In other ways, too, it was different from the north side, where the four Hatton children were born in the first decade of the century. It was more exacting and a great deal more expensive. The north side neighborhood had had certain advantages. It was packed tight with Negroes who "had more rheumatism from working in the steaming processing rooms of the tobacco factories, more accidents from laboring in the foundries, and more brawls and babies from uninhibited instinct" than any other group in the city, not excluding the vociferous Irish who lived in the next neighborhood to the east. There was no need for a telephone. "Out here in the north side," Frissie told me, "a few years back, people would just get out in the middle of the street and yell for Doc." There was no need, either, for a horse and buggy, or later an automobile, for the neighborhood, practically self-contained, was not many blocks around, scarcely a quarter-hour's walk. Dr. Hatton did not have to leave the neighborhood to earn a substantial living.

But as Rosalie grew up and her tastes were modified, refined, I suppose, by the kind of venal learning that passed for education, the Hattons moved to the west side, where there were almost no Negroes then. There the wide front yards, neat as spread green table covers, swept to old carriage houses in the rear. There northsiders never raised their brawling voices or drank up Sunday's dinner. On the west side Dr. Hatton needed a telephone, an automobile, and an office a mile and half away. The house needed a servant. And later, when the elder son also went, unwillingly, to college, Mrs. Hatton needed a job.

"I'm not throwing stones," Frissie Barlow said. "Your Cousin Charity is a sweet woman, a good, well-meaning woman. She has a good heart. All of us who are her friends know that. But she got one of those social welfare jobs dealing with the under-privileged, and she makes even those things she has to do for people look like acts of philanthropy."

The Hatton house was attractive and tastefully furnished, but it lacked the mellow warmth of human use. It seemed no longer lived in. I heard from Frissie that only Rosalie, in a wild tantrum of self-indulgence, now flung open the downstairs blinds, kicked up the rugs, and banged discordantly on the baby grand piano. It was a house in which lay morgued a corrupted kind of hope and pride and ambition. It was in a peculiar way the hearse of an American dream.

I was perfectly frank with my Cousin Charity. Even before my cheek was dry from the moist touch of her lips, I said:

"Cousin Charity, let me try to explain something. Don't tell me anything, well—on the basis of friendship. I'll listen, of course. I'll try to understand. Well, you see . . ."

"Oh," she said. A tremor passed over her face, and I saw that she was an aging woman. Her skin was blotchy and her hair had gone brittle and thin from lack of care. But I could not stop. As I talked, she listened, stroking her cheek with the back of her hand.

"Oh," she said again. "You mean you're not interested just because . . ."

I interrupted her.

"I'm more interested because we're kin. But it's not because we're kin . . ."

"Don't say any more," she said, smiling weakly. She took off her glasses—she seemed absolutely naked without them—blew on them and put them back on her nose. The silence was so long that I felt embarrassed. She sat stroking her cheek with the back of her hand, looking at me in a melting, enveloping way. Finally she sighed.

"Well, Cousin," she said, getting up, "let's have dinner. I gave the girl the afternoon off. She listens to everything."

We ate in the big back hall just off the kitchen. The table was spread for three, but one plate was turned down. Cousin Charity told me that the doctor never ate until nearly midnight. His food was kept warm in the electric warmer that stood on one side of the table. The hall, which was really as large as a small room, had none of the intimacy of rooms where families gather, none of the look, nor the homey, bready smell of such rooms. There were pictures of dead fish and fowl on the wall. There was also a decorative calendar, still turned to a February nearly three years gone. The back stairs led off the hall, and the bottom steps were stacked with newspapers and magazines still in their wrappers.

It was not a good dinner. It came from the electric warmer, and it was cold. Of the chicken, only the cracker meal in which it had been fried was done. The vegetables were flat-tasting, altogether unseasoned. Cousin Charity ate sparingly in pauses of speaking of my mother and of distant relatives who had gone far west and of whom I knew nothing. She seemed to talk in a kind of wistful desperation, against time. Her voice was animated and a little on the strident side. When she took off her glasses and blew them, which she did frequently, the nakedness I had seen earlier was clothed in a timorously aggressive trustfulness.

"Would you drink a little brandy, Cousin? I use it to settle my stomach."

It was good brandy.

"I've decided to tell you about Rosalie anyway," she said suddenly, placing an arm on either side of her plate. "After all, we are kin. When have you seen any of us?"

"Years and years," I said. "But listen, Cousin Charity, assume that I know nothing. Assume that we're not . . ."

"Oh," she said, and looked stricken again.

"Of course, I do know something," I said.

"Years ago your mother's children and mine all played together. Do you remember that? And now, and now— All right. I'll assume that you know nothing. But you do know something?"

"Yes, Cousin Charity," I said, trying to fill the place she wanted me to fill, trying to absorb her loneliness.

She took off her glasses and blew them. There was a red welt where they fitted across the bridge of her nose. A nest of fine, purplish veins lay on each side of the fleshy lobes of her nose.

"You knew that Clarice died?"

"Yes. We were sorry to hear it," I murmured.

"She was the fair one, and growing more beautiful. You could see that she would have been a beautiful woman. But she died. Then that left Rosalie as the only girl, and I don't care what it was, if Rosalie said she wanted it, she got it. I used to tell Doctor that Rosalie was his girl anyway. You see, he was very fond of girls, so Rosalie got all her own attention and Clarice's too, especially from her father.

"All our neighbors on the north side spoiled Rosalie too. They were all crazy about Rosalie. She wasn't as pretty as Clarice was. She wasn't half as fair. But she had nice, even features, and I'd dress her in little silk dresses and patent-leather pumps and she'd look right nice. She was the kind of girl that everybody would know, and everybody over there knew her. A lot of the things she'd do, too, they'd excuse. Never really anything bad, but she was full of life and mischief. She wasn't like Clarice at all. Clarice was quiet. But Rosalie was always up to something. Even the boys were quiet to her, and she ruled them completely. 'Tommy, do this' and 'Renny, do that.' She was always getting them into some mischief, and they were afraid to tell on her. Their father frequently whipped one of them for something she had done.

"There was an Irishman who used to go around with a little wagon selling ice cream, and Rosalie and all the children used to buy from him. One day Rosie didn't have a penny, but she ordered a cone anyway. You could buy penny cones and three-penny cones in those days, and I don't know what Rosalie ordered, but when he asked for the money, she put a stone in his hand and ran away as fast as she could. I was mortified when I heard about it. Of course he didn't do a thing but come straight to the house and tell me what Rosalie had done, and I paid him.

"Rosalie didn't come home for a long time. I sent the boys all over the neighborhood looking for her. When she did come home, I asked her about it, but she denied it. 'Rosalie,' I said, 'you know you did it.' 'Why, Mamma,' she said, her face just as straight, 'you know I wouldn't do anything like that. And if you don't believe me, I don't care!' I insisted that she was telling me a story, and she then went into one of her wild times, and by the time Doctor got home she was fit to be tied. She told him that I was taking sides against her with some old Irishman. She said she hadn't even seen the ice-cream man that day. We couldn't coax her to eat her supper after that.

"She got in the closet in the back parlor, which was Doctor's waiting room when we lived on the north side, and stayed there all night. We didn't sleep that night. We were afraid she'd smother, you know. Every few minutes we'd go to the closet and there she'd be sitting down in a corner looking at us. We thought she'd go to sleep after a while and then we could carry her to bed. But she didn't go to sleep. If we spoke to her, she wouldn't answer. She nearly worried me to death that night. But the next day she was just like nothing had happened.

"Rosalie had a lot of little friends. All the children in the neighborhood used to come around to play with her, and she could make them do anything she wanted. I would hear her yelling at them, 'If you don't do it, I won't let you play with my dolls any more,' and she could get them to do anything she wanted. And she'd bully the boys something awful. I used to feel sorry for the poor children, the way Rosalie bossed them. Sometimes I think they really didn't like her, although she could be sweet and gentle and simply lovely when she wanted to be. I don't know whether you remember about her, but a long time ago your family and my family spent nearly a whole summer together in New Jersey."

"I remember," I lied.

"Rosalie could be so sweet. Sometimes she'd be sweet to her little playmates and then change in a minute and have one of her stiffening-out tantrums. She'd change from one to the other quicker than you'd think, and she always had her way with almost everybody. Her teachers, and everybody. I don't know what she would have done if she'd been anybody else's child.

"I kept her out of school for two or three years, because after she got to the third grade, she decided she didn't like her teachers or the children or anything about school. I taught her at home, and such a time I had! She had a quick mind, and when she wanted to, she could get her lessons. But when she got in one of her moods, it was awful. She'd tease the boys about having to go to that old outhouse—that's what she called the school—and she'd hide their books and things. I taught her at home for nearly three years, and by her not going to school and coming in contact with the children much, they started calling her stuck-up and airish, and after a while she didn't have many friends.

"Doctor and I decided that the school on the north side wasn't the place for Rosalie anyway. The children were regular toughies, and dirty. They'd say anything and do anything. So we put Rosalie in school over on this side. We sent the boys, too, for company for her. Ashby was a better school and the children were nicer and there weren't so many of them. Evelyn Tate and Lois Empey and the Sturgis children all went to Ashby. They were all nice children, from good families. Rosalie got along all right there, and if she did anything, nobody ever told us. The only trouble seemed to be that she was jealous of her friends, and if one of her friends invited someone to go home with them it would break Rosalie's heart. Many a time she came home in raging tears because Evelyn Tate had invited someone to spend the day or night with her. If Rosalie liked you, she didn't want you to like anyone else.

"When she went to high school, she got a crush on one of her teachers, Maudestine Chambers. Maudestine was a pretty young thing, just a year or two out of college, and the young men were crazy about her. Rosalie made a great to-do over her. When she found out Maudestine was keeping regular company with a young man, it just about made her sick. It worried Maudestine. Rosalie would wait for her every day after school and go home with her. She'd save up her little change and buy her presents, and she always wanted to go over to Maudestine's house and spend week ends. Naturally, being a young woman, Maudestine didn't want any fourteen- or fifteen-year-old girl tagging after her. But just the same, she didn't want to hurt Rosalie's feelings. She knew Rosalie was a very sensitive girl, so she let her spend one or two week ends, and then she came to me.

"Maudestine was worried half-sick, you know, not wanting to hurt Rosalie's feelings and at the same time not wanting a real young girl tagging after her. Naturally I didn't know what to tell her to do. I thought Rosalie's crush would pass, and I told Maudestine so. She talked rather funny, and I don't think she was altogether frank with me. She asked me if I knew Rosalie was spending her movie money and her lunch money on presents for her. Rosalie used to write her notes too.

"But when Rosalie found out Maudestine was keeping regular company with this young man, the way she acted was mortifying. She waited for Maudestine after school, and Maudestine was going somewhere with another teacher. Rosalie went in Maudestine's room and started scolding her, just like she was her equal, and this other teacher came in. It got all over town and caused a lot of embarrassment. How Rosalie had said that

Maudestine was deceiving her, and if she didn't stop going with this young man she'd kill herself. She told her how she'd saved her money to buy presents and everything. Of course, the other teacher shouldn't have told it, but she did, and it got all over town.

"When Rosalie came home that day, she locked herself in her room. Of course, we didn't know what the trouble was then. Doctor didn't hear about it from some of his friends uptown until the next day, so we didn't know why Rosalie had locked herself in. She didn't go to school for a week. None of us even saw her for a solid week. Her father would go to her door—she was crazy about her father. She always had looked like him, his color and everything—but he'd go to her door and she'd tell him to go away. We put a tray outside her door three times a day, but she never touched it. We were all frantic. We got Evelyn Tate, her best friend, to come over and to try to coax her out, but that didn't do any good. Finally, that Friday evening Doctor went to Maudestine, and I guess she felt that since it was her fault in a way, she'd come over.

"Maudestine came, but she didn't want to do it. She said if this tantrum of Rosalie's would end it, it would be a good thing, and her trying to get Rosalie to act right might start it all over again. We begged and we pleaded, and finally she went up and knocked on Rosalie's door. Doctor and I stood at the foot of the stairs, and we heard Maudestine say, 'It's me, Rosalie.' Then the door opened and she went in. We certainly were relieved. She stayed in there an hour or more, I guess, and then she came down and told us she was going to spend the week end. She looked like she had seen a ghost. She was a pale young thing anyway, and she was very pinched and very pale when she came down. She looked like she had been crying too. But everything was all right again. Maudestine spent the week end, and Monday morning, when they went to school together, Rosalie was like nothing had happened.

"Rosalie had that crazy crush all year. Maudestine was nine or ten years older than Rosalie, but after a while it got so that

Rosalie bossed her as if she were a child. Sometimes Rosalie would treat her awfully shabby, calling her a half-white monkey, and asking her where her father was. She knew that no one had ever seen Maudestine's father and she knew what everyone said and believed about it, and she would get mean with her and ask her where her father was. But through it all, Maudestine never changed. She was just naturally a sweet, considerate girl.

"Rosalie got all wrapped up in moving. The Tates and the Barlows moved in this way, though not so far in and still near the north side. Really still in the north side almost, though a better neighborhood, where there weren't so many colored. And the Sturgises bought up in the thirty-hundred block. Rosalie started saying she was just as good as they were, and she didn't see why we had to stay on the north side. All her friends lived on the west side, and she didn't want her friends laughing at her. Then another time she'd say she didn't care, because if her friends couldn't come to see her on the north side, then she didn't have any real friends, and she'd always suspected that the real fair colored people were two-faced any-way, and she just didn't care. But just the same, she stopped inviting her friends, because she said she was ashamed of the house.

"It did seem that all our friends were moving out here. I was tired of the north side too. We had a good house, but the neighborhood was awful, and especially bad for the children. I knew they couldn't get anywhere over there, because over there they were lumped in with everybody else, the very low class, foundry people and factory people.

"We were upset about Rosalie's friends not coming to see her, and about the boys too. Tommy was smoking on the sly and playing truant from school, and Renny, well, you just couldn't tell anything about Renny. But Doctor was more concerned about Rosalie, and naturally I was too. It's a shame, and it shouldn't be the way it is, but it's so, and you have to own up to it: whether a young girl is fair makes a lot of difference, and all of Rosalie's friends were lighter than she was, and so had some advantage over her. Rosalie always did have nice, even features and fairly straight hair, but she wasn't light, and that can make a world of difference for a girl.

"Well, we sent Rosalie off to college with a promise that we'd move as soon as we found a place out here. We sent her off to Fisk with everything imaginable in the way of clothes. She didn't want for a thing. We sent her spending money every month, and pretty soon, from the reports we got, she seemed to be very popular. I'm sure no girl on the campus was better supplied with clothes. I just prayed that she'd get in one of her sweet moods and stay that way, for she could be a perfect lamb. And that's what she must have done, for every time we picked up a colored paper there was Rosalie's name, where she'd been to some party or a game or something.

"We heard from others that she seemed to have quite a few fellows too. But she never seemed to keep one long. She seemed to get tired of them. But once she came home wearing a solitaire and saying she was going to get married to a fellow in the dental school up there as soon as ever he graduated. We had been living in this house two years then, and had just about got it fixed like we wanted it. I didn't object to her getting married. I thought it was a blessing that she had got a young man. And Doctor didn't object either, but he seemed to think that since he'd bought this house for Rosalie, in a way, then if she got married her young man ought to come here to live. Rosalie might have been just fooling about being engaged anyway, though why she would do a thing like that I don't know. But after she went back, we never heard any more about it.

"Once in her senior year she got very sick, and without Rosalie knowing anything about it, her roommate sent us word. It seems that Rosalie didn't want us to know. Of course, Doctor and I got ready and went to Nashville. Doctor wired ahead to Dr. Glass and asked him to take charge of Rosalie, and when we got there, Dr. Glass had moved her from the dormitory to the hospital.

"But when we walked into the room, such a scene as Rosalie

went into! I thought she would fly out the window. Weak and thin as she was, she went into one of her fits, screaming and actually cursing, until I just knew she was delirious. Her father and Dr. Glass were afraid to administer a sedative, and I don't know how we got her quiet, but we did. But when she got quiet, she wouldn't say anything at all and she wouldn't look at anybody. You might have thought, sick as she was, she would have been glad to see us, but she wasn't. When her father and Dr. Glass went out, I tried to talk to her, but she wouldn't say anything or even look at me. I tried to rub her forehead, but she rolled her head away. She didn't even say anything or look when her father came back in and walked up to the bed and took her hand. She just snatched it away and started crying and that was all.

"I stayed a week, and in all that time she didn't even say she was glad to see me. Doctor came back here after he was satisfied she was all right, but I stayed a week, and sometimes when I went to the hospital I could tell she had been crying, but she never said anything. It wasn't from the pain or anything, and she seemed to have plenty of friends, for everybody came to see her and her room was full of flowers and fruit all the time. When her friends came, she was sweet to them. She was like an angel. After a week Dr. Glass said it was all right for her to go back to the dormitory, and I came back home.

"For a while, before Rosalie graduated, we were in hopes that she'd find a young student doctor up there and marry and they'd come here and set up so he could help Doctor with his practice. Doctor's practice was very good then, and it would have been just the thing for Rosalie to have married a doctor. Tom was in college, and so was Renny, but neither of them wanted to study medicine. As it turned out, Renny didn't study anything much, and Tom all but threw away four years and a good bit of our money, though he did at least get a degree.

"But after Rosalie graduated and came back home, the chances of her making a marriage like that were reduced to nothing. Nowadays most of the young men who come out of medical school are already married. And here it's not easy for an educated girl to find a young man. All the young men a girl could marry are already taken up with someone else, or else she has to marry somebody beneath her. But Rosalie didn't seem much inclined to get married anyway. One young man used to come all the way from Louisville to see her. Though I didn't care for him, I didn't like to see her keep him dancing like a monkey on a string. But he finally got tired and married a Louisville girl.

"Rosalie had a lot of new friends. Every day after school the house would be crowded with young people, and there was always someone new. A lot of them were new teachers in the schools here, and a lot of them I'd never seen before.

"There was a time when you could trust school teachers. You just knew they were good respectable people, but I wasn't always so sure of some of those who used to come here. But they used to have good times. They danced and played whist around at various houses, and some week ends a crowd of them would go to Chicago or Cincinnati or Indianapolis. We didn't know there was drinking going on among them, but after Doctor found out about it, he was afraid they might get ahold of some poison stuff that was going around, so he'd bring home bonded prescription whisky whenever Rosalie was going to have a bunch in.

"She was always full of life in her bunch, and always making some young man look ridiculous. She'd sneak up on some young man in a bunch of girls and snatch his shirttail out, or pretend to be fixing his tie and really untying it all the time. She seemed to get enjoyment out of annoying them, and I used to tell her not to do those things, but she didn't pay me any mind.

"I used to tell her to try to save some money too. She didn't have to spend a thing on the house unless she wanted to, but she decided of her own free will that she'd pay the gas and electric and the water and telephone. Sometimes she paid and sometimes she didn't, and I'd try to show her how expensive the house was with the boys in school. She'd fly off then and say I just wanted her to slave and sacrifice for her yellow brothers. That's what she'd call them—her no-good, yellow brothers. 'Tom and Renny aren't anything,' she'd say, and whenever I brought up the subject that was her answer.

"I really don't know where her money went. She didn't seem to spend much on herself. She got very careless in her dress about this time, and even sometimes when she bought clothes, she'd wear them once or twice and then give them away. But she spent money very fast, and then would go uptown and use my charge accounts. Later on I found out that she was borrowing a lot, too, but I didn't know what for. If she had helped carry the house, then each of us could have saved something out of what we made.

"By and by her friends started getting married. For a while there was a regular fever of marriages around here, and practically all Rosalie's friends who weren't teaching got it. There was a law in the city that married girls can't teach, and that left quite a few girls unmarried. But most of these were girls she hadn't associated with and were not in her bunch at all. They were girls who got through normal school here and got jobs in the north-side schools because they had relatives or friends who worked in service for influential white people. Most of them lived on the north side. They had come from that environment in the first place, and they stayed in it, where they could do almost anything they wanted.

"It was these people Rosalie began to take up with now. For a long while her really nice friends overlooked a lot, and she was still invited to parties and dances and things. But she was getting so that when they served anything to drink, she always took too much, and before the night was over she'd have a falling out with somebody. Pretty soon even the Sturgises and the Tates stopped asking her to things.

"She had two very bad wrecks with her car. Her father was forced to lay down a rule that whenever she went outside the city somebody had to drive for her. She was always wanting to go to Chicago or Louisville and take a friend with her. One Thanksgiving she had Tom take her and a friend to Chicago.

When they came back, Tom said he'd never take her any place else, she'd been half-intoxicated the whole time and he had an awful time with her and her ratty friend. Tom hardly spoke to Rosalie after that. He hardly speaks to her now.

"For years it went on like this and worse. She bought another car and lost it back to the finance company. Her father and I paid off any number of her debts, and it was about this same time that I found out she was borrowing money from other teachers. You know how things come back to you, and I was hearing on all sides that Rosalie would borrow and then fly off when she was asked to pay back.

"She began saying that people were talking about her. I know they were, because I was hearing things that Tom's wife was hearing and telling me, but it was the kind of talk you couldn't say who did. Rosalie accused various ones. She thought everybody was against her, other teachers in her school and all. She would go to another teacher's classroom and accuse her of saying something about her before the whole class, and perhaps strike her. I couldn't help hearing all these things, and I couldn't help believing some of them, because I knew how she was at home. Some days I'd come home and find her absolutely stupefied with whisky. Her father never has found it out. I'm sure it would kill him. He doesn't know until now that she drinks herself speechless every time she gets a chance. Some days and for a while she'll go along all right, but other times she'll alarm the whole block banging on the piano and singing at the top of her voice.

"Last year I had an insurance policy to mature. It was a fairly good-size policy, and I put the money in the bank. I didn't tell Rosalie anything about it, but she must have found the maturity notice or the canceled policy or something, though I didn't think when she came to me with a proposition that she knew anything about it. She was very sweet and considerate for several weeks, and I began to hope that she had changed for the better. Then one day about two months after the policy had matured, she came to me and said that some teachers at her school needed some money and they had asked her to ask me. 'Mamma,' she said, 'have you any money you can lend them?' That's what she said. Various ones borrowing money from me wasn't anything new, for I had let some have some before. Never any large sums, five or ten dollars at a time. Lending money was always a kind of saving for me, for if I didn't lend it I'd spend it.

"But this time it turned out that one, so Rosalie said, wanted fifty dollars and two wanted a hundred dollars apiece. I told Rosalie, I said, 'You know, Rosalie, if I lend that kind of money, I've got to have interest on it.' And her exact words were, 'All right, Mamma. I'm sure they'll pay you interest. It'll be better than the Jew loan sharks uptown.'

"I made arrangements then and drew the money from the bank and Rosalie took it to school. I had some notes drawn up, and I told Rosalie to be sure and have them sign the notes. 'Now, Rosalie,' I said, 'you be sure that each of them signs the notes they're supposed to sign.' Sure enough, she took the money and brought me the notes that afternoon. They were signed with the names of the people she said wanted to borrow the money.

"The arrangement with the notes was that they were supposed to pay me so much each month. But several weeks went by and I didn't hear from any of them nor see them. They were all some of the nice people who used to be Rosalie's friends in a regular way—Bernice Weedon, a very tall, awfully striking-looking girl, and Troy Moine. Lillie Sturgis too. All of them used to be Rosalie's fast friends until she took up with this other crowd. And when Rosalie came to me about the money, I thought, you know, that maybe they were all right again. I really loaned them the money, so I thought, more for Rosalie's sake than their own.

"Anyway, two months went by, and then nearly three months, and one day I said to Rosalie, 'Rosalie, I haven't heard from the loans yet,' and she said she knew that right then at that time they were all pinched, but that by the next month she was certain they would start taking up the notes. I didn't mind so much, but it seemed to me they might have come to me and said they were pinched just then, instead of avoiding me.

"When it got pretty late in the spring and I still hadn't received any money back and they were sending excuses through Rosalie, I made up my mind to talk to them. Something was coming up and I needed a little extra money. So I said to Rosalie late one afternoon, 'Rosalie, I think I'm going to stop by the school and have a talk with those folk on my way to the office in the morning.' Rosalie didn't say a thing but 'All right, Mamma.'

"The next morning she got up and dressed herself and went off to school. But just as I was getting ready to go out, the phone rang, and it was Rosalie.

" 'Mamma,' she said, 'don't come up to school this morning.'

" 'Why, Rosalie?' I said. 'They're honest debts they owe me, and I need my money.'

"But all she said was, 'Just don't come up here this morning,' and she hung up. I thought it was funny that she should call me up that way and tell me not to come to the school. But the thing I needed the money for wouldn't wait, and I went up anyway.

"Rosalie must have seen me coming, because when I got there she met me in the downstairs hall, and her classroom was on the second floor. Cousin, she looked like somebody wild. She certainly didn't look like Rosalie. She has changed a lot since you saw her anyway."

She took off her glasses and blew on them and put them aside. She placed her elbows on the table, locked her fingers together, and leaned her forehead against her locked hands. That was the way she remained during the rest of the telling, talking down to the scraps of food on her plate. It was better that way. I could not see her eyes. I could see only her lips moving woodenly over her words. She did not address me again. Sometimes her voice dropped very low, though it retained a desperate, forlorn, and strident quality.

"Rosalie met me in the lower hall of the school, and her first words were, 'Didn't I tell you not to come up here?' And I said,

'Yes, Rosalie, but I need my money, and it certainly won't hurt to talk to them.'

" 'School has taken in,' she said. 'You can't disturb them in their classes. You can't upset the school like that. You just want to embarrass me, that's all you want to do. You're just showing out.' Her voice kept getting louder and louder. 'You just want to embarrass me!'

" 'Why, Rosalie,' I said, 'embarrass you?' And then she did give me a surprise.

" 'You know they didn't borrow any money from you. You know it!' she said. 'You just wanted to make me feel cheap. You knew it! Damn you! Damn you, you yellow bitch!' she called me. 'You're just showing out! You're just showing out!'

"I was thankful we were in the downstairs hall, where there were no classrooms.

"I was crushed. When I went out of that building, I really didn't know where I was going. I wasn't thinking so much about the money. I was crushed by the awful names and the things Rosalie had said to me, her own mother. I didn't go to the office. I came home here. I waited for Rosalie, though I didn't know what I was going to say to her or what I could do. But four o'clock came and she didn't come. And then five o'clock. Doctor came in at six and, of course, asked for Rosalie, for she was generally always home at that time. Even when she'd had too much to drink she was home and sleeping generally, and Doctor would think she was just resting. He was never here for more than a few minutes anyway. I never have told him that some afternoons I'd come home and find her speechless drunk. That afternoon, when she wasn't home, I gave some kind of excuse, which seemed to satisfy him, and he went back to his office.

"Not long after he went out, the phone rang. It was Melba, Tom's wife. 'Mamma Hatton,' she said, 'Rosalie's up here and she's stone drunk. She says you put her out and you won't let her come home and she's got no place to go. She's talking and acting awful and Tom's likely to hurt her.'

"I didn't know what to say and I didn't know what to tell Melba to do. I could hear Rosalie shouting at the top of her voice, and before I could gather my thoughts, I heard Melba say, 'Get her away from me, Tom!' And the phone went dead.

"I guess they got her to bed all right, and she was all right in the morning. So many things happened afterward that I've never thought to ask Tom and Melba what they did with her that night. Anyway, she didn't come back here the next day. She rented a room over in Ehrinhaus Street, and the next thing I heard was that she was saying she was never coming home any more. She called up her father and told him that I put her out, and that as long as I lived she was never coming home any more. Some of our friends reported the worst kind of scandal about her. The worst kind of things! It nearly drove Doctor crazy. She wrote me a very abusive, obscene letter, and once when I saw her uptown she wouldn't even speak to me. She roomed in Ehrinhaus Street all the rest of that spring and summer, and I didn't see her but once. Doctor was running up there all the time, though, and I found any number of receipted bills that he had paid for her.

"The first week that school opened this past year, she came back. Doctor brought her back. She was half-sick and practically starved. Renny wrote about that time, saying he was coming home from Nashville to bring his wife for a little visit. He had just been married a few months, and we had never seen his wife, but Bea was from a fine family, and according to her picture, she was a beautiful girl. Of course, I spoke to Rosalie, telling her of Renny's visit, and she took it the wrong way. She put the construction on it that I was hinting something or other. 'You don't want me around when your yellow son brings his yellow wife,' was what she said.

" 'No, Rosalie. That isn't it,' I said. But I couldn't make her believe any different.

" 'Oh, yes it is. Oh, yes it is,' she said. 'Don't worry. I'll go before they come!'

"That afternoon she came home in a taxi, and the taxi driver had to bring her in the house in his arms, she was just that drunk.

"It was the first time she'd been drunk since she'd been back. After she first came back, I thought a change for the better had come over her. For days on end she didn't go out except to school, and some nights I'd hear her crying in her room. Of course, I was upset when she came home in that condition, and in broad daylight, too, with the taxi driver carrying her. I started to write Renny and tell him not to come, but I didn't, and they came on.

"Bea was a very sweet girl, and just as pretty as her picture, and every moment I was afraid. But Rosalie never saw them at all. She got up and went out every morning before anybody was up and she came home late every night after everyone had gone to bed. I always lay awake, listening for a car to drive up, or the gate to close, and when I heard it, I got up and looked out my bedroom window to see if she was intoxicated. She was a little bit once, and I rushed downstairs to head her off. At first she insisted on playing the piano. Then she said she was going to sleep downstairs, and even took off her clothes right there in the living room. I kept begging her not to do it, to come on up to bed. I begged and I begged. She said if I'd get her a drink she would. I didn't have anything but some brandy, and I got some of that and she went on upstairs.

"When I got up there, she asked me to take a drink. I warned her that her father was up on the third floor and he would hear. 'I don't give a damn about him, nor you either. No, not a goddam,' she said. 'Come on and take a drink with your black, drunken daughter.'

"She was getting loud by this time, so I drank some of the brandy. She took off the rest of her clothes and started marching around the room naked. I didn't leave, because I was afraid of what she might do. She marched and she quoted. She quoted the Song of Solomon. Then after a while she insisted that I take another drink, and I refused. I can't take more than a swallow of brandy. She said I'd take another drink or I'd be sorry. I didn't know what she might do, so I poured out a little bit and drank it, and then she threw a half a glass of it in my face and cursed and called me a weakling and told me to get out. 'You're a weak, yellow bitch, and I'm your weak, black bitchy daughter, and I want you to get out of here.' Then she she threw herself down across the bed and I went out. Later I heard her crying.

"Except for that once, I didn't see Rosalie the whole time Renny and his wife were here. But right after Christmas she started acting up again. These strange friends of hers started coming to the house, never the same ones twice. Sometimes one would come and spend the night and I'd never see her any more. Sometimes I'd know someone was visiting her because I'd hear them talking in the morning before they went out. It worried me.

"Up at school she was having trouble with the other teachers too. It was bound to come to the attention of the superintendent sooner or later. I was very mortified when the principal called me up and told me that there was no longer anything he could do, that things had gotten so bad that he couldn't protect her any longer. So last year the superintendent put her on probation from one month to the next. But even that didn't stop her, and she wasn't reappointed this fall."

I knew the story was ended, though the inflection of my Cousin Charity's voice did not change. She did not move. And after a while her voice came again, as if from a great distance.

"I don't know what's going to happen to Rosalie. She's nearly thirty-five and there doesn't seem much hope of her ever changing. When she's home, she just seems to sit around in her room doing nothing, and when she goes out, generally only at night, I don't know what she does. I've stopped listening for her to come in at night. She never seems to eat a decent meal, and she never eats with either her father or me. She's welcome to the food, but she acts like she has to take it on the sly. I haven't spoken to her in a month and haven't seen her for almost two weeks, but once in a while I hear her in her room late at night either reciting the Song of Solomon, like she does when she's had too much, or else crying as if she'd lost the last friend she had on earth."

Now Cousin Charity picked up her glasses and blew on them. She blew on them for a long time, it seemed to me, and then she got up and switched on the light, for dark was gathering. The whole dark hollow of the house was full of a kind of massy, sluggish chill, and inexpressibly melancholy.

Back in the living room, Cousin Charity laid her hand timidly on my arm.

"And you won't spend the night here with us?"

"I'd love to, Cousin Charity," I said, "but . . ."

"You passed over your own kin-people," she said miserably.

I looked at her, matching her face with the face of her second cousin, my mother, and feeling less the blood kinship than kinship of another, more abiding kind. It was a low, faint drum-beat of realization, but it was there, timidly beating in the common flux of blood, of experience, of memory and heritage that made me one with many—Charity Hatton and Mike Chowan, Chris, the sweet man, and Sabrah Keys. We were all buffeted by the same wind, hurtling in the current of the same dark stream. I looked at Cousin Charity, feeling this but thinking how really much like my mother she was. A little lighter, a little older than my mother would have been, but the same thin, fine hair, like a flower of snow, and the same straight nose over a mouth wide with downward curving lips.

"But you will see Tom?" she asked in a low voice.

"He won't remember me," I said.

"I'll call him."

"It's been a long time. More than twenty years."

"Wouldn't it be nice if all our kin from all over could come together?" she said, wistfully.

"So many of us are dead, so many lost."

"Yes. I guess you're right," she sighed. Then she brightened. "But I'll call Tom. He'll be expecting you."

"All right," I said, and Cousin Charity kissed me on the cheek.

But first I went back to Frissie Barlow. I went back to her to get my bearings, but she was not much help. "Come back after you've seen Tom," she said. "So you didn't see Rosalie?"

"No. And I don't really want to see Tom."

"Oh, go see him."

"It's been a long time."

"My God, the years fly! And Rosie, she's a wreck. And if it was just Rosie, it wouldn't be important. She'd be just another awful, drunken slut. But all over you can find girls like her— and boys too—butting around in a fog, not knowing what it's all about."

"Tom too?" I asked, not wishing to get into an argument.

"Go and see him. Go for Charity."

But it was not easy to go see Tom Hatton. I walked back and forth in front of the two-family house a long time before I went through the gate. The downstairs quarters were vacant, and I hesitated again before I rang the upstairs bell. A light gleamed through the glass door. A young woman, a sort of suntanned brunette with startling crimson lips, admitted me, and I followed her up into the apartment and took the seat she offered me. The room was carpeted to the walls and furnished in bleached wood of modernistic design. The curtains were of a metal-like stuff that dropped stiffly and evenly to within an inch of the floor. Clean glass ashtrays, embossed with the initials T. C. H. rested everywhere. There was not a book, not a magazine, not a bit of disorder.

I got up when Tom Hatton came in and stood across the room. He carried a paper cup in one hand and a cigarette in the other. He held the paper cup carefully under the cigarette and flicked his ashes into it.

"My mother called," he said. He did not offer to shake hands or to address me in any way, and I noted the formal "my mother."

"She said she would," I said.

He was a small, slender fellow, who looked as if he had been turned out by a machine. His features were sharp and immobile, like the profile drawings of ancient Egyptian statuary, and his skin and hair were as smooth as aluminum.

"We don't seem to remember each other."

"Why should we?" he asked insolently. His voice was machine-made too.

"Your mother . . ."

"Ha!" he said. He dropped the cigarette into the cup and handed the cup to his wife, who all this time had been sitting nervously crossing and uncrossing her legs in a chair against the wall. "Get rid of this, Melba," he said, reaching the smoking cup out and not looking at her.

"Your mother asked me to come."

"Ha! What was the sense of it?"

"I guess she had some sentimental notion that since you and your sister and I were about the same age and there was a sort of kinship . . . well, that sort of thing."

"My mother makes too much of these distant relationships," he said insultingly.

His wife came in and sat down as before.

"Besides, I have no sister."

"Rosalie?"

"She's a common drunk and a pervert."

"Tom!" his wife said.

"Rosalie is a drunken woman-lover," he said very slowly and distinctly, letting his eyes move slowly to his wife.

"Why can't you just say she's queer?" Melba said in a slatey voice.

"Ha! Face it. Face it! What's she to us?" He lit another cigarette, and though there was an ashtray on the table beside him, he held the burnt match in his fingers.

"She's queer all right. She doesn't want money, so she steals it. She hates the taste of whisky, so she drinks all she sees."

"Skip it!" Melba said, getting up suddenly. She went to the window, lifted the drawn shade and peeped out. She remained by the window.

"You keep out of this, Melba."

"Why talk about it?" Melba said.

"I'm not talking about it."

"Well, you were," she said, lifting the shade again. "Oh, Lord! Here they are." She turned back, gave me an oblique, impatient, frowning look, and said to her husband, "Your mother sure did her number tonight. She sure messed up."

"Oh, shut up! And go down and hold them for a minute," Tom said.

All this time I had been standing in angry bewilderment. The doorbell rang. I started to follow the young woman to the door, but she turned in the hall at the top of the stairs and brushed back into the room.

"I've got an idea," she said, going quickly to the closet and snatching out a coat. "Hold everything." Then she rushed out of the room and down the stairs.

"Listen," Tom said, "you can do me a favor." But there was no conciliation in his voice, only condescension. His cheeks had flushed a little and he was breathing somewhat rapidly. Carefully holding one hand cupped under the hand that held the burning cigarette, he seemed to be listening to the sounds below.

"I'm going to do myself a favor. I'm going."

There were voices drifting confusedly up the stairs now, and then a voice, unmistakably Melba's, speaking low, dominated them.

"Wait a couple of minutes," Tom said.

"O. K., Tom," Melba's voice called up the stairs. "Back in a minute. Now do your number." And then the door snapped shut.

"Ha!" Tom said, sneering.

"I'm going," I said.

Tom said nothing. He just stood there smiling insultingly, holding his hand carefully under his burning cigarette. I went down and let myself out.

I did not go back to Frissie Barlow's, but I wrote her, and in Knob, Kentucky, I got her answer written in a heavy, drawn hand on sheets torn from a cheap composition book.

". . . Nothing mysterious at all, but if I had known that they had got to the point of complicating everything I would have warned you and not played my silly joke. I didn't know they had moved, and I didn't hear until after I got your letter that they had been treating everybody for weeks just as they treated you. Tom works in a hospital across the river in Ohio as a laboratory technician, and I guess that passing in his job just naturally called for passing off the job too. I hear now that they're going to move across the river.

"I suppose passing is some kind of victory. A lot of people have given up more for less and I don't believe they, Tom and Melba, I mean, and especially Tom, feel that they're giving up anything. It's a funny point to get to. I often wonder what happens later. A long time ago I knew a young woman at Oberlin like that, and I've wondered since what happened to her.

"I saw your Cousin Charity the other day, but I didn't mention that you'd been by to see me. . . ."

CHAPTER FOUR

There Is a Balm

I

AFTER the Hattons I was road-weary and faint. I had need of rest and of finding some place where I could gather and renew my energies. I felt that my personality had been shredded by too many contacts with others, and that until I had patched it together again nothing would have any meaning. Indeed, for two weeks I felt that I had been losing perception and discernment, that my edge was gone. I was ragged, discouraged, and mired in abysmal futility. Nothing had been simple recently, not my job, nor the people I found, nor the things I heard. For a few days I wanted simplicity and ease.

It was in this state of mind and feeling that I set out southwest for Elizabethtown, where I found no place to lodge and no restaurant where I could eat, and came eventually to Knob.

Knob was not even a wide place in the road. There was a general store, which also housed the post office, and a milk station. Near the store a few houses stood with their backs to the road, as if they had not even awakened when the road was built. Between the houses stood the slatternly tobacco barns, the top half of their hinged walls lying open against the bottom, and the sun streaming in to dry the first of the gathered crop. Goldenrod and prairie grass stood high in the roadside ditches, and on a hill across the humming fields a copse of red maples burned in the sun. Scarlet autumn had come here on golden feet.

A quarter of a mile below the milk station I found the Phillipses. They were sitting in their front yard. There were

trees in the yard in front of the cottage, and they were sitting
in a spot of sun that fell through the trees. They were simply
sitting—she wide-legged, droop-shouldered, relaxed, her black
hands limp in her lap and a pan of green stuff on the ground
beside her, he straight and angular, but relaxed too, one leg
thrown over the other and his foot swinging. They did not seem
even to be watching the road. It was as if all the quiet of that
golden afternoon flowed from their breathing. Behind them,
their small, many-windowed cottage had turned quietly and
evenly from white to gray, as if the gentle wash of quiet time
alone had acted upon it.

I stopped. This seemed so indisputably the place I needed that
I felt no hesitancy at all. They watched me approach with quiet
interest. It was simplicity itself.

"Could you put me up for a few days?" I asked, addressing
the woman. There was no hurry, no agitation. There was nothing embarrassing in their kindly curiosity.

"Yes, I *could*," she answered slowly. And this I realized was
the absolute answer to my question. She smiled.

"Well, would you?"

She turned to the man. "What you think, Matt?"

"My name's Bess," Matt said, crackling with laughter. "I ain't
got a spoon in that mess."

"You ain't a bit o' help," she said.

"Let's git your things out o' the car," Matt said.

It was as simple as that.

They took me in and gave me a basin of water and a piece
of homemade, yellow soap. They gave me some yesterday's
biscuits crumbled in a bowl of milk sweetened with coarse,
brown sugar, and a piece of salted ham with corn bread. They
showed me a mountainous bed as clean as pre-dawn snow, and
how to prop the window open with a stick. They showed me the
knobs on the old parlor organ that would best hold my clothes.
Together, quietly, they asked me all they thought it polite and
needful for them to know. Then they left me alone, and by
sunset, when I was already in bed, I could feel the peace and

quiet flowing into me. The drugged sleep of utter fatigue poured over me.

It was a fine pleasure to sit in the Phillipses' front yard. There were many hills, for this was the cave country. The cave where Floyd Collins died was a few miles up the road, and Mammoth Cave was farther on a little way. The old Paducah road ran past the house, and beyond the road the soft green hills rolled slowly to the west. There were other hills, too, beginning at the eastern boundary of the Phillipses' tobacco patch and rising slowly, without effort, to an eminence of beautiful strength. When the wind was in the east, you could smell the cloudy odor of the oil fields of Le Grande.

"The trouble with you city fellers is you bathe too much. You whysh yourselfs clean away," Matt Phillips said. This was amusing, for he was a tall and bony man himself. We laughed. He liked laughter as something to live with.

"In this country, we don't bathe more'n once in two-three weeks in winter, an' that's something new. When I was a boy, we sewed up 'round October an' didn't peel out 'til May." He looked across the road, his head a little cocked, and drew slowly on his hickory pipe.

"Sewed up? What do you mean?"

"Sewed our underclo'es on. Sewed shirts to our backs. Git a gang o' us chil'ren together last o' April an' start peelin' us out, an' it would be something, I tell you." His laughter crackled like many dry twigs snapping.

"They might of did that in *his* family," Mrs. Phillips said.

"They done it in your'n too. Folks in this country don't keer for watah. It's been so cool lately, I ain't bathed myself in 'bout a munt'."

"Oh, Matt, quit!" Mrs. Phillips said.

"It's the truth." He cocked his head at me, for all the world like some designing, gray-peaked bird.

"It ain't not neither."

"This ain't no joke now," he said. "My son sent some feller here from Dayton, Ohio, one time. He was sick an' didn't nobody know what was the matter with him. He drooped 'round for a munt' or two, an' he got took so bad he went to bed. The doctor came clare from Glasgow an' looked him over, an' when he got done I ast him what ailed the feller. I'd took him in an' I wanted to know what kind o' sickness I had in my house. 'Matt,' the doctor said, 'that feller's goin'a die. He's done bathed hisself to death.' He did die, too, 'bout a munt' after that."

"I'm not going to die on your hands," I said. "Is that why you hesitated so long about taking me in?"

"She done the hesitatin'," he said, crackling and tossing his head in the direction of his wife.

"I didn't no such thing!"

"I seen you kind o' smilin' at my three front teeth an' I knowed you was a feller could laugh. Ain't they something, though?" And he skinned back his upper lip to show me the three front teeth that stood like slanting, yellow pickets in his red gum. "Them three teeth can do more damage than all them automatic teeth Retha's got."

"I don't think I hesitated so much," Mrs. Phillips said, giving a rising inflection to her words, as if she were testing them.

"Retha was thinkin' 'bout the trouble end of it. She don't like to steer her stumps no more'n she has to."

"I been steerin' myself for you for thirty-seven weary years," she countered.

"That's a long time to put up with one woman, ain't it? 'Deed it is now."

Three men, walking with rhythmic stiffness, came down the shoulder of the road in single file. Close behind them came a woman. All were dressed in dark, crumpled Sunday clothes. As they came into the yard, they looked at me with the same friendly curiosity, at once penetrating and impersonal, with which the Phillipses had greeted me the day before. One felt that these people, unimpeded by considerations of mere politeness, made contacts directly and arrived at instantaneous judgments of their fellow men.

"This'n's Ben Scott an' that'n's Gav Black an' this least'n here is Isaac Loper an' his wife," Matt Phillips said. "Mens, this here's a young feller come in on a east wind yestiddy. He's goin'a bide a while."

Each man gave me his hard hand. The woman smiled and nodded her head. They stood around like tree stumps.

"You on your way?" Phillips said.

"I was down thar myself, an' wasn't nobody thar. I come 'way agin. Met Gav on my way back an' we thought we'd ankle on back thar, an' passin' Loper's lane, he called us down an' we all come 'long together."

"I guess I bes' git ready," Mrs. Phillips said, and she and Mrs. Loper went into the house.

"Started cuttin' yit, Matt?" Ben Scott asked.

"No. I'm waitin' up on her. You?"

"Been cuttin' sence Thursday. Me an' the boys been bringin' in five hundred sticks a day."

"Weather ain't jus' right to suit me," Matt said. "I'm waitin' on her. Sun ain't jus' right. Still got a little flatness to it, kinda like barn paint. You cuttin', Isaac?"

"Done cut all I was 'lowed."

"You overplant agin? You the greates' little man for over-plantin' I ever seen," Matt said.

The men grinned at each other.

"Told him I th'ot he had too much," Scott said, with a lugubri-ous shake of his head. "Told him when he was droppin'."

"Th'ot I had her right. Agent come 'round las' Tuesday an' looked her over an' said I'd done putt in seven-tenths too much."

"Told him. Told him I th'ot he had too much," Scott said.

"Well, that ain't so much too much," Black said. "What you fixin' to do?"

"I don't know. That's been a-rilin' me some." He was a little man, with an old, tight, sad face. The sun had burned him to a crisp, and the wind had seamed and toughened him.

"I wouldn't cut it. I'd leave it a-standin'. They can't make you cut it down from thar. Time come to sow my wheat, I'd take my disc an' tractor in thar an' run it down," Black said.

"What do you think, Matt?"

"That's what I'd do," Matt said. "You got comp'ny, though, Isaac. You ain't the only frog done fattened hisself for snakes. The'dore Walker got bit worse'n anybody this year. They 'lowed him one acre, but he th'ot he could git away with three. He's been a-ridin' night an' day tryin' to make a 'justment. Clare wore out, he is. But he's got to cut her down."

"It sure riles a man," Loper said.

"What, Isaac?"

"Crop-cuttin', that's what."

"It oughtn'," Matt said. "All you got to do is what they say. You git 'bout as much for a idle field as for a crop anyway. They 'lowed me one acre, an' that's what I putt in thar, an' that's what I'm goin'a take out, an' that's what I'm goin'a sell. Gov'-mint's a funny thing. Uncle Sam's gov'mint 'specially. The'dore thinks his surplus's bigger'n the gov'mint. He shoulda knowed better."

"Them Prinn brothers who use t' raise so much 'backer an' make so much money, they ain't goin'a cut a bush this year," Loper said. "They got a hundred an' twenty-five acres, but they ain't goin'a cut a bush."

We watched the cars that were beginning to go steadily by on the road. It was about ten-thirty in the morning, and the Sunday traffic was thickening. The best caves were only a few miles down the road and the traffic to them was being detoured off the main highway, which was under repair, over the old Paducah road. Many cars went zooming by, and often the people in them waved at us.

"I'll jus' go my limit nex' time. By grab! I'll go under her."

"That thar wouldn't be no way to do," Matt said. "That thar sounds like spite talk, Isaac. You can't take no skin off the gov'mint's tail."

There was no answer to this, and again we watched the cars. Beyond the road the sumac made the hollow a blaze of crimson color, and farther away the slope rose like a green altar cloth suspended from the crest of the ridge.

"I wonder what them people thinks about when they goes by in thar cars an' sees mens like us a-holdin' down our shadders?" Scott asked of no one in particular.

For at least three minutes there was no answer to this either. Matt filled and lit his pipe. The women came out and sat on the rustic bench. Mrs. Phillips was dressed in a dark dress with a white sash and a straw hat tied over the crown and under her chin with a dull pink veil. She looked like a black doll dressed in cellophane. Mrs. Loper, I saw now, was really a young woman with a brown, empty, moonish face.

"I know what they're a-thinkin' about," Matt said quietly, smiling. "They're a-thinkin' we're some ol' country fellers ain't never been nowhar. They 'bout right 'bout that. Far's I'm concerned, what I can see from settin' right here is the world. But they're aimin' to make us feel good, a-wavin' an' yoo-hooin'. It does make me feel good, but not for thar reason." He spit a long stream sideways into the grass.

"It don't make me feel one way nor 'nother," Black said.

"Why it make you feel good, Matt?" Scott asked.

"I ain't been out o' this country more'n three munt's in my life. Ain't got no desires to go nowhars. But it makes me feel good 'cause mens from Ohio an' Indiana an' places can git in thar cars an' ride to Kintucky an' see me settin' under the trees on my own place, an' if I had a car an' the desires, I could go some place an' see mens settin' out on thar places. That's enough right thar to make me yoo-hoo to somebody in Indiana I ain't never seen before, jus' a-knowin' that they got a place o' thars an' I got a place o' mine."

After a while Black said, "I guess you right, Matthew."

"Dog my cats if I know if he's right or not, he's done said so much," Loper said.

The women got up. Their clothes rustled as they touched themselves here and there.

"If you mens is comin', you bes' come on," Mrs. Phillips said. "Sunday school'll be broke up."

"I ain't goin'," Matt said.

"All right," Mrs. Phillips said.

Matthew and I watched the men file across the yard and down the shoulder of the road. The women, like animated bundles, trundled after them.

"Do you have Sunday school every Sunday?" I asked.

"To the fo'th Sunday. Fo'th Sunday's preachin'. I don't hold with meetin' much no more like I use to."

I respected the silence he kept. I took furtive glances at him; his thick, dirty-gray hair brushed straight back from his brow, like a parakeet's crest, his lean, toughened face, his long hands with their ridged, purple nails. There was the same quiet about him that there is about an old, good dog, the same indescribable feeling of completeness and wholeness one gets in seeing an old, good dog resting.

"Meetin' is gettin' to be something like war."

"How's that?"

"My father was a soldier in the Civa' War, an' I heerd him say that a lot o' mens in thar didn't know what they was fightin' for. A lot o' folks in this country goes to meetin' an' don't know what they're in thar for."

"Whose fault is that, do you suppose?"

Matt crackled a little. "Well, that thar's 'bout like war too. It ain't nobody's fault, it jus' come about that way. Don't nobody know how wars come about. Don't nobody really know."

He turned to me and his forehead was pinched in a slight frown.

"I seen whar Inglan's called her surplus. What's that look like to you? Looks like to me she can't hol' out. I'd sure hate to see that happen. I would now. Looks like to me we ought to do something. We got near 'bout all we got in this nation from Inglan'."

A sudden wind began to scatter parts of the Sunday paper about the yard. We got up and collected them. We folded the paper under the leg of a chair and sat down again, hopping our chairs squarely into the sun, for the wind was the breath of autumn. It was delicately scented with autumn greenery, and especially with juniper from some distant, drying hollow. This odor, I knew, if one lived with it long, could break the heart. Cars went by on the road, now several in a line, now one alone. Matt knocked out his pipe and laid it on the ground.

"I 'member when no more'n one or two cars a day come that old Paducah road. I 'member when this here was the old Fed'ral road from Louisville to Nashville an' coaches come over it, the downstage an' the upstage, once a day. I was born behin' that knob," he said, nodding toward a cluster of hills in the west.

"It's beautiful country," I said.

"The purties' sight in this country is the win'er, when snow's on them hills an' green cedar's stickin' up through the snow. In the win'er time we use to go to the pond an' git us a block o' ice when I was a boy. We'd make a hole in the top of it an' git a stick an' job in the hole an' push to give us a runnin' start. When we got her started good, we'd hop on an' skeet clare 'cross the pond an' a half-mile down the holler. We had win'ers then. I 'member the win'er o' eighty-two. Snow near 'bout leveled off all them hills."

"The stage didn't run then, I'll bet," I said.

"Not for weeks. That snow blocked up things so high we never seen our stock for nine days, an' then it was dead. 'Cept for that, it was sure peaceful in this country that thar win'er. That's what I like, peace."

A hitchhiker went east on the road. He had a pack on his back, and he walked with a free, ground-eating stride. Something was chalked on his pack, but we could not read it from our distance. He threw up his hand to us and we watched him until the goldenrod on the ditch banks hid him from view.

"Better feed that dog 'fore Retha gits back," Matt said.

I followed him around the side of the house to where the dog was chained to a running leash. He was an underslung dog, with the heavy sagging dewlaps of a bloodhound and the deep, hoarse throat of a dog bred for the hills.

"Why do you keep him chained?"

"Always have had a dog, but this is the firs' bugger I ever had to tie up."

"Is he bad?"

"No. That thar's a out-country dog," Matt said, crackling. "My son brung him to me from Dayton, Ohio. He's a hog dog. Never could train him for nothin' else, an' yet an' still he's s'pose' to be some kinda hunter. Ain't no wile hogs in this country now."

We went back to the front.

"Thar's three things a man's 'bliged to have—a dog, a plat o' land somewhars, an' a woman."

"And just like that? The dog first?"

"Near 'bout like that. Firs' thing I ever owned was a dog. Pip could do near 'bout everything on a farm 'cept milk. I learned him to sucker terbacker an' gather eggs. 'Deed I did. My father didn't keer nothin' 'bout dogs, an' when Pip firs' come 'round, I had to study out ways to keep him. Built a little shelter for him behin' the 'backer kiln, an' ever' chance I got I was down thar learnin' him something."

Just as he was getting into his story and my disbelief was in suspense, we saw the file of men and women coming down the shoulder of the road from church. The three men were in front and now a third woman brought up the rear. They came into the yard and the women found seats, while the men squatted on their haunches, their arms locked about their knees.

"Let me blow a bit," Mrs. Phillips said, "an' then I'll git you all some watah." She thrust out her legs and took off her hat and blew. Her face was slick with sweat, for it was warm in the sun, even with the wind blowing.

"Who'd you see, Retha?" Phillips asked.

"Well, I seen everybody," Mrs. Phillips said, with her peculiar rising inflection.

"How's all?"

"They all right, 'cept Cledie."

"What ails Cledie?"

"She jus' complainin' all the time."

"Ain't nothin' ails her," Matthew said. "Cledie'd complain in the Kingdom."

"That ain't no maybe-so," Black said.

"Well," Mrs. Phillips said slowly, "I don't know."

The talk was slow and as quiet as breathing. It had nuances in it that one learned to recognize only after long listening. No one ever seemed to interrupt anyone else, and following every utterance there was a full weight of silence, the quiet recognition of each man's right to have his say considered.

"I'm goin'a git you all some watah now."

Matthew said to me, "Ain't nothin' but Scotts, Blacks, Gavins, Phillipses, Woodsons, an' Lopers much in this country, an' they're all tied up one way or 'nother. An' ain't a one of them don't own him a piece o' land."

" 'Cept Laury," Isaac Loper corrected.

" 'Cept Laury," Matt said. "He woulda had his plat, too, if they hadn't took him off to the army. He los' his right senses in the army. He ain't been no good sence."

The men pulled at the grass with their hard fingers and threw the grass up into the wind. Only Isaac Loper wore a tie or had his stiff, high shoes laced. Loper's tie was machine tied and fitted to an elastic clamp that hooked under his collar.

"This here new war's gittin' serious," Black said, after a while. "Keep on an' she'll be critical, like las' time."

"It's critical now," Matt said.

"One thing, they ain't likely goin'a take none o' you all this time," Loper said.

"But 'fore this regist business is done, every man's got to regist. Ain't that the way of it, Matthew?"

"Oh, ma Lord!" Mrs. Scott, the new woman said. "Like las' time?"

"Thar you is, gittin' all riled agin," Mr. Scott said. "Uncle Sam don't want no gran'pappies."

Mrs. Phillips came back with a galvanized pail of brownish water and a gourd dipper. They asked me to drink first, and then the dipper passed from hand to hand among them. The water had a brackish taste, but it was so cold it paralyzed the throat.

"Why you reckon they fixin' a new regist for ol' mens too, Matt?" Isaac Loper asked. "Ain't nothin' in the paper 'bout it today, is thar?"

"So Uncle Sam'll know jus' how many mens he's got."

"I gotta talk with ma Lord," Mrs. Scott said, rolling her eyes in anxiety and bringing her hands together. She was a big woman, with a sebaceous yellow skin and a broad nose with flaring nostrils.

"This here's a country o' old people," Matt said. "Old folks an' right young ones. They won't hardly git nobody from this country this time."

"They putt me in the las' class the las' time," Gav Black said.

"They putt Ben in the firs' batch las' time, an' I knowed thar was boun' to be something wrong with that. I got down on ma knees an' prayed to ma Lord."

Scott looked around apologetically. "I'd wake up in the middle o' the night, an' thar she'd be out on the floor talkin' with God. Kep' pesterin' me to take her to Munfordville. Worried the life outa me."

"I was distressed, an' when I'm distressed I don't know nothin' to do but pray."

"That's right, honey," Mrs. Phillips said. "Take it to the good Lord in prayer."

"I knowed if he took me over thar to Munfordville, I felt like I could git things straight."

"Uncle Sam ain't gen'lly wrong, though," Matt Phillips said.

"Well, when we got to Munfordville, I found out the man who was signin' the mens up hadn't asked me none o' the questions he was due to ask me. If he'da asked me them questions, they never woulda putt him in the firs' batch no way. I jus' felt like thar was something wrong with it," she said, rolling her eyes. "An' I knowed God would fix it right."

They left when the sun reached long fingers straight across the land and flung struck matches in the farthest fields. We watched them go, the men up ahead, the women following. Then we just sat. There was a definite chill in the air, but we sat in the quiet contentment of the day's end until Mrs. Phillips suggested the evening chores and supper. There was a cow to milk and a few chickens and turkeys to feed. A sort of godly gloom lay in the hills when these things were done and we sat down to green beans and cold joints of fried chicken. The kitchen smelled of fresh milk. Bright tins and the insides of a cream separator stood in a clean row on a bench against the wall. Suspended from the ceiling were drying gourds, red peppers, and seeds in little cotton bags. Beneath the yellowed newspaper picture of Theodore Roosevelt hung a small white-silk flag, in which were worked the red and blue words "GOD BLESS AMERICA." The low, strong hills, heavily purpling now as dark ascended them, seemed close outside the window.

"Well, it's been another good day," Matthew said.

There was no answer to this. The dark hills shoved their strength and sweetness right into the room.

"We'll make a terbacker farmer out of you yet," they said, laughing.

"It's only when you sucker 'backer that you wisht it was some other crop," Mrs. Phillips said, "an' then not much hardly."

"Don't you grow anything else?"

"Corn an' wheat, but not hardly no more'n we can use ourself. 'Backer's 'bout the only money crop thar is in this country. But we don't need much cash money now. Money ain't been urgent with us since two years after we was married an' a long dry spell turnt this whole country to a flour bin. I had to steer my stumps then. Picked up carpenter, plasterin', and paper hangin' myself. Went off an' stayed three munt's plasterin' once, an' I hung nearly all the paper thar is in this country."

We were sitting in the sun against the back of the house making loops in short lengths of string. The loops would later go around the stems of tobacco leaves, which would be suspended from sticks to dry. The sun was getting right for Matthew now.

It no longer had that "flatness," perceptible only to him, of which he spoke. It sparkled on the hills. It set a thousand blazes in the hollows. In a few days now Matthew would be cutting. Fresh clay had been worked in the interstices of the drying kiln, and already the bins were piled high with brushwood.

"Sometimes I git worried thinkin' 'bout what's goin'a happen in this country."

There was so unaccustomed a gravity in his voice that I looked at him.

"It's the young people," he said. "Fast as they git growed, they leave. When I was a young boy comin' up, we didn't think 'bout leavin'. All the folks you seen Sunday growed up here together. But thar chil'ren." He shook his head. "An' our'n."

"The land's still here," Mrs. Phillips said, her voice lifting on the final word, as if it were a tentative suggestion.

"Land ain't no good with nobody on it, Retha."

"Somebody'll be on it."

"But not none o' our'n. I don't like the th'ots o' no total stranger on my land," he said in a hard, even voice. Then he went on more gently. "When my father died thar was still a little something owin' on this plat, an' my mother was blind, an' my sisters was too young to work. I went to work an' finished payin' for this piece o' land."

"Ain't no use a-worryin' 'bout that now," Mrs. Phillips said quietly.

"No. I guess Gav ain't no better off, nor Ben neither. Ben an' Eunie with five chil'ren an' not a one o' them in this country. An' not a one o' our'n. That thar's a queer thing," Matt said.

"But they're in this nation, Matt," Mrs. Phillips said. "An' bein's they're in this nation, they can fin' a plat o' land somewhars. That's the beauty part about it. That's what you said Sunday."

"But this here's . . ." And then he sighed and said no more.

I sensed that they had discussed this often and that now the subject was not closed. But they spoke no more about it in my presence. On the organ in my bedroom, among the tintypes and warping postcard photographs, I had no trouble picking out their son and two daughters. The son was somewhere in Ohio, the daughters married and living in Chicago. They had been caught in that restless, unending tide of migration which swept, now with lesser, now with greater force, all the rootless young Negroes not only from these hills but from the sandhills of Georgia, the valleys of Tennessee, the flats of Arkansas and Mississippi, and the swamps of Florida. It was the same tide that had begun to wax in my childhood. Now, perhaps, it was beginning to wax again.

After supper that night there was chill enough to warrant a fire in the grate in their bedroom, and we sat in there finishing up the string. It was a homely room. On the floor was the worn matting that gave its strawy odor to the whole house. On the walls were cheruby pictures, many of them cut from calendars. The bed was piled high with quilts, and other quilts covered the two chests and a flat-topped trunk.

"Now would be a good time to tell me about Pip," I suggested.

"My Lord! Has he been doin' that boy-talkin' brag 'bout that dog?"

"I man-talked brag 'bout you when you was younger an' leaster. But this ain't no brag 'bout Pip. That thar dog was so."

"Don't know nothin' 'bout it," Mrs. Phillips declared.

"Pip was 'bout as smart as me, or Retha either," he added slyly, looking up from under his brow at her. "If he'da went to school like me an' her, thar ain't no telling. 'Course he couldn't talk his smartness, but Pip conducted hisself like a human. Look like you could see him reason things out.

"Use to set hens, my father did, an' we had one old settin' hen one spring that jus' got mulish. We th'ot we was goin'a have to give her up, but my father tried her again. He give her another settin' after she'd already ruint two. She jus' wouldn't stay on the nes' nohow. She stayed on for a coupl'a days, then right off again. Pip musta knowed she wasn't tendin' to do right.

"That evenin', when it come time to feed Pip, I called an'

whistled, an' if he come, you come. Couldn't git no rise outa him a-tall. Firs' thing I th'ot was my daddy had got in a temper an' runned him off. I went everywhar looking for him. I waded all the sink holes. Pip was fonder of swimmin' an' fishin' then anything, an' I didn't know but what he'd went for a swim an' one o' them big ol' turtles had got a-holt to him. Thar's some mighty big turtles in this country. I went to all the neighbors an' everywhars, but I couldn't find him. Firs' time I ever recollec' cryin' was that night. I cried myself to sleep.

"All nex' day nobody seen Pip. That evenin' I went to the henhouse to gether eggs. I hadn't fooled with that thar pob for a long time, 'cause Pip had did all the getherin'. He'd nuzzle in the shed kitchen an' git the egg baskit an' take it out an' set it by the henhouse door. It was a roun'-bottom baskit, an' he'd done pawed hisself a little hole to set the baskit in. He gethered them eggs jus' as good as I could.

"So I went in the henhouse, I did, an' started feelin' 'roun' in the nes'es. It was dark in thar anyway. I putt my han' in one nes' an' putt it smack on somethin' that I knowed wasn't no hen. An' then I heerd a little growl. It got my yeller up, an' 'course I jumped back. I went to the barn an' got me a lantern an' come back to take a look, an' I looked an' thar was Pip curled up on that thar nes' broodin' them eggs same as a hen."

Matt spat into the fire and scratched his face, looking at me quizzically. At any moment I expected him to crackle with laughter, but he did not. Once or twice Mrs. Phillips shook her head, but Matt ignored her. He did not expect her to believe him. He really did not expect me to believe him either.

"I didn' know what that thar dog was up to, so I called him. But he wouldn't steer. I drug him off the nes', but he acted like he wanted to snap me, an' got right back on. Pip brooded that thar nes' for nineteen days an' didn't lose n'ary a egg.

"When them biddies was hatched, Pip marched outa that henhouse same as if he'd laid them eggs. 'Spected any minute to hear him cackle an' cluck like a hen. He did brood them chicks for a while, though, but my father said it looked so plumb unnatchel that he made me tie Pip up right short under the house.

"Pip was the knowin'es' dog ever was in this country."

I did not say anything. Mrs. Phillips went on making loops in the strings that were gathered in her lap. In the act of lighting his pipe, Matt looked at me, and then he nearly choked. A great cloud of smoke spouted from his mouth; his hands, heavy with laughter, slapped his knees; the pipe wobbled uncertainly in his almost toothless gums and then fell to the floor, scattering sparks across the tin hearthplate. When the fit was over, though tears still rolled down the seams in his cheeks, Mrs. Phillips was the first to speak.

"If a man in a stage show can tell one bigger'n that thar, then I'd like to hear him," she said.

The hand wiping the tears from his cheeks made a sound like toast being buttered.

"I did have a dog name Pip," he said.

For eight heart-warming, hope-kindling days I lived with them. It was not easy to leave. I told them that I would be back again some time. They came out to the shoulder of the road— he as lean as a fence picket, and she narrow-shouldered, wide-hipped, shaped like a clumsy wigwam.

"Whatever you do, son," she said, "remember God."

I thanked her.

"That thar's a good piece of advice," Matt said, beginning to crackle, "but you don't want to forget neither that you got to turn that thing on curves."

I could see from my rearview mirror that they were still standing on the shoulder of the road when I rounded out of sight on the first curve.

2

I went southeast from Knob, through Horse Cave and Cave City and Bowling Green and on to Fairview, where a shaft marking the birthplace of Jefferson Davis needles the sky. I crossed the Cumberland River, strikingly beautiful at this point, and, less than a mile farther on, the Tennessee. At Gilbertsville I went up to see the dam.

Guarded by giant machines and tended by men who crawled insect-like up ladders and over the huge structure, or scooted about in swift boats in the river among the monumental pilings, the great bastioned walls of steel and concrete rose like a thunderous song. I walked the high catwalk the breadth of the river from west to east. Pile drivers, rattling cranes, power-driven hammers, clanging steel on steel made a deafening noise. Men in steel helmets scuttled like circus performers along narrow ledges high up in the air. Far below, others in life jackets scampered about a multiplicity of tasks, reaching, pulling, pushing, twisting, clamping, digging, loosening, scaling. Huge scoops sucked at the mushy bed of the river and great tractor trucks hauled the bubbling clay to heighten and lengthen the fifty-foot, half-mile-long bulge on the eastern shore. Beyond the north wall of the dam the green waters of the Tennessee seemed placid, unruffled by the gigantic scale of activity, by this industrial, creative America at its roaring, blasting, thumping best.

Industrial America at its best? I thought so until I talked with P. H. Bynum, the Negro official whose title as Recreation and Education Supervisor for Negroes did not begin to cover his duties. He had been many things to many men in his six years with T.V.A. and he had much to say. We sat in his little office just off the entrance of the recreation building and looked up the treeless street of tan and green temporary houses. In the crowded bookshelf against the wall behind him I saw a row of books on sociology—Schrieke, Johnson, Frazier, Reuter, Dollard and Davis' *Caste and Class*. On the desk before him lay spread Green's *Negro Labor* and a pile of penciled notes, for he had been reading when I came in.

"It burns me up," he said. "T.V.A's been only a huge relief project. All the signs you see, 'Build for Defense,' are brand-new, just put up a few days ago. It must have occurred to somebody in Washington just since the campaign and Germany started to raise hell. T.V.A. was just a glorified relief project until then. We were told that these men were to be returned to their normal life in the localities from which they came. We were told that their work here was to give them training in skills that would be useful to them back home. Sure. That's all right for the white fellows. They didn't come from farms. But what about work on a dam is training for farming? the sweating? Negro workers here are puddlers, firemen, common laborers. It shows bad planning. It shows that we're an afterthought. The rule is there. I'm not grumbling with that. I'm quarreling about the damned red tape and finagling that makes rules inoperative. The T.V.A. is putty in the hands of the labor interests; the government is putty. Democracy's taking an awful beating here on T.V.A.

"What happens? All right. It's simple sociology for the whites. They've got a great social program. I mean really great. Some day the whites will go back to their normal lives with an increase in the skills of their normal pursuits. They have classes in the work which they do here, the same work they'll do when T.V.A. is done. Steel workers increase their skills by attending classes in construction engineering, mechanics by classes in Diesel engineering, the latest stuff. The same goes for carpenters, electricians, steam-fitters, right on down the line. But what about Negroes? All right, I'll tell you.

"In the first place, there's only one Negro skilled laborer in the whole darn set-up. But suppose a hundred came on to the job tomorrow? There's a rule to take care of that. Only union men can attend these training classes," he said very slowly, through tight lips. "Labor made that rule. Labor practically dictated that to T.V.A. That rule would get 'em. The hundred skilled workers who came on the job tomorrow wouldn't be union men. That rule was made to take care of the last eventuality. To take care of the situation as it is, they didn't need a rule as drastic as that. They had a simpler one. Only men engaged in the occupation with which the classes are concerned can attend the classes. There aren't any Negroes engaged in these occupations. Labor has induced T.V.A. to believe that it is not to the best interests to have more men taught these crafts. Neat, isn't it? Absolute monopoly. Boy, it really burns me up!"

All this, of course, was contrary to the glowing accounts I had heard of T.V.A., and I told Bynum so.

"I know. I know," he said. "I wrote up some of that bunk for the colored papers. But I was young on the job then, and blind as hell. Now I stay in hot water trying to make some of those things I thought true then true now. But I do it alone. You know, I hate to say it about my people, but they're cowards in a thing like this. There're other men who're in good positions, key spots, to do something about this thing. But do they? Do fish sing? I've discovered that there aren't any big niggers when it comes to something like this. There're just big-mouth niggers.

"You know what? At Wheeler there were some skilled Negroes. Rookers, hookers, concrete finishers, carpenters. Then what happened at Gunawald? Negroes were shut out from working as riggers by taking riggers into the metalcraft workers union, from which Negroes are systematically excluded. Get me? At Pickwick, other steps were taken to exclude Negroes as concrete workers and carpenters. Out here there's only one skilled Negro laborer, and he's not classified as such. He knows more about a Diesel engine than anybody around here, but he's not classified as a Diesel engineer and he doesn't draw a Diesel engineer's pay."

"But these steps you spoke of which excluded Negroes from certain occupations. Do you suppose they were taken for that specific purpose?"

"Do I suppose they were? Don't make me laugh!" Bynum said. "I know it. But it's not T.V.A. It's organized labor."

"And the workers?"

"They know it. Sure they know it.

"The funny thing about it is, I believe in democracy. I believe in it right on down to the bricks. I'm not discouraged, and I tell my men so. But I get damned embarrassed sometimes.

" 'But, Mr. Bynum,' one ol' slow-talking Georgia boy said to me one evening out there in assembly. 'Mr. Bynum, you been talking 'bout Thomas Jefferson an' Abe Lincoln an' I don't know who-all. But they was all white. I know that,' he said. You know how a slow-talking Georgia boy would say that to get his laugh. He might be serious as hell—and this boy sure was serious—but he had to have that laugh. 'You done tol' us all 'bout them mens an' all the good things they done by an' through democracy. But what I wants to know is, if democracy's so good for white folks, why ain't it good for niggers too?' "

When we got through laughing, Bynum went on.

"All right. What could I answer? You tell me and I'll tell you. Hand him that baloney about the slow, sure processes that I heard over the radio the other day? Hell! You understand it, maybe, and are content to wait the processes out. Maybe you know that a hundred and seventy-five years is no time in the life of a great ideal and whatnot. Maybe I understand it. But what do boys from Georgia know about it? They want something right now. I don't see why white people don't understand that. They might save themselves a lot of trouble if they implemented some of the everyday program of a democratic order. Just plain old justice in the distribution of work and wages would help a lot right now, and it might save a mess of trouble."

"You sound very ominous," I said.

"Not at all," he said, waving his hand. "It's simple two and two. You just can't go on finagling with this business forever, denying people forever. It's too damned demoralizing, state of emergency or no state of emergency. The average Negro worker, on T.V.A. and everywhere else, says, 'I'm going to live today, and to hell with tomorrow'; and if that isn't a threat to democracy, I don't know what it is. It's planning for tomorrow that makes democracy."

Bynum had some dismaying figures on the way in which the Negro worker on T.V.A. "lives today." Using a financial index, he had studied two hundred of the three hundred and forty workers at Gilbertsville. Out of every dollar earned, they spent twenty-one cents for the support of their families, twenty-eight cents for alcohol (whisky, beer, and wine), thirty-three cents for "outside women," and the rest on incidentals—gasoline, tobacco, and burial insurance.

"But that proves nothing," I said. "You have no comparative figures for whites."

"All I can say is, if the white index here is even comparable to this, then things are going to hell sure enough," he said conclusively.

But nothing at Gilbertsville looked as if it were going to hell. The houses, the school, the recreation building, the hospital, all of which I was told were temporary, looked stronger and were far better equipped than similar facilities for Negroes elsewhere. The children I saw in the school looked brighter, healthier than other children, and the housewives I saw sweeping the fronts, hanging clothes, or simply talking across their yards had that air of protected security which, it is said, in all the world none but American women have. They at least had faith in the present. If for the support of themselves and their children they were getting only twenty-one cents out of every dollar their husbands earned, then these wives were wringing the last value from every penny. They looked happy; and perhaps, as Bynum said, this was because their poor little was the greatest plenty they had ever known.

At Paducah I stopped only long enough to see what I had been told I must see—the waters of the Tennessee and Ohio meeting and running unmixed side by side. The home of Irvin Cobb and the "best Kentucky Colonels" disappointed me. A dust of viscous density lay thick over the Negro section, and the young Negroes loafing in insolent and curious awareness before the unpainted, boxlike houses reminded me of nothing so much as sullen animals darkly guarding their lairs.

From Paducah to Wickliffe. There the flat and marshy land suddenly erupts into great mounds where long ago the Indians, whose savage wars gave the state its name of the dark and bloody ground, buried their heaped-up dead close to the shores of the river. At Wickliffe I crossed the Ohio at the barren stretch below Cairo, Illinois, and in five minutes, crossing the Ohio again, spanned by a bridge which also spanned the Mississippi, I was out of Kentucky and Illinois and into Missouri. Speeding over the flat land, I went southwest toward Arkansas.

There was a big cotton crop, and the gins were working overtime. Though it was Sunday, I passed wagon after wagon load of cotton. The shoulders of the road were white with cotton blown there by the wind, and on the wind came the rich, baked-ham odor of cottonseed oil. Fat bales of cotton stood on lonely loading platforms along the single-track railroad. Great heaps of it and of gray cotton seed lay piled in the skimped yards and on the sagging porches of ugly farm shacks. It stood dusty and unpicked in field after ragged field. Somehow the land seemed shackled and degraded by its fickle king.

On the edge of Missouri, where the cotton gin and compress towns grow planlessly out of the Missouri earth, the very color of the earth, I picked up Paul. Although he was a little drunk, I was glad to pick him up. It was beginning to be mean-looking country, darkness was not far away, and I was glad for the company even of a drunken man. Paul looked harmless and unhappy, as if he had been trying for a long time to thumb a ride that would take him away from New Madrid, Missouri. I stopped several yards past him and sounded my horn, and when with drunken, slow realization he was aware that I waited for him, he snatched his derby from his head and ran drunkenly spraddle-legged to the car.

"Where are you going?" I asked him.

"Pittsville," he said, as if even now he could not believe I had stopped. His loose lips mumbled something that I could not catch and with sudden resolve he clambered in beside me. He was making an elaborate pretense of being sober, holding tight to himself and concentrating very hard, as drunken people who do not want to be found out do.

"Where'd you come from?" I asked.

"Cairo. That's it. Cairo. Gran'pa's dead. Fune'al, you unnerstan'. See what I mean?" His words got lost on his thick tongue.

"Your grandfather's dead?"

"Tha's it." His eyes rolled and the lids closed slowly, drunkenly, and then opened wide quickly. "Some ol' man. Wake him tonight. Fune'al 'morrer. See what I mean? Sen' for me yestiddy to Cairo."

He spoke with careful concentration, still holding his derby in his hard, thick-skinned fingers. From underlid to chin the left side of his face bore a curious pattern of shiny, crusty scar tissue.

"Wake him t'night, unnerstan'. Come on go. What say, buddy? Come on go. Fren' to fren'. What say?"

"Only relatives and close friends go to wakes," I said.

"Ain't you my fren'? Tell me 'at. Ain't you my fren'?"

"Sure."

" 'At's all I want t' know." He settled back against the cushion, but was up again almost immediately, wobbling his head close to my face. "Treat me right. See? Treat you right."

It was mean-looking country we were passing through. There was a disquieting lack of Negroes. Outside the towns, white boys strolled the roads and sat on the ditch banks. Some of them, especially those with girls among them, amused themselves by yelling obscenities at us, after which they pushed and pulled and slapped each other in spasms of mirth. With diabolic grimaces and gestures, others pretended to throw themselves in the path of the car. Lank-haired women and scraggy men, dressed in the thin, faded, soft-blue overalls of the rural South, sat on the earth-gray porches in angular immobility, as if movement had been suddenly arrested midway of a violent action. Cotton possessed the land. It grew to the very steps of the cabins. The flat land, the ragged cotton fields, and darkness spreading over the gray sky contributed to an atmosphere of indescribable depression. Ignorance lay on the land and in the hard, drained, bitter faces of the people like a blight. Here man was not master of the earth; he was earth's slave, and the bitter essence of his bondage thickened on the land like phlegm.

"So your grandfather died?"

"Some ol' man. Min' if I take a drink?"

He pulled from his shirt a bottle half-full of whisky and drank.

"Here. Take one."

"No, thanks," I said.

"Aw, come on. Fren' to fren'," he said, sticking the bottle under my nose.

"I'm driving."

"Aw, come on." With drunken persistence he tried to force the bottle to my lips. I pushed it away.

"I'm driving, I said."

"No harm, buddy. Fren' to fren'. No harm. See?"

"That's O. K.," I said.

He took another drink and sat holding the bottle in one hand and his derby in the other. He was neither concentrating nor pretending now, and he seemed less drunk. I kept the car going steadily at sixty, for we had not come to Blytheville, and Pittsville was many miles beyond that town.

"Tough titty," my companion said lugubriously. "Thought the ol' man was comin' on like Gang Busters, then, pop! Sen' for me yestiddy. Some ol' man. Ain't no more real men lef' no more."

"Do you have any kin-people?"

"Plen'y folks. Uncles an' aunties. Got a auntie in Chicago, unnerstan'. Ol' lady's dead. Lem' me tell you something. Fren' to fren'. See?" He leaned close to my ear, and in a wet whisper, said:

"Gran'pa use to play ball wi' a cracker team. 'At's what they tell, unnerstan'."

"In Pittsville?"

Twisting his mouth and contorting his features, he brought his face very close to mine. "Don' believe me? Hunh? Hunh?"

"Sure. Why not? Was he passing?"

"Ssssssush," he said, putting a finger to his lips and winking at me confidentially. "Got it now? O. K. Fren' to fren'."

"Friend to friend," I said.

"Tell you something else an' see can you make me out a l'ar. My gran'pa could scent rabbits same's a dog. He done it for some white men oncet. If I'm lyin', I'm flyin'. Ast Mr. Jim Gregg. Ast Lawyer Lee Scott. Any white man in Pittsville'll tell you 'at. If he wasn't dead, you could ast the ol' man hisself, cause if it's a lie, he tol' it. Here, take a drink."

"No, thanks," I said.

We went through Blytheville and sped out again into the flat country beyond. The headlights did not taper off into the darkness, but were shut off against the wall of blackness with the abruptness of magic. My companion went to sleep. When he awakened we had passed through Grandy and were approaching the outlying lights of Pittsville. He was loggily sober. I asked him about lodging in Pittsville. He insisted that I go to his grandfather's first. I would at least get something to eat there.

"It's too late," I said.

"Ain't they wakin' him tonight? Hunh? O. K., then."

The little house stood on an unlighted, unpaved street at the far end of a thin row of other little houses. It was lighted up as if for a party. We passed from the porch directly into the living room, where an open coffin stood on a wheeled stand in the center. The old man lay with his head toward the door. A silk handkerchief covered his face. A little yellow lady in a crushed hat sat at the foot of the coffin. She looked up when we came in but she said nothing. From behind the closed door opposite us there came the low hum of talk, but there was no sound and no sight of mourning. The flowers had the smell of death and that was all. They were wrought into curious garlands of hearts and stars and crowns. The old man seemed very comfortable.

The room into which we passed from the living room was full of women sitting in two circles, an inner circle around a table in the center of the floor and an outer circle sitting in chairs around the wall. Close relatives seemed to be at the table. The gasoline lamp with its milky, opaque globe filled the room with hard light. No one was crying. They might have been at a quilting. On the crude mantel above the homemade holdall, the clock had been turned to the wall and a sheet covered what I suspected was a mirror. When we came in, a woman whom I later heard called Jamie jumped up from the table.

"Paul's come," she said, and in another moment several women were trying to hug Paul, and two or three big-shouldered men, like harnessed bulls in their tight clothes, were grinning from the kitchen door. Paul let each of the women hug him and kiss him on the cheek. He smacked the rumps of the younger ones. No one paid any attention to me. I followed him when he pushed his way through to the kitchen.

There were a half-dozen men in the kitchen, and it was hot in there, for the wood-burning range was going and something in a huge, black pot was simmering on the back of it. There were two distinct strata of smells in the room. The steaming odor of the cooking refused to mingle with the thin, sickening odor of flowers. In a moment it was as if Paul had not just come from Cairo and I was not a total stranger. Three of these men were Paul's uncles, his dead mother's brothers, and the others were family friends. Between Paul and his uncles there was a casual camaraderie.

"This is my fren'. See? Unnerstan' what I'm sayin'?" Paul said, establishing my relationship. He looked at each in turn. No one questioned him. Except the uncle called Neely, all of us found seats. There were two cots in the room, one against each side wall, but no chairs. The cots, the oilcloth-covered table, and the range used up all but inches of the floor space. One corner of the room was shut off by a faded piece of cretonne stretched on a wire.

"I thought Gran'pa was comin' on like Gang Busters," Paul said. "How did he come to die?"

"He jus' blowed out, Paul," Neely said. He was the biggest of the uncles, a shaggy fellow of about sixty.

"A strong win' come up Friday night," Henry said, "an' he went away with that."

"Gone wi' the win'," Paul said, with no intention to amuse, and no one laughed.

We could hear the women talking loudly, I thought, for a house of death, and we could see through the doorway their dark shadows massed against the wall. Jamie, the first to greet Paul, had a thin, E-string voice, which pierced dagger-like through the voices of the others.

"What'd Gran'pa say?" Paul asked.

"Pa didn' say nothin'. It were jus' like Neely said, he jus' blowed out," Henry answered.

"Nex' thing I wanta know, did any y'all buy some grog?"

"Pa lef' some," Neely said. "Pa lef' dang near a jug o' his special."

"Dat'll make you drunker'n a fool, too," one of the men who was not a relative said.

"Ain't nobody fixin' to git drunk. I been drunk," Paul said. "If you gotta stay up all night, you gotta have a eye-opener."

"Pa sure would be put out if he knowed somebody jus' natcherly went off to sleep wakin' him," Neely said.

"Ain't no way for him to know it now, though."

"Sure ain't," Walter said. His voice was the masculine counterpart of Jamie's, high, but without the edgy quality. Like his brothers, he was a big man, the raw, brownish-red color of old brick.

For some minutes we had heard a man's voice in there among the women's, but now in the interval of our silence it seemed to dominate everything. We looked toward the door, but we did not see the man. His voice dropped oil, condoled. Neely frowned. Walter wiped his face with his hand.

"I tol' my buddy 'bout Gran'pa's pitchin' arm an' 'bout him scentin' rabbits," Paul said.

Neely chuckled. "Pa had all the kids bamboozled. Go up on them school groun's an' tell them kids more lies then a moo'in' pixter."

Everyone laughed but Paul.

"I seen him pitch a ball faster 'en I could, an' he was already a ol' man," Paul said.

"He had a good pitchin' arm," Henry said.

"What'cha mean? Didn' he scent no rabbits?"

" 'At's what he said," Henry said.

"Pa was a l'ar," Neely said.

"What'cha mean?" Paul demanded again. His loose lips hung incredulously.

"Everybody knowed it but kids an' white folks. I thought you knowed 'bout that rabbit-scentin' business. Pa was jus' foolin' them men, Mr. Gregg an' them. They was talkin' 'bout it not bein' no huntin' by the dogs bein' sick an' Pa 'bout butted in."

"Pa sure was a mess," Henry said.

"Everybody near 'bout knowed how Pa was, always buttin' into something an' gittin' hisself all knotted up like a eel line. White folks or not, didn' make him no dif'ence. Pa jus' 'bout heard 'em talkin' front of the bank or somewheres an' busted in on the tail end. He been talkin' 'roun' for years how he could scent game like a dog, an' Mr. Gregg an' 'em jus' 'bout took him up on it. There wasn't a rabbit dog that was good for nothin' on account the disease, an' them men prob'ly was half-jokin'. But you know how Pa was. So Pa prob'ly jumped in 'fore he'd fig- gered a way to git out good. Pa was a mess."

"Pa come by my house that day," Walter said in his high voice. "He was hikin'. Didn't have no time to stop, though he musta knowed there was something unusual with me to be home from the railroad that time a day."

"Wasn't nobody home but Jamie when he got here," Neely went on. "Me an' Henry was to work, but Jamie said Pa come on home an' poked 'roun' lookin' for some ol' box traps. He foun' two. Jus' two was all he foun', an' them wasn't enough, 'cause when we come home he was buildin' some more. But he wouldn't tell nobody what he was buildin' them for. I thought he was buildin' 'em for possum, 'cause he never did like no gunshot possum. But you ast him an' he jus' shake his head. He built him 'bout eight o' the fastes' box traps you ever seen. Then one ee'nin' 'bout night-dark he marched off with 'em.''

The women were getting loud in the next room. Henry got up and closed the door and then lifted a glass jug from behind the cretonne curtain and poured some water and some whisky into an agate pitcher on the table. The pitcher passed among us.

"When Pa come back 'bout ten that ee'nin' he wouldn't tell nobody where he'd been at, nor nothin'. But he was beat down when he got back. He poked 'roun' for a little while, an' then he hit the sheets.

"Soon that Saddee mornin', long 'fore day, I heard him sneakin' outa bed an' feelin' 'roun' for his clo'es in the dark. I laid there an' he didn' say nothin'. Henry musta heard him, too, didn' you, Henry? 'cause you come in from the shed room 'bout the same time I come out here in the kitchen followin' Pa. Pa was out here in his drawers, gittin' in his clo'es. He wouldn' tell me nor Henry nothin' neither. He got out a bunch o' bindin' cord an' lit him a lantern an' went out.

"He was back 'fore bre'kfas', but he still didn' say nothin'. Me an' Henry went on to work. Mr. Gregg an' 'em come by for him, Sis Jamie said—Mr. Gregg an' Mr. Broomhead an' some more—an' Pa, he went off with them as big as you please.

"That ee'nin' me an' Henry an' Walter was all comin' from work. On Saddee we gen'lly comes right up Main Street, 'cause Walter always have to buy his ol' woman them lickrish chews ol' man Hargraves sells to his store. Ol' man Hargraves' the only place you can buy 'em, an' we us'lly walk up Main Street with him Saddees. Well, we was comin' 'long an' we seen this gang o' men standin' way up by the bank where the hitchin' postes was, an' all we could see was guns. By it bein' Saddee an' all an' us bein' down in the railroad yards, we didn' know but what some country niggah had did somethin' an' them men with guns was the startin' of a mob. By it bein' Saddee, there was a mess o' people in town, an' it ain't hard to start somethin' when you got a gang o' people.

"We started to turn off, 'cause we didn' see no colored people, seem like, nowhere. An' then we seen Mr. Broomhead up there, an' we looked agin an' seen Mr. Gregg, an' they both had guns. So we knowed it was all right. An' by me rememb'rin' the huntin', I commenced to laugh.

"Well, when we got up there, we sorta slowed down to a creep, an' there was Mr. Wade Briscoe tellin' these men 'bout Pa, an' there was a mess o' rabbits on the groun'. I looked at Walter an' Henry an' they looked at me. We knowed Pa had been up to some trick o' foolin' white folks. Pa'd ruther fool a white man 'en own a hundred dollars. Pa was a mess."

Neely stopped. Henry, who was sitting on the cot directly opposite me, rubbed his hands together and chuckled indulgently. From the next room came the strident voice of Jamie and then the unctuous masculine voice that we had heard before. Jamie was beginning to sound hysterical, I thought, but no one seemed to notice, except Neely, who was frowning.

"Well, what was Gran'pa's jive?" Paul demanded. He kept running his tongue around his lips.

"Well, now, here's what Pa had did," Henry said, taking up the story. "He tol' us about it that ee'nin'. I thought Pa would kill hisself laughin'. I can see him now settin' there with his shoes off an' his feet bakin' in the oven, laughin' so hard he like' to fell outa the cheer.

"Them box traps Pa made he set out on Schlesinger's place, where they use to have carnivals. He caught him nine rabbits in them traps, an' soon that Saddee mornin' they was to go huntin', Pa went out there an' robbed them traps. He took them rabbits over behin' the woods back o' Mr. Ed Finney's pasture an' tied up two of them to a stake he driv in the groun' behin' a clump o' bushes. He took another rabbit an' tied it up some place else, an' then he took two more. He tied all them rabbits up one place or another in a half-mile square.

"Wasn't nothin' to it after that, Pa say. By him s'posin' to be a dog, he was up ahead like a dog was s'pose' to be, an' he led Mr. Broomhead an' them up on the blin' side o' them clumps all spread out. Pa, he'd go down on all fours an' creep ahead, an' all at once he'd dive in the bushes an' cut the cord, an' the rabbits would start hikin'. Them men caught eight rabbits that day."

There was no general laughter. The brothers made a kind of happy and sober communion of their laugh sounds. The three men who were not relatives laughed as if they had laughed at the story before. One of them said:

"Did the mens ever fin' out how yo' pa had fooled 'em?"

"Didn't nobody know it but us," Henry said, "an' we wouldn'a tol' it. No, sir. I figger by him bein' able to fool 'em, he could feel prideful to white folks, an' if he didn't have that, he wouldn'ta had nothin'."

"Gran'pa was a l'ar from way back," Paul said. Already he was beginning to see this as a mark as distinguishing of his grandfather as ballplaying and rabbit scenting.

"An' he wasn't 'zactly a l'ar neither," Walter said. "I don't know what you'd call Pa, but he wasn't no common l'ar."

On the periphery of awareness was the sound as of someone praying with quiet insistence in the next room. Flat and solid in the very center of consciousness was the heat in the kitchen. No one seemed to think of opening the window, though the air was thick and foul with the odor of simmering food, of flowers, and of our own yeasty body sweat. The pitcher went around a third time, but no one seemed to be drinking much. A thin scum of sweat put a sheen on all our faces. Slowly one took refuge in the sound of the praying voice from the other room. It rose and fell with expert, insinuating cadence, broken now and then by the fierce, low keen of a woman's voice. Gradually all sound retreated, became lost, became indistinguishable from heat.

The door was flung open suddenly, and there stood Jamie. Sweat glistened on her swollen face. Her wild eyes darted about the room, licked at our faces, and came to rest on Neely.

"Neely, that's your pa layin' in there dead!" she said fiercely. Her fists came to her chest. Like predatory birds, her eyes darted to the other brothers. "Henry, Walter, that's your pa an' my pa layin' in there dead. An' here you set drinkin', drinkin'! You oughta be prayin' wi' us. You oughta be prayin' to Gawd!"

Then her face cracked and her voice utterly collapsed and she was weeping into her fists with a long, wailing sound. Neely gently guided her back into the room and closed the door after her.

"I could bus' him one," he said feelingly. "I could sure bus' him one."

" 'At preacher'll do it ever' time. He got Jamie all worked up when we was wakin' Sarah," Walter said.

"Trouble wi' Jamie is she ain't sure she feels nothin' till she's all tore up an' cryin' 'bout it," Neely said.

"If Pa could git outa there an' hear 'em," Henry said, shaking with an irrepressible chuckle.

"He sure would if he could. That's jus' the thing Pa would like to do, raise up from the dead an' th'ow a skeer in 'em."

Everyone laughed quietly.

"Pa tol' a tale 'bout the dead comin' to once. It got put in the paper. 'Member that, Walt? Pa was more proud o' that then if it was a hundred dollars. They took his pixter an' put it in the paper. When I seen this other piece 'bout him in the paper Saddee night, I thought 'bout it. Wonder what ever come o' that other piece, Neely?"

"Pa 'bout wore it out showin' it," Neely said. "Jamie looked for it for his journey package."

"Gran'pa was there when this woman raised up, or something, wasn' he? Seems like I 'member something like that," Paul said. But a minute afterwards, when he remembered, his lip curled. "What ol' jive did he have this time?"

"It wasn't hardly no jive, as you call it," Henry said patiently. "It was too seri'us an' times was too critical. Even Pa wouldn't been up to no foolishness in times like them. There's one thing 'bout it that nobody got the straight understandin' to, Pa nor nobody else. What ever went wi' the resurrected woman? Don' nobody know."

"You don't reckon the white folks know?" Walter piped.

"I b'lieve to my soul it woulda looked so bad on young Doctor Leary an' Undertaker Blair that the white folks come together on that thing an' done something. They might o' took her outa town an' paid her to stay out. Some says they mighta took her clear to Oklahomey. Some says they mighta killed her anyhow. She wasn' nothin' but a po' country white woman noway. I b'lieve the white folks knows. Big white folks like Doctor Leary an' Undertaker Blair sticks together."

A silence followed this. Henry got up and went to the stove and lifted the pot on to the table. With a long fork and a spoon he lifted from the pot a hog's head, so well done that the meat slithered from the skull onto the large tin lid where he placed it. The white skull, with its ragged eyeholes, gleamed sardonically. Henry dumped the viscid slabs of meat and ladled great mounds of black-eyed peas into plates, and each of us got a steaming plate of this and a tin fork. We settled down to eat where we were.

"Times was pretty critical," Neely said slowly. " 'At smallpox sickness that run th'ough here took 'em off like flies, 'an didn' nobody have time to lay 'em away proper. Pa said he seen many a body come there to the graveyard in ho'made coffins you could see th'ough. Pa said he put many a white woman in t'ground without a stitch 'tween her an' the pine box she was layin' in. They brung the dead people out in wagon-loads, an' hardly no colored was took a-tall. Times was critical, an' it could be by times bein' so critical, Doctor Leary might could los' his head an' sent a live woman to the undertaker."

"Didn' the white folks put it in the papers?" Paul asked, in bitter outrage and incredulity.

"There's things I b'lieve 'cause I know, an' then there's things pas' b'lievin', an' there's other things I b'lieve 'cause they's so pecul'ar you say they's God's doin'," Henry said. Smiling with a touch of tenderness that softened his whole big frame, he moved the pot back to the stove. "There was things that Pa said that he wasn' askin' no b'lief for, an' when he didn' ask no b'lief he jus' tol' it like he say it happen. Pa was upset 'bout that resur-

rected business, though. He come clean down to the railroad
yards an' tol' us 'bout it. 'Member, Neely?"

We had nearly finished eating when the dining-room door
opened again and a heavy-muscled black man, not much over
five feet tall, stood there. Above his piped vest his shirt was wet
with perspiration. His face was as black as a thundercloud. It
quivered in a fixed, beatific smile. Behind him the room seemed
more crowded than it had been when Jamie flung open the door.
A thick murmur of hushed voices beat gently behind the
preacher. He was looking at us, but he seemed also to be listening in pious satisfaction to the murmur behind him.

"I brings you the word of the Lord, brethren," he said, raising his short, heavy arms in a gesture at once grotesquely
pompous and reserved. "Weep not at the out-goin', but take joy
an' be comforted that Gawd's great will is done. Amen! Who's
goin'a say amen?"

From the women behind him there was a chorus of amens;
from the men, not a word, only a shifting of feet and a dropping of eyes. Arms still upraised, he began his prayer.

"Oh, Gawd, we come this evenin' beared down wid the sor-
rows of this worl'. We come as paupers to Thy th'one o' grace.
We been down in the valley o' the shadder, an' our hearts is
heavy this evenin', Lord. Thou's done thundered fo'th Thy will.
Thou's done took from out our mist one o' Yo' lambs. Thou's
done took a good brother who's done lived his 'lotted time an'
died, Gawd, like we all mus' die. Ummmmmmmmmm. Thou's
done come into this house o' sons an' dotters, o' brothers an'
sisters, an' wid Yo' own han', Yo' own great han', Gawd—
ummmmmmmm—Thou's done dashed down the vessel outa what
Yo' po'ed life into them. Thou's done took a father an' a gran'-
father. Thou's done beared down hearts. Thou's done put bur-
dens on 'em. Thou's done whupped 'em wid stripes. 'Member
dese hearts, great Gawd. Relieve 'em. You know when t'sun's
been a-shinin' too long an' the earth's all parched an' barren, You
sen's Yo' rain, Lord. You relieve the earth. When wars rage,
like the one ragin' now, an' the thunder o' the guns an' the

cannon drowndes out Yo' own great thunder, an' mens dies an' makes widders an' orfins, den, in Yo' own good time, Gawd— Yo' precious time—ummmmmm—You sen's peace. You takes the burden off'n the hearts o' nations. An' you promise', Father, by the sweet-flowin' blood o' Jesus, to rescue the perishin', suckle the needy, give health to the ailin' . . ." He did not pause at a piercing scream from Jamie. His extended fingers worked spasmodically, as if each had a life, independent of him. ". . . an' sen' balm to the hearts o' sufferin'. Sen' it now, Lord. Let it flow like the healin' waters o' Gilead, an' ease the burden o' dese hearts broken by the fulfillin' o' Yo' almighty will. Amen."

The preacher opened his eyes and looked around as he lowered his arms, shooting his cuffs as he did so. The three brothers stared at spots about six inches beyond their toes. One corner of his thick mouth drawn in a hard snarl, Paul lifted the pitcher from the table and drank. In the other room there was a general snuffling and loosening of throats. Walter was the first to recover.

"That was a fine prayer, Rev'ren," he said. "Mighty fine."

"Thank you, brother. I s'pose the arrangemen's ain't been changed none sence I talked wid y'all?"

"No they ain't, Rev'ren. Not's I knows of," Walter said, looking at Neely.

"Ain't been nothin' changed," Neely said.

"That's fine. That's jus' fine," the preacher said pompously. "Uncle Henry's goin' a smile up there wid Gawd tomorrer. I'm aimin' to do him proud."

With that, he went back into the other room. Neely closed the door.

"He can lay a pow'ful prayer," Henry said.

"Yeah," Paul said. "He comes on like Gang Busters."

We kept quiet again. These silences fell like something physical, like unhurried periods of gestation. It was increasingly easy to fall into the habit of them. After more than three hours of standing, Neely had at last lowered himself to the floor, and now sat nodding against the wall. Others nodded too. One of the men who was not a relative was sleeping deeply. Only Henry remained wide-eyed. As the fire died down, the house began to crepitate. At something after two I thought of leaving, but remembering that I had no other place to spend the night, I remained where I was, uncomfortably crowded on the cot between Paul and the heavy sleeper.

"If all the kin-people goes to sleep at a wake, it's the sign o' somebody else amongst 'em dyin'," Henry said in a low voice.

"Are you sleepy?" I asked.

"No."

After a while Henry eased himself up from the cot and went to the dining-room door. It cracked protestingly when he opened it.

"They all 'sleep too," he said. "Pa would be some kinda put out if he knowed folks was sleepin' at his wake. What time you reckon it is?"

"Twenty of four," I said, looking at my watch.

"Reckon I could git th'ough there wi'out 'sturbin' nobody?"

"Might."

"Jus' happen to feel in my pocket. We done lef' the main thing outa Pa's journey package. I don't know how come us to leave it out." He pulled a scrap of crumpled newspaper from his pocket and smoothed it between his hands. "This paper'll do Pa more proud an' give him more comfort then anything else whilst he's waitin'."

"Waiting for what?" I asked.

He looked at me in mild astonishment. "To cross the river Jerden. To git to Glory," he said simply. He smoothed and smoothed the crumpled scrap of paper.

"May I see it?"

It was a rather long obituary torn from the *Pittsville Sun* of two days before.

UNCLE HENRY BRISCOE DIES FRIDAY
KNOWN TO MANY

Uncle Henry Briscoe, a former negro slave who came to Pittsville in 1860, died in his home on Matthew Street about ten o'clock Friday night.

Uncle Henry, according to his own statements, was about 95 years old.

The old negro was a familiar character in Pittsville for many years, known to almost everyone who had ever lived here more than a few years.

According to Edward Ransome's history of Jefferson county, to which Uncle Henry contributed considerable data of early days in the county, the old negro came here as a slave in 1860 owned by the late Rev. T. S. Mocrum.

The history says that Uncle Henry made the trip from Jackson with Rev. Mocrum and after a brief sojourn at Wittsburg, came on to Pittsville, arriving here just shortly after the town was settled.

The old man was a favorite of many of Pittsville's most prominent citizens having seen many of them grow up. For many years Uncle Henry was the keeper at the ball park, and in that capacity came to know many youngsters of the present generation. His homey philosophy, always expounded in a quavering voice, was a source of amusement to almost everyone who knew him. One of Uncle Henry's favorite stunts was reeling off what he said was his full name, a string of some twenty-odd first names winding up with "George Washington Abraham Lincoln James Henry Briscoe." Funeral arrangements are being made.

I handed the paper back to Henry.

"I b'lieve I can make it," he said, opening the door wider.

Shifting Paul's dead weight off my cramped shoulder, I got up too. We closed the door behind us and stepped carefully into the dining room. Some of the women had left, for there were only five now, and they were asleep as if drugged. Two of them, legs and arms tucked in, slept in chairs against the wall. Jamie and two others slept with their heads cushioned on their arms on the table. The air was even more foul than in the kitchen. The sharp odor of the funeral flowers, like a solid thing, had putrefied in the stagnant air. The gasoline lamp shed a hard, hissing light. Scraps of food lay balled in greasy tissue on the table.

In the living room everything was as I had first seen it, except that now the little yellow woman in the crushed velvet hat was sleeping. Her hands were fastened over the edge of the casket and she was sleeping peacefully against her raised arms. The old man lay as rigidly comfortable as ever in his narrow, lavender-lined bed. His withered yellow hands were folded on his stomach, as if he had just taken a deep, releasing sigh and rested them there. I saw nothing in the coffin that looked like a package of any kind. A blanket of thin, tufted silk lay folded over the old man's legs and perhaps the journey package was beneath that, I thought.

"Reckon I'll 'sturb him much?" Henry whispered. "I got to lif' him up."

With that he bent over the body and worked his arm under the shoulders. The old man's entire length rose rigidly. The handkerchief that covered his face slipped a little, but did not disclose the features. Holding the old man up easily, Henry drew the flat, silk pillow from under the head and laid the body down again. From the open end of the pillow he took a small package done up in ordinary wrapping paper and tied with string. He fumbled with the string and finally undid it; then he laid the package on the old man's chest and folded the paper down. The package contained several pictures, some of them tintypes, several pages apparently torn from a Bible, a sheaf of rough foolscap written upon in an uncertain, drawn hand, and a small American flag, such as used to come folded in boxes of cigars and candy when I was a child.

"Pa'll be mighty proud," Henry whispered with unmistakable satisfaction, tucking the ragged newspaper clipping among the things. Then he remembered something and drew the clipping out again.

"There's a thing on here none o' us couldn't make out," he said, peering at the print. "What's that mean here?"

I looked over his shoulder. "Homey philosophy?" I felt suddenly inadequate. "Oh, those are the things he believed in."

"What kinda things? Like the gov'mint?" Henry whispered, beginning to wrap the package up again.

"Yes," I said.

He replaced the pillow and straightened the blanket that had bunched around the old man's feet. Then he removed the handkerchief and I saw the old man's face. It was just a dead old man's face, waxen, yellow, drawn hard in the lines of death. We looked at it together.

"Pa b'lieved mostly in mens, like God an' Abraham Lincoln," Henry said, looking down on the pinched, gray-yellow face. "But there wasn't many things he b'lieved in, less'n it was comin' an' goin' like he wanted to. Pa said there was a time when he couldn't come an' go like he wanted to, but after he got so he could, Pa sure done it. Yes, sir. I reckon he b'lieved in 'at more'n most anything."

3

A few sharecroppers were already on the move in northeastern Arkansas. One saw their coughing, rattling cars piled high with bedding, cans, and children moving southwestward from the lowlands bordering the Mississippi. They were not moving because of fear of the water, but because annual migration had become as instinctive with them as with the birds. Most of them were white, and one could tell they were sharecroppers by the furtive, diffident, and yet brutalized look of them. One saw them parked for repairs, or simply parked for an indefinite time a mile or two outside of towns, living by seasonal work in gins or compresses or cotton-oil mills, or making and selling baskets of reeds of guinea corn, which grew in great abundance in deserted fields.

On Saturdays one saw them and their women and children shuffling in straggling lines on the main streets of the towns. They were droop-shouldered, lank-haired, slack-kneed, with absolutely no resilience of either body or mind. More pitiful were they than the Negroes one saw on these streets. And one saw Negroes everywhere, provisioning themselves with meal and salt pork in the narrow, crowded stores, standing on the curbing on the sunny side of the street and arguing loudly about nothing at all, or mumbling stubbornly as they haggled for bargains at the curbside rummage sales.

These sales, too, were everywhere. They were conducted by white women from jalopies along the curbing. Rumpled dresses and coats hung over the open car doors and on the fenders and tops. Though there was frequently an air of confident bargaining, nothing ever seemed to change hands. But every Saturday the rummage sales on wheels were there. I saw them in town after town. They seemed to be an institution.

An institution also were the Saturday movies, where Tim McCoy seemed always to be playing in "Blazing Guns" or Gene Autry in "Singing Saddles," or where there was an extra-special called "Wages of Sin." All through the week the movie house would be a boarded, desolate store front crowded between a feed store on one side and a plantation or lumber camp commissary on the other. But about noon on Saturday the boards would come down as if by trickery, and a man, invariably wearing one of those broad-brimmed felt hats that begin to be common in Arkansas, would put fresh lurid posters up. Boys with stenciled handbills would dart about shoving handbills everywhere. If it were a special at which soap or china or a few dollars were to be raffled off, a Negro, outlandishly dressed in posters from head to foot, would saunter through the crowd bawling the attraction.

At two the crowds gathered, Negroes on one side, whites on the other, of the door where the man in the wide-brimmed hat sold tickets with one hand and stale popcorn with the other. By nine at night the three continuous shows had been run off, and by nine-fifteen the movie house was again a placard-ragged store front on an almost empty street. In every town it was the same—same building, same show, same crowds.

And in southeastern Arkansas the fields lay unvaried. The full-grown cotton, turning a pale blue-gray now, lay like a burden on the land. Along the road, nailed to the posts of plantation gates, scrawled in lime on the concrete, lettered on crude posters, everywhere were signs, "Cotton Pickers Wanted." In the fields one saw black men, women, and children at work, toiling slowly down the long rows. But each day the fields had a new quota of them—hungry, trusting folk who came out from the towns and villages before dawn, singing perhaps as the truck which bore them lurched through the chill darkness, unbelieving that the wage would drop from fifty to forty cents a hundred pounds by noon and to thirty by quitting time. But the wage always dropped, and the remaining crop threatened to rot in the bolls until the cloud of migratory workers—Syrians, Cubans, and even some Chinese—on their sweep to Mississippi and the southwest stopped long enough to pick for wages considered too high for Negroes.

"White folks ain't what dey use ter be."

Mary Grant said that to me, though she was not thinking of the cotton. When I first saw her she was thinking of the pain that knifed through her chest and the long yards she had still to carry her water pail. With every uncertain, heavy step the water sloshed over her black ankles and her broken, man's shoes. Three young children watched her apathetically from the doorway of a weathered, unfinished house. Once, resting the pail on the ground, she remained bent over it, pressing her hands against her withered breast. When she took the pail up and started again, her steps were slower, more uncertain than ever.

All this I saw from the road. By the time I had locked the car and overtaken her she had not staggered more than a half-dozen yards. I took the pail from her a bit too suddenly and she floundered, as if, flexed to the burden, her old body found relief insufferable. She leaned against me, and I could feel her heart pounding and hear her breath hissing in and blowing out through her gray lips.

"Thank'ee, son. Thank'ee. Ah laike ter fainted," she gasped. She kept her eyes closed and rested heavily, as if my chest were a refuge she had not known in all her life before. Her body was thin and brittle.

When she was ready to move again, we went slowly around

the unfinished house to a blackened cabin immediately behind it. The cabin rested on high log pilings. There were two rooms in the cabin, one on each side of an open hall, and a flight of crude steps led up from the hall to a dark loft. "Dat's where we goes when dat ol' river rise," she said.

We sat on boxes in the hall. There was a door in either end of the hall and on one side we could see into the back door frame of the unfinished house and on the other into a weed-grown yard, where three goats stood tethered in the watery sunshine. The old lady sat bent over, her elbows resting on her knees and her fingers plucking at her blue headcloth.

"Ah ain't felt right in many a year. Ah jes' messes eroun', steers mo' den Ah should, but sometimes ma haid gits so drunk Ah's forst ter set down." She talked with painful slowness.

"Have you been to a doctor?" I asked.

"Son, Ah ain't be'n ter de doctor in twenty years. Doctor tol' me den dat some niggah hed putt a lizard in me. Seems laike Ah hed a twitchin' all ovah ma body an' Ah couldn' git shet of it. He gimme some black med'cine, an' dat holp me some, but he didn' git nothin' outa me. Twitchin' jes' eased off atta while. Don' know whether dat doctor foolin' me or not 'bout dat lizard."

The children had followed us. There were two boys of six or seven and a smaller girl. All of them were practically naked, and shivering against the damp chill in the hall. They sat on the loft steps. Except for the boxes upon which we sat and a soiled dress hanging from a nail, the hall itself was empty. Chicken droppings and mud tracks stained the warped floor. Through the doorway of the room opposite us I could see stained news-paper blistering on the walls and the floor space filled with un-made beds.

"Doctor tol' me den de niggahs was gittin' so bad he didn' know how ter doctor dem no mo'. Sayed dey was chawin' roots an' conjurin' an' he couldn' doctor dat stuff. He died, an' Ah ain't be'n ter de doctor sence."

"You ought to go. A doctor might help you," I suggested.

Her wheezing was like nothing so much as the spent and spasmodic breathing of a whipped child. It was painful to hear. Her speech was labored, but unpitched to any emotion, as if the source of her words lay in sensations long dead.

She shook her head slowly and gazed at the floor.

"Ah misgives it. We hed all kinda doctors fer ma man, an' dey didn' holp him none. We paid a heap o' money. Ma dauter stay ter Helena, an' he was dere eight weeks. She paid out a heap, but he died jes' de same."

"How long ago was that?" I asked.

"Dat younges' dere was jes' gittin' big inside Leila. Ah reckin she be five nex' munt' ur two.

"Ah birt' seben yokes o' chilluns an' dey all livin' ter ma knowin'. De farthes' 'cross in Texis. Ah got chilluns in Helena an' some in Saint Looes an' some in Lit'le Rock an' dey's two yere. We sunt dem all word when ma man died, but didn' none o' dem come ter de buryin', 'scusin' dem dat's yere. He kep' a-sayin' he wants ter see de oldes', an' Mistah Jaspah we gi'd him de numbah an' he went ter Deewit an' sunt him a telegram warr, but he never come."

Knotting and unknotting her hands against her forehead, she made a murmur of misery.

"Maybe he didn't get the wire," I said.

"Hit's a right fur piece ter Texis," she answered, "but Ah reckin he got it an' his woman kep' him from comin'. He weren' no boy laike dat. He were ma bes' chillun. 'Course, he's a growed man now, twix' fifty an' sixty, Ah reckin. Ah wus big wid him when ma mammy died, an' dat wus in eighty-five. Don' dat make him twix' fifty an' sixty?"

"Yes," I said.

She went on with her own thoughts. The last flies of the year crawled unmolested over her face, her hands. The children walked solemnly up and down the stairs, up and down, absorbed in some wordless game of oppressive seriousness.

"When ma man died, dey tol' me Ah wus goin'a git a penshun, bein's Ah wus so ol'. White man come yere an' say he goin'a git me a penshun. Come yere wid some kinda papers wid readin' on it. He axe me how ol' wus Ah'm an' Ah tol' him Ah didn' know, but Ah wus bigged up in eighty-five an' Ah hed be'n sleepin' wid mens long 'fore dat. 'Well, you ovah fifty, a'ntie,' says he, 'an' Ah'm goin'a git you a penshun. Jes' gimme fifty cent laike all de yuthers done an' in a lit'le bit you be gittin' check money from de gov'mint.' Ah gi'd him fifty cent an' he come eroun' 'bout a week atta dat an' Ah gi'd him fifty cent mo'. He come fo' ur fi' time, but Ah didn' have no fifty cent las' time. Dat wus fi' year ago, an' Ah ain't got no penshun yit. What you reckin happen ter dat man?"

"He was cheating you," I said.

"You reckin?" she asked, as if she doubted me, as if her mind would not accept the simple evidence. "Ma dauter Leila say dat. What you reckin he do dat fer? White folks ain't what dey use ter be. White folks didn' use ter be laike dat. Dey didn' use ter cheat us po' niggahs. Der use ter be good white people."

"Yes," I said.

"Mistah Jaspah 'ud ruther cut his th'oat den cheat a cullud pursen." She heaved a forlorn sigh and plucked distractedly at her headcloth.

"Who was Mr. Jasper?"

"Mistah Jaspah? He were ma mammy's young mausa. He live' up Boyer road tel he got tuck an' died. Las' time Ah seen him wus when he tol' me Ah could bury ma man in de wes' corner o' his fiel'. Weren' long 'fo' he died, an' dey's some new white folks livin' dere, an' Ah reckin Ah'll git buried in de swamp. Mistah Jaspah wus one good man."

She turned her head toward me and a tremor passed over her old, gray face.

"An' you reckin dat white man come wid it in his min' ter cheat?" I nodded and she turned her eyes again to the floor. " 'Cause maybe ef Ah wus gittin' penshun money Ah wouldn' be buried in dat gum-tree swamp. Ma dauter in Helena 'ud take an' buy me a buryin' space ef Ah wus gittin' penshun money."

I thought at first that she was tired of her hunched position and was merely sitting up to lean her back against the wall. But then I saw her eyes bulge and her face twist in pain. I leaned toward her, not knowing what to do. She was altogether oblivious to everything but the cruel pain. A quivering band of muscle appeared on her thin neck, and she thumped and twisted her head against the wall. Meantime the children kept up their wordless, solemn game of walking up and down the ladder-like steps.

"Is there anything I can do?" I asked.

But the old woman made no sign that she had heard me. One spasm after another passed over her face. But the pain was beginning to spend itself, for her hands dropped from her breast and she closed her eyes. She leaned against the wall and breathed in short, quick, furtive gasps. Her face grew less twisted slowly, until by comparison with its former distortion it looked beatifically calm, as if the pain had deterged it.

"Seems laike Ah worked enough an' done enough ter do nothin' but set an' rock," she said after a while. "Ah be'n workin' all ma life. Now ma blood need turnin' down an' Ah gits a tur'ble pain th'ough ma ches'. Ma med'cine's near done run out too. Ah fergits what you call dat med'cine, but Ah gits it from de sto' an' Ah takes it keerful so's it wun't run out too fas'. Ah be'n po'ly sick laike dis eight er nine years now."

"But certainly you don't stay here all day alone with these children?"

For answer she raised her voice and called in a kind of weak, strained scream, "Dan Edward." From the unfinished house there came the sound of heavy shoes shuffling across loose boards, and a massive black fellow, dressed in overalls and a denim jumper, came to the door frame and looked across at me sullenly. His shoulders sloped like massive bastions from the black tower of his neck.

"What you want, ol' woman?" he asked.

His mother ignored him.

"Dat's Dan Edward. He stay yere wid me. He got a bitty stan' o' cotton out dere needs pickin', but he wun't do dat."

"Dat ain't ma cotton!" Dan Edward said. "Damn've Ah'm goin'a pick Bung's cotton fer him. Ah ain't planted it."

He stood leaning massively against the door frame. I remembered the old woman's staggering along the rutty path with the pail of water. I thought of the small field of scraggly cotton and the weed-choked vegetable patch I had seen flanking the path.

"Your mother's just had a spell," I said. "She ought to go to a doctor."

"She ain't goin'a die tel she have ter," he said. He stomped down the plank that served for steps and disappeared around the side of the cabin.

"Ah got 'nuther boy don't live fur, an' Leila, de yoke ter Dan Edward, she live yere. Bung's got a white man thinks a heap o' him. He got a piece o' lan' 'bout two mile, an' he tol' Bung dat ef he clare it an' work it he could have eva'thing off'n it fer two years. Bung ain't skeered a work. But he ain't makin' nothin' yit. Totes me home a lit'le som'pin ter eat sometimes.

"Leila, she pickin' cotton. She be'n fo' places, an' evah time dey tells her dey give her dis much an' den dey turns right eroun' an' give her dat much. Dese chilluns is her'n, an' dat boy dere," she said, pointing to the largest child, "he go ter school. He 'ud be in school right now 'cept school done close down fer de cotton. Ah'm proud he's l'arnin' som'pin. Leila, she wus good wid books herownse'f. She de only one what tuck ter l'arnin'. Seems laike dey minds wus on cuttin' an' grabbin' an' mawlin'.

"Mistah Jaspah sayed he goin'a sen' her off ter a mo' better school somewheres, but she got bigged up an' den she got mai'ed. Her man use ter beat her, an' Ah tol' her ter git shet o' dat niggah, but 'fo' she did, he got shet o' her."

She beat her hands quietly together. Sluggish flies swarmed over her bare, scabby legs and crawled drunkenly across her face, but she made no move to brush them off.

"Mr. Jasper was a kind man," I said.

"He wus de mos'," she said, and the words had an emotional content, a quaver in them. " 'Fo' Ah mai'ed Ah use ter go ter de woods wid anuther white man, an' he were nice too. White folks is jes' dif'ent now. Mammy an' me stayed yere tergether den, an' she use ter axe me ter bring him ter de bed an' she sleep in de lof'. But Mistah Piner, he wouldn' never come ter de bed much. He come a time ur two, but he laiked de woods. He wus a nice man, too, but not laike Mistah Jaspah."

I looked at her, trying to peer beneath her age, trying to hear the murmurings of warm remembrance beyond the robot words. It was hard to imagine this withered old gray crone as having once been black and comely and desirable.

"When Ah firs' got mai'ed, Ah couldn' git use ter ma man. Ah wus wile, Ah reckin, an' Ah reckin Ah wus twix' an' 'tween. A time ur two Ah runned away wid Mistah Jaspah, but he allus got ter worryin' 'bout his niggahs an' his craps an' sunt me back. Den atta while Ah hed chilluns so fas' Ah fergitted how ter be wile, Ah reckin. Ah birt' chilluns right along. Dere wus one evah year fer a while, an' den dey shet off, an' by'n'by dey come on agin tel Ah hed seben yokes."

She kept her silence for a moment.

"De Lawd's be'n pretty good ter me. He lem'me live ter raise all dem chillun."

"Did your husband farm?" I asked.

"He farm' eroun' a lit'le," she said. "But he hed be'n los' his he'lt' fer hard work. Me an' de chilluns worked dis place, but atta while de boys dat wus de oldes' lef', an' de man ter de bank jes' kep' eatin' away an' eatin' away tel dere wusn' nothin' lef' but dis yere bitty lan' an' dis house from de thirty acres de ol' Mistah Jaspah hed gi'd ma mammy when she wus free.

"Ah work' out too. Ah work' fer some folks nigh 'bout thirty years. Dey paid me t'ree dollahs a munt', an' a time ur two fo' an' five. Dey useter pay me right good wid som'pin ter eat. Hawg-killin' dey'd gi' me hawgshaid an' chitlin's. Dey gi' me clo'es. Den when de ol' folks die, de chilluns lef' from yere.

"Ma man, he wusn' laike me. He nevah did have no proper un'erstandin' 'bout his pay money. He work eroun' an' de white folks 'ud gi' him mos' any lit'le bit o' change. Mistah Jaspah sayed ter me right much, 'Maeey, Ah don' see how come you mai'ed Sam, when you could o' hed mos' any niggah in de county."

The sudden appearance of Dan Edward startled me. His form blacked out the light from the rear door of the passage. He thrust his burred head out and glared at his mother. The old lady hunched over and rested her elbows on her knees, while her fingers began that distracted plucking at her headcloth. Dan Edward was so visibly evil-tempered that I stood up and my muscles hardened.

"What you jawin' 'bout so much, ol' woman?" he demanded.

"You go pick dat cotton, Dan Edward. Dat's what you do." She did not look at him. "Ah kin tell what Ah pleases ter tell. You don't feed me."

"You bettah mind what you talkin'. How you know dis man anyhow? Might be some niggah ter beat you outa som'pin," he said, glaring at me.

I explained with some asperity that I meant no harm either to him or to his mother. He thrust his neck out further.

"You bettah not mean me no harm," he said. Then he stalked away.

"Set down, son," the old woman said. "Set down." She reached out her brittle hand and touched mine. "He ain't comin' back no time soon."

I sat down again, but she did not speak for a long time, as if she were trying to reknit the thread of sympathy between us. I watched the children at their solemn play and thought of all the Negro children I had seen being raised by their grandmothers. As often before, I wondered what significance this phenomenon had for the future.

"Look laike, ol's Ah is, Ah ought ter git a penshun," she was saying with a kind of stubborn insistence. "Look laike ter me Ah ought ter could set an' rock now a time ur two, 'd'out worryin' 'bout de weeds dat ain't chopped an' de cotton dat ain't picked. An' Ah don't want ter git buried in dat swamp. Gawd knows Ah don't want ter be buried dere."

She paused and her rheumy eyes looked at me with a certain brightness.

"Son, Ah got som'pin ter axe ya."

"Yes, Auntie?" I did not know what else to call her.

She scrabbled to her feet before I could help her, and went into the room whose door opened into the wall against which I was sitting. When she returned, she was bearing something wrapped carefully in a white cloth. Her face was strangely glimmering, tremulous, fleetingly stripped of the wooden grossness of age and changed in the way I had seen the faces of the devout change with hope and faith at prayers. Sitting down again, she undid the cloth with great care, displaying finally a biscuit-like Ingersoll watch of the kind that sold for a dollar when I was a boy. It lay bright and untarnished in the cloth.

"Ain't it purty?" she asked. The children had crept silently closer, and she guarded the watch by lifting the outer edge of the cloth over it. When one of them reached out to touch it, she covered it quickly with her hands and made the children go away.

"Ma man gi'd it ter me jes' 'fo' ma dauter taken him ter Helena. It wus de only thing Sam evah hed wort' anything. He was in tur'ble mis'ry den, an' he smelt tur'ble. Ah could not, Ah jes' could not lay in bed wid him."

She straightened the cloth on her lap and picked the watch up in her brittle fingers, letting it slip into her creamy palm.

"D'ya reckin dis'll git me a buryin' place somewheres? Mistah Jaspah, when he seen it, sayed Ah didn' have ter worry wid dis. But he's dead now, an' de fiel's full, an' dey's strange white folks stayin' on de place. D'ya reckin, son?"

"Of course," I said, not looking at her. "Of course."

She quavered a sigh of deep satisfaction and got up again. When she came back, I was already standing. The children were in the doorway now, and when we went toward it they backed across the narrow alley and leaned against the unfinished house. They were the shiest children I had ever seen. I called them and gave each a coin and they scrambled away out of sight. Then I gave the woman a coin.

"Ah'll git me som'pin dat tas'es good ter ma mouf," she said. "Don't know what dat mought be, 'cos eben sweet'n watah makes ma head drunk."

It was much warmer and drier in the doorway. The sun slanted down across a corner of the new house and fell in a wedge directly in the door. I brought a box from the hall and helped the woman down onto it.

"Bung wus puttin' up dat rail house dere," she said. "Dat's one good boy. He wus workin' money-work den an' he went ter work an' buyed de lumbah an' commence. Den when he got it 'long where 'tis now, mens come wid a truck an' tuck de res' of it an' tuck out de winder pos'es an' de do' pos'es an' sayed Bung hed'n nevah paid dem fer dat. Las' win'er Dan Edward an' his woman, dey commence ter tearin' it up fer farwood. Him an' her stays in dere. She pickin' cotton now off somewheres."

Through the unframed doorway I could see that the house was no more than a shell and that clumsy boards had been laid over the floor joists to make a footing. A cookstove stood against one wall. Some of the boards had been wrenched from the walls just below the roof and the lumber there was black and splitting with weather rot. Rags and potato sacking were stuffed in the holes under the eaves. The windows were boarded up with cardboard display pieces.

I left the old woman sitting in the doorway with the sun falling in her lap. The children appeared and followed me around the house and stood in a solemn row to see me off. I walked down the ragged path through the weeds. I waved good-by, but they did not answer, and when I crossed the fill over Black Gum swamp, where the old woman did not want to be buried, they were still standing as if rooted to the path.

4

Across the state line and the Mississippi River east of Lake Village, Arkansas, sprawls Mississippi. The natives of Greenville say that their town is the geographical center of the Delta. Indeed, it may be, though the subtle, penetrating, and unnameable something in the atmosphere seems no more concentrated here than in River City.

River City is not on the river, as Greenville is, or on a bluff above the river, as Vicksburg is, and therefore, say the natives of River City, they know the river best. Until 1887, when, through the power of prayer, old Joshua P. Brockery pushed the shores of the river back, they say, River City lay in water, and the first settlers knew that the red fury of the river never sleeps. They knew that it is multiform and manifold. It had boiled around them hundreds of times. It had lashed out at them while they slept. It had stolen up on them with the malignant quiet of a great prowling red cat. It had heaved and tossed like a monstrous woman in insatiable passion, and then, when the fit was spent, with enormous limbs outflung and turgid, lay in deadly, smothering quiet over all she had destroyed. Then in the summer of 1887, Joshua Brockery, the black Moses who had led them through the wilderness to this place, saying, "This is for my people a place where God dwells and liberty," prayed against the water. And in the morning the water was gone.

That is the legend. Beyond the limits of the town, the natives will show you the great sink holes through which the water was sucked by God's own breath.

River City does not look like a town with such a legend. It is a gray town, flung like rubble into a dull-red field just off the highway that runs north to Memphis and south to the Gulf. Only two of the town's buildings boldly face the road—a church on one side and an undertaker's shop on the other.

I turned off the highway into the town's fifty-yard length of main street. There was no one on the street, and I had passed the block of low, tired buildings before I saw anyone. The man was standing below the levee beyond the railroad. He seemed to be looking for something. He was spattered with mud, and a moment later I saw why. Down near an idle cotton gin between the levee and the cart track that served as road, his two-mule team was mired down. He glanced up as I approached, but he seemed in no mood to answer inquiries, and I crossed the levee and the road to a shallow block of buildings facing the paint-scaled railroad station. The larger, two-story building housed the post office. Next to it the narrow, frame building was the telephone exchange. I went into the telephone exchange.

A young man in headphones was reading a comic book at the small, toylike switchboard. I inquired of him for a place to stay.

"Sure," he said. "Lem'me get Judge." He stuck in a plug, jiggled it around, and pulled it out again. He looked at it and rubbed it on his sleeve before he replaced it.

"Sometimes I can't make connections for hell," he said, grinning amiably. He pressed the headphones against his ears. After a moment he got up and went to the door, calling, "Harry, Harry!" apparently into space. Then he came back in.

"Fix y'up in a minute," he said.

Harry was one of the town officials. He, too, greeted me amiably.

"Where's Judge?" he asked of the young man in the headphones.

"He's about gone to Melton," the telephone operator said. "I tried to get him."

"Did you ring the house?"

"Couldn't make no connections there. He's about gone to Melton."

Harry turned to me. "Judge's not here," he said. "I'm goin' to send you around to Mrs. Tilman's. She'll fix you right up."

He sent me to Mrs. Tilman's in company with a young man named Coley. On that short, muddy ride over roads nearly impassable, I learned that Coley was new around there, having been in River City only six or seven years. Prior to that he had been a twenty-dollar-a-month teacher in a three-months school up in the hills. But he had come to River City as to a place of opportunity, and now he worked in the district office of the Sons and Daughters of Lance. On the strength of this job he had married and was the father of four children.

Over and over, while the car switched and slung itself in the muddy cart tracks, Coley made me a little speech of apologetic welcome. He took a kind of happy, sadistic pride in River City's deficiencies, apparently loving it all the more for having them. Already he had been a minor civil official. He wanted another office. "Some day I want to be mayor," he said, glancing at me sharply.

We passed no one on the roads. Many of the scattered houses looked deserted. The houses were the drab, colorless gray color of wet newsprint, the same color the sky was that November afternoon. There were many fire-blackened heaps of rubble. With no tree in the landscape to soften it, the naked ugliness took on the concrete hardness and reality of a brick wall.

"Suppose some colored fella in Melton or Lofland would of said to you he wanted to be mayor? You would of laughed, wouldn't you? You would of thought he was crazy," Coley said.

"It would have sounded rather visionary," I admitted.

"Well, it don't sound that way for me to be saying it here. And for why? Because here we're all colored together. That's something to be proud of. Take my kids," he said, shaking his head in wonderment so great that he did not finish. "You got any kids?"

"One," I said.

By the time we reached Mrs. Tilman's I had had an enthusiastic exposition on the advantages of living and rearing children in an all-Negro town, though this town was more dead than alive, and though there were not a dozen other children in it. Even in its heyday there had not been enough children to support an elementary school or the Methodist Seminary, and public education had practically died until the county built the colored high school.

"It's mostly a town of old folks an' folks getting old," Mrs. Tilman said. "It's nothing here for young people."

And there was nothing there except the honky-tonk upstairs over the restaurant next to the grocery in the block of buildings on the main street. That was for young people. It specialized in frozen bottles of beer, and two bottles of beer were more potent than half the amount of whisky. There was a lucite music-vending machine, which provided nearly all the light in the place, and toward sunset on Saturday I saw the young people flock there like birds to a dark nest. They were not native young. They were men (with hands big and tough and supple from the cotton, quick to grab a girl or clasp a knife) and girls (with short hair pressed back from narrow, knotty foreheads) in from the big plantations and the little hamlets strung out along the Delta road like flawed beads on a string. On Saturday afternoon I saw these gather and fill the place with a kind of massive, brooding energy, while the bottles grew thick on the agate tables and the music became a sluggish sea of lustful utterance.

The two groceries and the drugstore were neither for the young nor for Saturdays. They were for coal oil and baloney and stew meat, cotton stockings and pins and threads, cough medicine and snake oil and tonics on any day but Saturday. On Saturdays they were closed by sunset. In ancient cars, in mule carts, and on foot, the natives and the small farmers went south to Lofland or north to Melton to shop on Saturdays. The migrant cotton pickers walked in to River City from the big plantations. They ate the fifteen-cent dinners of greens and neckbones and sweet potatoes in the restaurant. They shot cautious five-cent crap between the two idle cotton gins below the levee, while their women companions changed overalls for dresses in one of the cabins far down the row along the levee. Then when the night grew late and there was no light anywhere save the blue light from the vending machine, the massy energy of these people wakened and swelled incarnate in the music in the honky-tonk. It was as if the jungle had come back again.

It had been jungle in 1886, jungle growing in the fertile mud of the Mississippi, when Joshua Brockery flung wide his arms and said, "This is the place where God dwells and liberty." His big body was a fervent prayer, his great voice the deep, sweet trump of freedom. "Brothers," he said, "this is the place where God dwells and liberty. I consecrate it to you and our people forever. Let us pray." And he got down on his knees in the mud. The nine men who had come with him bared their heads.

"Dear God, I feel like You just made this place this morning. In Your great bounty You filled it with trees for our cabins, and in amongst the trees are bear and deer to eat, and in the water under our humble knees are fish. . . ."

His blood taught him to pray, but Lee Hazlitt had taught him the use of words.

Lee Hazlitt owned the big plantation, Eagle Island, and Joshua had been his slave, as was his father also. Joshua's father had been a headstrong, runaway slave in Virginia, and he was sold down the river and bought off the block in Vicksburg. But Lee Hazlitt really never broke Tom Brockery's contumaciousness. Tom ran away, was caught, ran away and was caught again. Lee Hazlitt made him a boss slave and married him to the most desirable black woman on the plantation.

When the Civil War broke out, Joshua, oldest of Tom's sons, was twenty, and Tom was in charge of Eagle Island and of Longacre, another Hazlitt plantation. Following the capture of Corinth, Lee Hazlitt took his stock and slaves (excepting the Brockerys) into Alabama, where the capital of the Confederacy had been set up. He left the plantations in the care of the Brockerys. Joshua was given charge of Eagle Island.

Joshua saw a lot of the fighting. He saw the United States gunboat *Indiana* sunk in Vicksburg harbor, and Commodore Porter, who led the rest of the Union fleet safely past the forts at Vicksburg, sent for him. The commodore wanted to know exactly where the *Indiana* went down. He wanted to salvage her armament. Joshua would not tell him. "You are a prize of war," the commodore said. The other Brockerys he sent north to Cincinnati on a ship with Captain Richardson.

Joshua served Commodore Porter on the gunboat *Benton* and on others, ships that were constantly in the fighting. He saw the battle of Grand Gulf. His ship carried reserves up the river to fight at Port Gibson. He saw the early desperate skirmishes at Vicksburg and, back from a scouting trip up the Red River to

Alexandria, Louisiana, he served as gunner's mate. In the fighting following the fall of Vicksburg he was dangerously wounded, and Commodore Porter, assigning a nurse to accompany him, sent him north to Mound City, Illinois. After a month of convalescence, Joshua went overland to join his family in Ohio.

After the war the Brockerys moved South again to Longacre, Lee Hazlitt's four-thousand-acre plantation. For five successive years they raised fifteen hundred and more bales of cotton. Then came flood and the panic of 1873, the carpetbaggers and the scalawags, the intimidation and the violence of the election of 1875, death and a devastating fire. Tom Brockery and his wife died in Hazlitt's old mansion. One son was lost to the river. Three others moved north to the Dakotas. Joshua, married now and with a family, moved to Vicksburg. There, courageously, with stubborn, instinctive ethics and a deep sense of necessity, he was finishing the clean-up of the mess left by corrupted Negro political leaders when Colonel Harold Dermott found him. That was in 1884.

A few years before, the Louisville, Louisiana, and East Coast Railroad had completed its line from New Orleans to Memphis. The road had been built in defiance of the river and the muddy wilderness of the Delta from Vicksburg to Memphis after a struggle as epic in its way as the struggle to win the West. Only a few scattered town sites lay along the right of way, for only the hardiest had dared the wrath of the river and the dreaded Delta fever. The fever was the great enemy. It lay in millions of Delta acres like a viper in a pot of gold. The railroad offered all sorts of inducements to white settlers to populate and exploit the wilderness, but there were few takers. But the Negro was supposed to have a natural immunity to the humid climate and the miasmatic atmosphere. Colonel Dermott, of the land department of the railroad, knowing the kind of man he needed, remembered the giant Negro who was once the slave to Lee Hazlitt.

If Colonel Dermott thought Joshua Brockery's hesitancy was fear, he was mistaken. It was because the offer the railroad made was too attractive. It was because the carpetbaggers, and more particularly the scalawags, had made all white men suspect. A lot of good white men had been corrupted by wealth and the prospect of wealth in a South still reeling from the impact of war. There was some trick to this offer. Secretly in 1885 and again in '86, Brockery waded into the Delta and followed the line of the railroad nearly to Memphis. He was gone a month the first time. When he returned from his second trip of two months' duration, his mind was made up. He would accept the offer of the railroad on the condition that he be allowed to pick a site approximately midway between Vicksburg and Memphis, and on the further condition that the specific grants of land to the first settlers for clearing and draining the town site be raised to forty acres a man.

Joshua got his conditions. Moreover, he induced the railroad to bestow acreage on Ten Hamm, an ex-slave master mechanic who could "rig up anything." These two, Brockery the knight to Hamm's yeoman, with seven others dropped from the coach behind an old wood-burning engine one hot summer day in 1886, and, with the train crew looking on, dedicated their wilderness colony to God and the sanctity of freedom. It was decorum, perhaps, that made them wait until the train had smoked away before they prayed. Then they left the high roadbed and went down among the cypress trees and ankle-deep into the water and knelt to Joshua's "book word" prayer.

By the end of that summer, with tree saw and ax and dynamite they had cleared ninety acres. Ten Hamm rigged up a groundhog sawmill, and sawn timber was laid by for house raising. In the late fall the water came and washed out the road bed, floated away their lumber, wrecked their saw. The winter was made bitter by swarms of savage mosquitoes. Sleep was impossible. The railroad gave them permits to ride the night train that went up to Memphis and returned at dawn. Cramped in odd places among the baggage and freight, they slept. Sometimes Joshua and Ten argued all night long; Ten, practical, with hard money sense, arguing for a permanent sawmill and the marketing of lumber, for mercantile establishments based on agriculture; Joshua arguing his nebulous dream of an ideal farming community, uncorrupted by wealth or the competition for wealth, arguing churches and schools and brotherly love, and that these could be established by a spiritual rule of thumb.

In the following spring the first log huts went up, practical one-room affairs with broad stick and dirt chimneys and a window in each wall. Deep drainage ditches sliced the clearing and shot away west to the ever receding woods and east toward the river. The first eleven families moved in, forty-seven people in all, including the aged and the children. The first timid planting was begun. In the spring, too, Ten Hamm started a mercantile trade in cotton, timber, and staves, and on a plot between the railroad levee and the empty town square commenced the building of a cotton gin. All day the men cleared the land. All day the women worked the fields. At night the dozen children gathered in the Brockery hut and studied reading from the Bible and Almanac and writing from the *Universal Letter Writer*. Joshua was the teacher. In midsummer three other families came. Came also the first death from swamp fever.

In ten years River City looked much as it looks now, except that it was peopled, its buildings were in use, and there was but one busy cotton gin instead of the three idle gins there are now. There was a sawmill then, too, and the town was clamorous with the chuff-chuff bung of the gin and the metallic grind of flatcars hauling lumber from the sawmill. Now a deadly quiet smothers the town, and more buildings are empty than in use. The wooden awnings that made a roof over the pavement around the L of the square have been ripped away by wind and water. Across the railroad and the levee below the square, Hamm Street stretches a tenth of a dreary mile. The Episcopal church is the home of bats. The Methodist Seminary leans halfway across the broken pavement. Through its sagging doors and broken windows can still be seen the tattered bunting of the last commencement in 1917. The two-story bank building now houses the post office below, the district office of the Sons and

Daughters of Lance above. Beyond it, Ten Hamm's mercantile house is a whited sepulcher, and Joshua Brockery's twenty-one-room brick house is empty now of all but the screaming ghost of his daughter Nella.

"Yes," Mayor Tennant Hamm said with a wry smile, "both Joshua Brockery and Father would be disappointed today. And their dreams were not really incompatible. Father simply didn't live long enough to see where he was going. He was murdered in his store back in '98. And old man Brockery, well, after all, even he could not live all his idealism. Understand me now. Time makes subtle changes, and Joshua Brockery had to bend with the times or be broken. I've never known a man of more integrity, a man less corruptible than he."

We were sitting in the mayor's inner office in a one-story frame building near the post office. We faced the stove, for it was chilly and a cold rain was falling. The mayor was a dapper-looking man in his fifties, though neither gray nor bald. College at Howard and law at Yale had given him center and poise as natural as his flat, accentless speech. Except for one window, out of which we could look across the muddy road to the dilapidated building opposite, the walls of the office were hidden by crammed bookcases. The modern desk, the carpet, the filing cabinets and other furnishings were quiet and rich. Only the glowing, old-fashioned wood-burning stove saved the office from an incongruity as profound as a comfort station in the middle of an uninhabitable wasteland.

"I was the first child actually born in River City, and I'd like to have something besides that to boast about," he said, again smiling his twisted smile. "This seemed a good place to me after law school and a year of the war in France. I know it seemed a good enough place to me when I was a kid. I didn't even see its great contradictions when I came back in 1919. I guess I wasn't looking for them."

"Contradictions?" I asked.

"The town was founded on a contradiction," Mayor Hamm

said, "a priori contradiction. I have read over and over the speech that old Joshua Brockery made to the Mississippi Constitutional Convention in 1890. Frankly speaking, the purpose of that convention was to disfranchise the Negro. Oh, it wasn't openly said, but the chief proposal put forth in that convention was to establish an educational test for voters. And Joshua Brockery conceded to that proposal, offering up as a sacrifice on the altar of liberty—those were his own words—the ballots of a hundred thousand Negroes. 'I am come here,' he said, 'to bind up the wound that has been festering for a generation, to propose a shelter from the storm that might destroy us all.'

"He was talking about reconstruction. The wound was reconstruction."

"But the contradictions?" I asked again.

"Well, I don't see how he expected Negroes to run a political institution like a town all by themselves if he thought them incapable of taking a hand in running a political institution with the help of the whites. And besides, Lynch and Revels had proved themselves nobody's fools."

We listened to the rain, and we heard also the dead quiet through which it fell. The quiet was not merely the absence of sound; not a negative thing at all, but positive and even visible in the dilapidated building opposite the window and the empty, rain-soaked road.

"Perhaps Joshua Brockery didn't expect Negroes to run a political institution in that sense," I said.

"The democratic sense?"

"Yes."

"He did. I've collected all his early speeches. Before he died, I knew him very well."

He talked very quietly, like a man whose disillusionment has been transmuted into a vitiating philosophy. Disillusionment had come slowly after the war, when he had returned to River City, and slowly he had begun to realize things. But the town was already dying then, and he was left without the wish to save it, even if he could have.

"I hope you're not one of those cynics who attribute the failure of the town solely to the fact that it is a Negro town?" he said, smiling.

"No," I said, searching myself and finding my answer true.

"Because that's less than the truth. You don't think, do you, that we're really less capable than anyone else? No. River City proves nothing about the Negro. It proves plenty about humanity. Not black humanity, nor white humanity. Just humanity."

We could have talked on for years without disturbance. Atrophy and desuetude were contagious. The mayor talked in quiet snatches. Between snatches his forehead creased in a look of mild, habitual worriment and he folded and unfolded his hands.

"My father was a more practical man than Joshua Brockery," he said. "They were cousins, you know. My father didn't know very much about the principles upon which he was supposed to act, and he didn't bother to learn. But he lived according to certain principles by instinct, and he lived in harmony with old Joshua's idealism. Father made a little money for himself and a little for Joshua too. But here's where they were worlds apart: Father just didn't like whites and thought that both races would get along better by separation. He used to boast that after he was free he never lifted an ax or a hoe for a white man. That was Father. He was practical about it. But you can't just say this is a practical world and put all your thinking in that frame of reference. Oh, no," the mayor said, shaking his head.

"I tried that once," he went on. "I said, 'This is a practical world, and in the American democracy segregation is an accepted principle.' And do you know what started happening right away? Almost immediately I began to lose my sense of pride and equality. As a kid in this town, these things had been established in me, you see. Everything here was Negro, from the symbols of law and authority and the man who ran the bank down to the fellow who drove the road scraper. That gave us kids a sense of security and power and pride that colored kids

don't get anywhere else. But as soon as I started relating everything to my practical frame of reference, I began to lose all
that. I didn't want to be without them."

"And now?" I asked.

He shook his head sadly. "They have become habits of
thought, no longer germane to the real situation at all. The men
who founded this town were taking flight from the real situation anyway. They were trying to find an easy way to democracy and the democratic principles. I don't believe there is an
easy way. If we had been willing to be the reagent and if the
whites had been willing to really test democracy by us, we'd
have been nearer to it in the South. But neither side was willing.
The South has never really wanted to test democracy.

"But pride and power and a sense of security no longer apply
to the situation here in River City." He smiled again wryly,
and immediately afterward his brown, sharply molded face set
itself in the patient lines of perplexity which was its habitual
expression. "I don't know which is worse," he said, "cynicism,
apathy, or a false sense of security. They are the fifth columnists
of the mind. They all and each prepare the way for corruption."

I knew at once what he was talking about, and I knew also
that the integrity of his profession would not permit him to
reveal all he knew or even as much perhaps as I had already
learned from other sources. As lawyer and as mayor for twenty
years, he probably knew the story better and more objectively
than anyone else in the town. It was the story of River City's
past twenty-five years and of Calhoun Russ. It was not a pretty
story as I had heard it from various sources.

The separate stories of River City and of Calhoun Russ began
to be one story in about 1904, when Russ made a visit to the
town long enough to win and marry Clara Brockery. His
father-in-law, Joshua, gave the young couple a wedding trip to
Mexico, and when they returned in 1905 they settled in a house
on the Brockery estate at the southern extremity of the main
street.

Russ had gone to River City at the instance of his brother-in-law, Stewart Hall. Hall was quite a figure in the town at that time, and he remained so for a few years after. He filled the place left vacant in the town's business and commercial life by the death of Ten Hamm, who was murdered by a common footpad in 1896. Hall was cashier and chief stockholder in the bank, financial officer of the sawmill, and president of the cotton-oil mill company. But by 1908 he had lost everything. His wife, Hettie Russ, left him. "A woman that bright didn't mean a black man like that no good 'noway." Calhoun Russ somehow acquired most of Hall's holdings, and Hall left town.

The Russes were very light of skin, and they were comparative strangers, both of which circumstances tended to make them suspect in a community in which only a few persons, mostly women, were lighter than medium brown. They had come, it was said, from Natchez, where social cleavage within the race was based largely on color and a little on wealth. Color differences within the race affect men much less than women, but at the turn of the century the light-skinned women in River City had had neither the time nor the inclination to establish a color line. Common interests and common pursuits had left no time for social distinctions, and even after a few families such as the Brockerys, the Hamms, and the Duncans had acquired economic well-being and could afford hired help, the frontier spirit of absolute equality was strong. The washerwoman and the general man ate with the family, for they had often raced the mistress of the house down a cotton row. Another important factor in preventing the establishment of a color line was the homogeneous state of sexual relations. There was practically no opportunity for relations between the races, and the sexual pattern of intimacy between Negro women and white men, so frequently found in the South, was not established. The prestige value of intimacy with whites did not apply. The children born in River City were of nearly the same color.

Calhoun Russ was blamed for splitting the town on the color line. He did it, the natives say, by inducing Joshua Brockery to donate land and twenty-five hundred dollars for the erection of an Episcopal mission. There were already four churches in the little community of less than eight hundred people, but "none of them was good enough for Calhoun Russ." The mission was never successful, for only Clara of the Brockerys, the wife of Russ, attended it, and none of the Hamms. And the Brockerys and the Hamms were still the town's leaders, though Joshua was withdrawing more and more from the purely local picture. The Brockerys and their daughters, Nella, Edna, and Connie May, kept their membership in the Methodist church. For four or five years the mission was forced along on twice-monthly meetings attended by the Russes and a few light-skinned Negroes from the county. Then it closed. But its purpose had succeeded. Color became a factor in the town's life.

Russ professed to be civic-minded. He was always getting up committees. He ran for mayor as regularly as election time came every two years, but he was never elected. "We jes' didn' trus' dat half-white niggah. Eben de mins who worked fer him didn' half vote fer him, dough dey'd swear t' him dey did. But he'd done cheated an' scrouged so many folks out'n deir 'longin's dat nobody didn' have no confidence in him." By the end of the war, he had acquired extensive holdings in farm properties. No one ever proved anything against him, but he bore a bitter reputation for sharp dealing. He had long since liquidated his holdings in the bank and the gin and other commercial establishments. People said that this was because he did not want anything "on the books." He could not cover his tracks if things were on the books. Later the bank failed at considerable loss to the farmers, and the gins would have done better had not Cal Russ's cotton gone to the white gins in Melton. A financial blight settled on the town. Women who formerly had kept their own homes and worked their land were forced to seek domestic employment in white homes in Melton and Lofland. Men became sharecroppers on the big plantations to the south. Homes were broken. Houses stood vacant, and boys flung stones through their windows, and later doors began to gape, roofs to fall in, and weeds to grow to the eaves.

The legal end of Russ's business interests was handled by a white lawyer, with an unsavory reputation among Negroes, from the town of Melton. One of the greatest causes of the distrust in which Russ was held was his association with white people who were somehow not quite reputable in their own communities, or who were known among Negroes as cruel and predatory. "Cal Russ coat-tailed for such trash as them."

It enraged and baffled the townspeople that Joshua Brockery seemed to set a lot of store by his daughter Clara's husband. They felt so convinced that Russ was a scoundrel. They felt certain that had it not been for the Brockery nephew, who was the old man's lawyer, Cal Russ would somehow have got the old man's property even before he died in 1924. Joshua Brockery, they said, had money and other property to the amount of fifty thousand dollars when he died, and he made only one meager provision for his only unmarried daughter—an invalid. But his daughters Edna and Nella, along with the latter's children, seemed to be dependent upon him too, after their divorces. In 1919, when Joshua was building a new house, he was heard to remark that his children and his grandchildren had to have some place to live. Certainly he and his wife alone had no need for a twenty-one-room house. But no provision was made for anyone but Connie May. It was thought that Russ, who was the administrator of the estate, had something to do with this.

The Brockery money, so far as Nella and Edna were concerned, just seemed to disappear. No will was ever probated, and within a few months of their father's death, Edna and Connie May were living in a dilapidated shack and Nella, evicted on the order of Russ by a county deputy sheriff, who broke her arm in the process, took her children to live in New Orleans. It seems that a transaction, believed by most to have been spurious, gave Clara, Cal's wife, title to the house. For a long time the house stood empty. Then it was used as a lodging for teachers in the county. But something happened and it stood

empty again. Finally in 1939 the rumor flew that the Brockery
house was up for taxes. The rumor reached Nella in New
Orleans, and she returned to River City—some said on the
advice of a lawyer—to take occupancy.

Nella arrived on the noon train on a Sunday in the fall. By
one o'clock the whole community knew she was back and alone
in that empty house. Many persons claimed to have seen her. If
the Russes, who lived in the next house on the estate, knew it,
they told no one. Calhoun Russ was seen on the road and in the
drugstore, and he was stared at in inimical silence as usual and
as usual he offered no information about his private affairs. It
was chilly that day, and toward evening a little smoke was seen
to hang over one of the chimneys, and the townspeople knew
that in one of those empty rooms Nella had made a little fire in
the grate to keep herself warm.

It was late at night when Cal Russ came back from Lofland
with the deputy sheriff. The deputy's name was Conner, and it
was a name held in dread by the Negroes of the county. He
had among them the reputation of being mean, ignorant, a
nigger-hating killer. "You think Cal Russ didn' know it? You
damn tootin' he knowed it! It didn' make him no dif'ence.
Why'n' he git the town marshal right here? He seen his chance
to git rid of Miss Nella, that's what."

Russ let the sheriff in with a latch key. The only light in the
house was the probing finger of light from the electric torch
Russ carried. Nella had locked herself in a room on the second
floor. She is said not to have answered the sheriff's command
to open up. The door was wrenched open. The sheriff started
shooting at once at the huddled figure in the cone of light from
Cal Russ's torch. Nella had a paring knife clutched spastically
in her hand. There was a curl of apple peel on the floor. She
was shot six times.

"I heard some of those shots," Mayor Hamm said. "Of course
I don't know what happened up there in that room. They say
she attacked and they killed in self-defense." He smiled wearily,

and I thought he was carrying disillusionment and apathy a little too far. "Would you like to see the house?"

We stepped into the road, lowering our heads against a sudden gust of rain. We climbed the two steps onto the slope of the levee which bulged sharply up at the crossroad. Just before we reached the post office at the corner, Mayor Hamm stopped and tapped the ground with his foot.

"Right about here Cal Russ himself was shot to death a month to the very day after Nella was killed," he said. "No one knows who killed him. He had brought ruin to so many of these people. He hired two bodyguards after Nella was killed. Two bodyguards in a hamlet like this. It was a queer sight."

We moved on, and at the post office we turned and walked down the path in the shoulder of the levee between the road and the railroad track. There was no one on the muddy road.

"But one of the bodyguards was shot too. It was just before dark in the evening, and the shots came from the direction of that empty house you saw opposite the post office. His bodyguards left him there on the levee to die."

The Brockery house stood up the road facing the railroad. It was a huge stone structure, bleak with the utter desolation of the rain and emptiness. From appearances, time and the weather had not worked on it appreciably, but there was something else about it, some quality of barren decay and brittleness that made it seem it would collapse at a touch. In the yard the weeds had grown high and palings from the fence lay about. In the back of the yard stood a row of kennel-like structures whose original purpose I could not imagine, but which served now as the playthings of the wind and the rain. We entered the house through the basement door on the side and walked through the service rooms. We heard rats in the walls.

"The furnace was a great marvel to the people when the house was first built," the mayor said. "It never worked properly."

On the first floor all the oppressive silence seemed suddenly to plunge and roar with outraged dreams and faith and violence.

Doors stood open everywhere. Like a child's static drawing of the ocean, the hardwood floors lay in frozen waves. Trash lay about in moldy piles. We stood in the middle of the library floor and read the little cards stuck in the glass doors of the bookcases. "Negro History," "Religion," "Pleasure Books." The shelves were warped and furry with dust.

"When I'm in this house," Mayor Hamm said, smiling diffidently, "I always have the feeling that I'm in the center of something important. I don't know what it is. Perhaps," he went on slowly, with increasing diffidence, as if by hard compulsion, "perhaps it is the corruptive power of human weakness I feel. I don't know. I don't know. Ruins always get you. . . . Maybe just the weight of everything. . . . But this house . . ." He looked around the bare, rain-stained walls. "But this house is the abstract and the epitaph of River City."

He shook himself, as if to throw off a chill. Then he smiled his habitually weary smile.

"Would you like to see the other floor? Nella was killed in the room just above this. Bullet holes are in the walls. Her blood is still on the floor."

"No. I don't think so," I said.

"Some folks like to," the mayor said.

5

From River City I followed the line of the river south until at Yokema the river broke sharply and my road cut into the sandhills, deep into the raw, red bowels of Mississippi. South and to the west I knew lay Natchez and the wooden warrens under the bluff above the river which some friends wanted me to see. "They are our shame and our pride. They give you a strange sense of our strange history. And certainly that is one of the things you want," my French-descended Negro friends wrote.

But I did not need to go there for that. Not historical markers, nor colonnaded old buildings and ancient slave quarters, nor the cubicles of dead passion in the hillside under Natchez were necessary to a sense of our strange history. On dusty roads deep in green country, in one-street towns sprawling in the mud, in teeming cities I had been overwhelmed by it. I had heard it in voices, seen it in eyes, and touched it in the rough pressure of hands. I did not need to go to Natchez. I wanted to go into the back country, for out there east of Port Gibson lived the biggest Negro landowner in Mississippi, and the legend I mistakenly thought I would find him to be was at least of the historical pattern.

But first I got lost in a network of clay roads that plow deep into the earth through the red hills. Tangled, ropey growth hung from the walls of the roads, and cattle and foot paths burrowed through the walls to hilly clearings, where staggered blackened shacks and outhouses propped with rotting logs. The clearings were seldom clear. Tough grass and leathery bushes, slash pine and scrub oak grew everywhere over them. The land was not fecund, yet even the stones grew weeds.

Toward late afternoon, when I had found my maps no good at all and my gas tank was nearly empty (there had not been a service station for miles), I parked my car near a sloping cart track and went up into the clearing. The usual shack and outhouses stood in the plot. Sloping down behind the shack was a ragged patch of corn left to dry for fodder. In the yard, two men were slowly pushing and pulling a two-man saw through a log. I inquired my way of them.

"Yums gawn ter Lo'mins," the younger man said, as if that was all anyone needed to know. Like the older man, he was short and stocky. The cold had turned his black face slate-gray.

"And how far is Lorman?" I asked.

"Purty fur piece, an' yit b'ain't so fur neythur. Too fur ter roll," he said, grinning and showing blackened teeth. He wiped the drip from his nose across the back of his hand.

"And are there colored people there with whom I could spend the night?"

"B'ain't gawn ter Lo'mins jes' ter slaap?" he asked in astonishment. "Lor', Cap'n, yums kin slaap yere."

I looked at the shack and the outhouses and the unwalled well on the same little rise of ground with the privy. The log shack was chinked tight with red clay, and gray smoke was pouring from the wide stick and dirt chimney. I was conscious of the quizzical, naive gaze of the men, and I was also conscious that I was good and lost and that even if I found Lorman over the unmarked roads there might not be a stopping place there. I accepted the invitation, and then I stopped worrying. Never once in five months had these people treated me other than generously, given me other than their best. Even when I discovered that there were a woman and four children and only three beds in the single room, I did not worry.

The space in the room was judiciously used. Three double beds stood end to end along the wall beyond the fireplace. Against the wall opposite them stood a bench holding two buckets of water, a dipper, and several dishes. Near the fireplace was the cookstove, and above that, within arm's length of the front door, stood the table at which we ate sweet potatoes and greens for supper. There were no window frames—just a square opening in each wall closed by a hinged cover.

The three younger children went to bed in the middle bed, but the older girl and the woman sat up with us. Both of them had the protuberant underlips and the brown teeth of snuff users. The girl was tall and gangling, and she was dressed in overalls and an old army tunic, for she had been gathering Spanish moss all day, and now it lay drying before the fire in a black scattered heap. Like her mother, the girl was wide between her eyes, and her temples were exceedingly high and narrow. Over her long head her harsh hair stood a short, even length. In a hard, undecorated way there was something beautiful about her. She was the mother of the youngest child.

We sat before the fire as "snug as ticks on a goat," as Leroy Stepteau put it. And indeed, we were cozy. The woman and the girl said scarcely a word the whole evening. Now and then the wind sucked down into the chimney and blew the fire and a thin cloud of sweetly acrid smoke toward us.

"Dat win'! Dat win'!" Leroy Stepteau said, with the satisfaction of a man who is housed against the weather. "Be blowin' fair in dis p'recshin presen'ly, sho's Ums bo'n. An' when she do blow, Cap'n, yums bettah watch out. Make fer kiver den. Las' winah larnt ums som'pin. See dem stices chunked, don' ums? Las' winah, when hit blowed up so col', dat ol' win' cut t'rew dem stices same like a hawg knife. B'ain't gawn ketch ums dis winah." And he laughed a mellifluous laugh of triumph.

"Las' winah wus de blowin'es' time in hist'ry. Ums gawn-on fo'ty-seben an' Ums ain't seed nuthin' ter ekal it. Tell um cross de rivah hit blow f'om Semtembah t'well May. Dat right. Sho' wuddn't like ter stay dere. Ums b'ain't ter stay no place but wh'ar Ums at. Ma daddy, dere, he done stay yuther places. He done stay one time ter Tesas. He done be'n cross de rivah. B'ain't yums, Daddy?"

The old man's eyes flared like embers with the wind upon them. Now that he was shed of the coats and ragged sweaters that swathed his body when I first saw him, he looked scrawny and fibrous, like hide that has been cured black in the weather.

" 'Twix' an' 'tween," Father Stepteau said enigmatically.

"Dere y'go. Dere y'go," the girl said sharply. "Why'n' you talk plain?"

"Peavy like good talk, b'ain't ums, Peavy? Peavy lis'n all night ter ums talk, ef'n ums talk all night," Leroy said.

But Peavy was staring into the fire.

" 'Twix' an' 'tween de dyin' o' Roy's mammy an' gittin' tied up wid anudder woman, Ah hed a spell o' travelin'. Roy's de leas' age'ble chile me an' his mammy come by. He wus jes' mew'in' when Ah lef' out fer Tesas. Ah stayed fi' y'ars, an' when Ah hit back yere, Roy wus a growed chap. Dem yuthers wus all growed. Some done lef'. Ah got me anuther woman an' she drapped me some mo' chilluns. Ah hed two craps. Some daid an' some gone off. Hed a patch fulla chilluns. Ah still got some chilluns in me. K'int git no woman ter drap 'em fer me." He cackled lewdly and rubbed the tip of his nose. The girl laughed a sudden burst of sound.

"Dere yums go," Leroy said reprovingly.

"He crazy," the girl said, not taking her eyes off the fire.

"Well, Ah is. Ah got 'em in me. De truf's de light," the old man said.

"Don' ums bring in de holy scripture nuther," Leroy said.

The old man was quiet, but he shook his head and smiled into the fire a long while after, remembering heaven knows what. The girl, too, remained silent. Her face and the face of her mother were now drawn in identical lines. A subtle change had come into the atmosphere since the old man's words.

After a while Leroy said, "Ums don' wan' no fight 'bout dat." His father, still smiling, did not look up. "Yums yere ums, ol' man?"

"Aw, skip it," the girl said. "He crazy."

"An' Um nevah did fight," Leroy said darkly. He remained silently staring at the old man for a full minute, but the old man did not even glance at him. The girl shuffled her feet and then she took off her shoes and placed her feet in the warm moss. The woman spit into the fire.

"Nevah did hav' no dis'greemun er no kin' t'well Daddy be's de way um is. Ums all chop de rows tergidder. Ums nevah fit wid nobody 'bout nuthin'. Seed many a fight. Seed many a fight when de rivah run ter Rodney an' dere wus a steamboat lan'in' dere. Rivah done shif' now. Hit don' run ter Rodney no mo'. Er long while ergo, when Ums wus a chap an' tooken Cap'n Singleton's cotton ter de lan'in', Um seed de whole boat fightin' wid de Rodney mins t'well de cap'n come out wid a fo'ty-fo' an' ca'm ums down. Ums seed Lem Whitney drawed a boat hook clean t'rew a niggah's chis'. Ums knowed a man what Lem Whitney hed chawed ums y'ars off. Ums wus settin' on de lan'in' once an' Ums seed de mate boss spit in de watah an' kill a niggah wid a fo'ty-fo' an' den spit ag'in. Ums seed plen'y fights, but Ums nevah fit none."

Whatever it was he did not want any fight about, he had apparently forgotten. He was no longer thinking about the old man.

"Um cud er fit. Um wud er be'n white folks, Um wud er fit. But Ums don' like no sheruff. Ums don' like no dis'greemun. 'Scusin' once fer a witness, Ums b'ain't nevah in no co't in ma life, an' den de niggah wus wrong. Niggah allus wrong ter go an' measure ahms wid white folks."

The old man had been listening to this with rising excitement. Now he stamped his foot on the floor and crackled, half-rising from his stool.

"You wus wrong! De niggah wus tryin' ter perteck what wus his'n an' you shud'a he'ped him. You wus wrong. You knowed dat wus dat niggah's hawg! You talk 'bout fightin', Ah cud'a fit you dat time!" He rose entirely from his seat and made an old man's stiff gesture of anger, curving his clumsy fist across his chest. He stood unsteadily in a crouching position waiting for Leroy's answer.

"Set down, yums, fer ums fall," Leroy said, looking steadily at the old man. "Yums larnt dem wil' notions ter Tesas."

"Don' keer wh'ar Ah larnt 'em. A man's a man," the old man crackled, still standing, and now beginning to tremble violently, as if a great wind shook him. The woman, who was sitting next to him, reached up and took his scrawny wrist and held it. The old man tried to jerk away, but the woman held him firmly until he sat down. Then she spat into the fire. The girl laughed shortly.

"What about the time you were in the law court?" I asked Leroy.

"Niggah fo'thin' a piece er lan' in de Thirty Hills," Leroy said, already having forgotten the old man's outburst. "Niggah hed hum some hawgs, done got um off'n ums. Buy se'f t'ree hawgs. Niggah tote dem hawgs home, an' fo' he-un cud pen dem hawgs, one er dem come up missin'. He-un hunt de hawg. Seed what hum claim he-un hawg on white man's place, an' hum claim de hawg. De white man wud'n turn hit loose, natcherly. Niggah tuck hit ter co't.

"Jedge Truly come out yere f'om Fayette an' say ter mums dat hum want um ter be witness. Jedge Truly say, 'Roy, Ums

want y'uns ter tell de truf in dat guv'ner's co't.' An' Ums axe
hum which side he-un on. Hum say, 'De right side.'

"Co't day come an' Um hitched up—hed a mule den—an'
wus dere. Niggah wus dere. A whole patch er white folks wus
dere. Dat co't wus pack' like 'vival meetin'. White folks settin'
down; niggahs stan'in' up b'long side de wall ter de back. Jedge
settin' on he-un th'one an' white mins settin' down ter fron' o'
hum. Jedge Truly settin' down dere wid some mo' white mins.
Man say som'pin loud an' niggahs laugh in ums bellies. Jedge
knock de wood.

"When de niggah what buy de hawgs wus witness, um talk
so easy Jedge kep' axin' um what he-un say. De man what wus
axin' ques'uns kep' a-sayin', 'Niggah ef yums b'ain't lyin', yums
'ud talk out.' Den Jedge Truly commence ter axin' hum ques'uns.
Jedge Truly say, 'Talk up, boy. Dis yere's a co't o' jestis. Don'
ac' skeered.' Hum talk a lit'le outer, but Ums cud'n y'ar. Jedge
on he-un th'one b'ain't pay no 'tenshun.

"Den call mun. Dey hed de hawg in a coop. White mins
settin' down front ter jedge look at mums peep-eye. Evah las'
one er dem mins looks alike ter mum, an' dey all look wid peep-
eye, 'scusin' Jedge Truly. Make skin peel off'n mums back. Jedge
Truly git up an' axe um ques'un. Jedge Truly say, 'Roy, did um
sell dis boy some hawgs?' an' hum p'ints ter de niggah.

"Ums say, 'Think Um did, Jedge.'

"'Think y-uns did?' den he say. Den he say, 'Dis un de
hawgs?' an' den hum p'ints ter de hawg in de crate.

"An' Um say, 'Um dun'no, Jedge.'

"'Boy, what ails yums?' Jedge Truly say, an' Um say,
'Nuthin'.' Dem white mins wus gi'en muns de peep-eye.

"Jedge Truly say, 'Bain't yums know y-uns own hawgs?' an'
Um say, 'Yas, suh.' An' Um say, 'Un red hawg same like nudder
red hawg ter mums, Jedge.'

"Den hum say, 'Yums sol' some hawgs, didn' y'uns?' an' Um
say, 'Yas, suh.' 'Bain't yums sol' hawgs ter dis boy yere?' Jedge
Truly say. Um say, 'Dat look like de niggah.'

"Den Jedge Truly set hum down ag'in, an' nudder white folks

hi'stes humse'f up an' axe um whedder Um knowed ef'n dis wus de hawg an' de niggah wus de niggah. Um say, 'Hawgs an' niggahs looks alike ter mums.' Dem white mins settin' down ter front de Jedge smile ter each yuther. Yuther white folks laugh out loud.

"When dey le' mums git down f'om dere, Jedge Truly say ter me-uns, 'Roy, yums 'bout de lowes' niggah Ums evah seed.' But Ums didn' keer nuthin' fer dat; hum a-livin' wid a yellah niggah woman on Broke Nose road.

"An' dat niggah wus in de wrong. Hum knowed de white folks' way. . . ."

"You wus in de wrong," the old man interrupted, but his vehemence was gone. He did not even look up from the fire. "Dat's de trouble wid de niggahs. Dey don' stan' up fer each udder. Dat's de trouble, dat's de trouble," he repeated quietly into the fire. "Ah took ma chances when Ah wus a young man. Ah wauked like a natchel bo'n man. Ah wusn' skeered like him. Ah wusn' skeered er nothin' on two laigs."

"Yum talkin' ol' man's talk now," Leroy condescended.

But the old man did not answer, and after a time he fell into a doze, from which he would snap awake now and then, mumble something, look sheepishly around, and doze again. The wind was quite high. We could hear it whistling in the top of the chimney and soughing around the corners of the cabin.

"Um hed a bruddah wud'a fit comin' an' gawn," Leroy said. "Hum wen' off wid de wo', an' Ums b'lieves hum got shot in de wo'. We-uns ain't nevah heerd no mo' 'bout hum. Wus talkin' 'bout hum wid Hosey Rice yuther ee'nin' ter de relief.

"Um knows dis. Ef'n Cap'n Gehagan b'ain't mo' freer wid dem guv'ner's rashun tickets an' we-uns has ter eat cow peas an' dem guv'ner's apples all de winah, Ums mought's well git shot. Wuser den Red Cross rashuns.

"Las' winah! Las' winah! Dat wus de wuses time Um evah seed. White folks ter Goldblatt's sto' talkin' 'bout runnin' de lan' cheap an' mo' bettah wid munt' han's den wid share han's an' fo'thers. Talkin' 'bout de Delta white folks git a tracker an' b'ain't has ter furnish nobody. Talkin' 'bout a'ter while b'ain't

nuthin' 'cept mis'ry fer we-uns. Um ain't 'sputin' hum. Dey's
apt ter know mo' bettah den we-uns. But der kain't be no wuser
mis'ry den las' winah wus.

"Seed de time when er bad crap y'ar come, Um cud make
mums fo' bits er a dollah. B'ain't no mo'. Ums munt' han' fer
seb'nteen y'ars 'fo' Ums mai'ed, an' den b'ain't nevah widout er
ten cent er two. Den Um meets up wid me-uns wife an' her'm
speakin' 'bout what er nice place her'm got by ums daddy lef',
an' we-uns git mai'ed an' come yere. Um b'ain't hed nuthin'
sence.

"Daddy speakin' 'bout 'ginst white folks. Bes' be fer hum.
Don' none de white folks love no niggah noway. Niggah un'er
he-un thumb. Niggah allus gawn stay dere. Niggah speakin'
'bout dis an' dat. Ums heerd niggah speakin' 'bout de new wo'
ter de relief. Dat dere's white folks' look-out. Niggah's b'ain't
ter hav' no min' 'bout dem things. Niggah b'aint' ter keer
whichaway de worl' go. Ums don' keer who own de guv'ner.

"Coun'y agen' say ter mum, 'Bruddah Stepteau, wud youms
like ter git er loan f'om de guv'ner an' gits y-uns some nice lan'
an' er house an' bawn?' But Ums knowed hum wus jokin'.
Heered de guv'ner do dat fer white folks, not no niggahs. Dat's
white folks' look-out. Dat don' in'erfere wid mums. Guv'ner
mought tell de niggah what hums boun' ter do, like plan'in'
vetch, er what hum 'blige' not ter do, like not plan'in cotton.
De guv'ner mought gi' ums de priv'ege er makin' de mark ter
he-uns checks fer Mistah Choen. But hum b'ain't gi'in' we-uns
no house an' lan' an' loanin' wums no cash money.

"Ums gits 'long all right wid white folks. All de bad wedder
b'ain't wet, an' all de sunshine b'ain't warm. Ums allus speakin'
'bout dat. De rain's mo' wetter fer de niggah den 'tis fer de
white folks. White folks kin gawn out wid new rigs on an' hit
come up ter rain an' um not git wet. Caize why? Caize mos' eny
do' hums knock ter gawn let hum in out de rain. Niggah jes'
got ter stay out de rain. Ums stay in out it."

The women went to bed first, undressing in the dark lower
end of the room. Then the old man was awakened and the

three of us undressed by the fire. The old man was irritable after his nap, and he complained of being hungry. Finally the woman called from the bed and told him to get a sweet potato from the pot. Both the old man and his son wore long, gray underwear, and the old man's was ingenuously patched and extremely dirty. Both had little black bags suspended from their necks with soiled string.

I was to sleep with the old man in the last bed. The woman was already asleep in the first bed, but as I passed the second bed, where the girl lay with the three young children, the girl's eyes stared brightly up at me in the gloom. And then, when the old man passed, she gave a short, hard burst of laughter. The old man stopped for a moment and raised his hand, but the girl lay perfectly still looking up at him. She laughed again.

"Yums!" Leroy called warningly.

Then the old man came to bed still sucking the sweet potato. "Thank Gawd dat chile b'ain't pissin' ovah me dis night," the old man said irritably.

He was up many times through the night.

6

The largest Negro landowner in Mississippi was a disappointment. He conformed to the legend surrounding southern Negroes with extensive landholdings in only two particulars: he was uneducated, and he lived in an ordinary weatherboarded farmhouse. As for the rest, he was not a man of wealth, nor of sharp business practices, winning the baffled, grudging admiration of local whites. He did not lend money to whites, nor underwrite their bank loans, nor have them for tenants. He was no bastard son of some rich but degenerate quality white man. And it did not seem likely that he would die and leave his family destitute.

The legend which Phondus Midgett contradicted is not accidental. Too many Negro communities in the South have such a legend. It is as purely compensatory as the spirituals. It has not grown moribund because it is of a piece with the historical social pattern of the old South, and the old South is as active a ghost as there ever was. The legend is the still-green epitome of the cultural pattern from which sprang that weakling, admiring, envious phrase, "Dat niggah's got white folks." It is not now so desirable for a Negro to have white folks, though most of the more influential and affluent still have them—they hope, secretly. To have white folks was good a quarter of a century ago. Now it is contemptible. Now attaches to it all the distrust, suspicion, and fear that attaches to a "white folks' nigger"—all the contempt of outraged faith. Now it is held much better to be "like white folks," enough like them to best them in business, to lend them money, and to hire them as tenants. The legend is green.

But Phondus Midgett confounded it. He was black, without a trace of white blood. I saw this from a photograph, beneath which two rusty guns were crossed on the wooden walls of his front bed room-living room. He was not at home the cold, gray Sunday I went to see him. He had gone to Copiah County with the son who was a preacher. On the first and third Sundays he always went, for there was no service in the local church on those Sundays. But his wife, his two sons, and his old wage hand, Ras Toddy, were there, and when their talk began to flow after the first somewhat strained hour of making up their minds about me, I knew the legend was confounded.

"Turn that radjo off, Millard. We can't hear ourse'ves talk," Mrs. Midgett said. "A radjo's a fine thing, but you ain't wantin' it talkin' when you got somebody to talk to."

We had been talking nearly two hours when this remark was made, and Mrs. Midgett's inconsistency amused us all. We laughed, quietly tearing down the last barriers between them and me. Negroes were remarkably easy to get acquainted with, I had noticed, once they knew you respected their defensive attitude of equality. Restraint dropped away, supplanted by a freedom and simplicity that was at once rugged and sweet, and within an hour or a few minutes they would be talking of the most intimate things in their lives as if they had known you always. What barriers there had been to this freedom of intercourse had always been in me, hurdled with the greatest of difficulty and remaining to be hurdled again. But lately, more and more were the barriers disappearing; more and more the stuff of their lives was filling up the emptiness of my own, leaving no room for barriers.

"It's good comp'ny when you ain't, though, ain't it, Maw?" Millard got up and turned off the battery set. Still in his thirties, he was already gray and a little stooped.

"With your Paw always goin' to Po't Gibson or somewheres, an' always wantin' me to listen to the prices, it ain't no comp'ny. It's work."

"Aw, Maw," John Henry said.

"Yo' maw ain't got no nose for work o' no kind no mo'," Ras Toddy said.

"I reckon we tied her up too soon," Millard said. He was the jolly-seeming one. John Henry was more serious.

"Humph!" Mrs. Midgett said.

" 'At's about it."

"Reckon yo' paw better let her plow dat no'th holler nex' spring."

"I been outa the fields twelve years, but I could do it," Mrs. Midgett said, jerking her white head emphatically.

"If'n you had a tractor plow, an' if'n a tractor plow would plow up stumps," Ras replied, winking at Millard.

"With a mule!" the old lady said.

"Aw, Maw," John Henry said.

"You's pretty good, Maw. But you ain't that good."

"Humph!"

"When yo' maw was a bitty, though, she were a good one."

"I'm a bitty now, Ras. I ain't near's old as you."

Indeed, her face was strangely youthful, almost free of lines. Her hair was white, and the flesh of her hands puckered over the bone.

"But you ain't no man. Dat's where the diff'ence comes in."

Around us, as characterful as speech, were the things these people lived with. Overalls and worn jackets hung from nails in the wooden walls. In the corner behind the ornamental iron bed stood an arsenal of guns, their gunlocks sheathed in greased rags. Piled with odds and ends of clothes, a hoe blade, a few limp issues of the *Pathfinder*, and a collection of oil lamps, a low, boxlike piano stood beneath the narrow front window. In each corner of the inside wall an open door led to other rooms.

"Y'all boys wasn't bo'n to know nothin' 'bout it," Ras went on, not entirely joking now, "but when yo' maw an' Phondus firs' was married, yo' maw had this thing 'bout all figgered out, jus' like there wasn't no Almighty to interfere. Heard her say then they was goin'a own some day. We was all wage-handin' together then, an' that was fo'ty years ago. But they done it."

"It's been a long year ago," Mrs. Midgett said, with a kind of humble pride.

"But you done it, Maw," John Henry said. His voice seemed tight, vibrant.

We all reacted in our different ways. For the Midgetts, Ras Toddy's words must have unlocked a door behind which lay their most meaningful sensations, the blood tie, the communal memory of time lived and suffered, the essence of their days on earth. As I sat on the end of the semicircle around the hearth and watched them, I thought that lately I had been reading in too much, like one who dares not be content with the simple evidence of his eyes and ears, for fear that once the sight and sound are gone they will have left no meaning for his inner self. I thought this as I watched them. The old lady lipped her pipe in squint-eyed silence. Millard's face was thoughtful. But John Henry was more darkly brooding.

"Y-all can't git the best of yo' maw."

"Wait 'til Christmas," Millard promised. "Jus' wait 'til the girls get home from their schools an' Willie an' Ike comes. We'll make her step then. An' Willie an' Ike. Lawd! Them rascals ain't learnin' nothin' down there to Alcawn but eatin' an' sleepin'." He laughed indulgently, a good laugh to hear. "Them rascals ain't never done a real long day's work in their life. I don't b'lieve them rascals ever been over these seven hundred acres."

"They ain't had no call to," Mrs. Midgett said.

John Henry got up. He thrust his fists into the bib of his overalls. The corners of his mouth turned downward.

"But they ought to, Maw," he said.

"In the Christmas," Millard said softly, "we'll take 'em fox-huntin'."

"Fox-huntin'!" John Henry said. "Them rascals ought to have a firs' name, workin' 'quaintance with they own place. They ought to know ever' hook an' holler in it. Them rascals couldn't find they way up here from the road if it wasn't for the tracks. They ought to work this land."

No one said anything. The old lady smoked her pipe. Millard stooped over and played with a sliver of wood on the hearth.

"They ought to work this land," John Henry said again. Then he hesitated, as if he were not sure of himself, as if their silence was a factor he had not foreseen. He looked first at his mother and then at Millard. His fists made knotty breasts inside the bib of his overalls.

"Y'all think I don't lay no weight by learnin'. But it ain't that. It's jus' that I think them rascals ought to cut some timber in the timber lots, an' plow in some o' the hard places, an' fetch in the stock from way over the big holler. This place'd mean something to 'em then. They was too young, wasn't even borned, to cut down the trees an' clear the land for this very house. They was too young to stick dynamite under stumps an' run like hell to keep from gettin' blowed up. They never made tracks to the road, an' split rails for the fences, an' track yearlin's to auction in Fayette. But I done it, an' Mill done it, an' Joe done all them things."

He stopped and licked his dry lips and looked fixedly at his mother. Then he took his fists from his bib and spread his dark fingers.

" 'At's why we ain't never lef' it, Maw." Now he turned from them and walked between the bed and the piano, so that their backs were altogether to him. " 'At's why in nineteen, goin' on twenty years we ain't never spent a night off this place."

The silence was as heavy as water in a paper bag. John Henry had stopped by the window and stood there staring out into the gray, late afternoon. The old lady's pipe had died, and when she took it from her mouth spittle ran down the stem. She made a sigh whose sound filled the room. John Henry spoke quietly from the window, without looking around.

"We-all didn't feel like that when we was fourthin', Maw. Them rascals don't know that. Them rascals ain't got no re-membrance of the diff'ence. Come day, go day, long's we made a crop an' stacked something away, we didn't care 'bout the land. Paw was always sayin' when the place we was on was worked out, we could always move some place else. But Paw don't say it now. Paw don't force this land. We-all don't cut no timber careless on this land. We don't kill no possums on this land with a litter in her pouch if we knows it. It's our'n. We ain't workin' nobody's land 'cept our'n, an' we work it careful."

"Them rascals is all right," Millard said softly, still stooped over, still playing with the slivers of wood on the hearth.

John Henry turned from the window.

"I ain't disputin'. They's all right. But if they had to choose 'tween this place an' some place out yonder, what'd be their choosin'? An' if they marry, will they do like me an' Joe done an' bring their women here an' put them up a house over yonder on the ridge?"

But he was not looking for answers.

"I 'member when Paw firs' took a-hold o' this place, ol' square-head Con'l Bushrod come out here from the Po't. We all knowed what he wanted. He wanted to 'stablish domination over Paw, that's all. We hadn't cleared 'nough land to make a crop o' nothin'. The hollers was full o' trees an' the ridges full o' stumps. He come out'chere an' what'd he say? He say he fur-nish us till we make a crop. That white man talk 'bout he was Paw's frien' an' he furnish him till we make a crop. An' what did Paw say?" He took a step from the window and again thrust his fists in the bib of his overalls. "What did Paw say?"

"Paw say, 'No thanks, Con'l,'" Millard said.

"What else Paw say?"

"Paw say he aim to stay out from under ever'body."

"What else?"

It was a curious catechism.

"Paw say . . ."

"Paw say, if we can't eat our own crop, then we goin'a eat mas' with the hogs. Didn't he say it? Didn't he? Then the Con'l got on his horse an' rid away. Me an' Joe went to Blanton's sawmill an' drawed down pay for a year to get money to furnish us. An', Maw, you an' Paw an' Mill an' the rest slaved the land."

He relaxed now. The tightness around his mouth loosened, and he looked almost cheerfully relieved in a heavy, sober way. Perhaps he had had all this on his mind for a long time, and now that it was off he felt better. He fastened his jumper across his chest.

"I'm goin' on 'cross now," he said. And then, his rubber ankle-high boots making no noise on the bare floor, he was gone.

When we heard the dogs, we realized that they had been barking for a long time. From far away, it seemed, we heard the long, mournful belling of a deep-throated dog. It was a sound strange and thrilling. Millard jumped up.

"That's Glory!" He listened intently for a moment. "She's got something. I sure hope it's that rascal been stealing geese."

Behind the house the dogs were beginning to yap boisterously. Then came the long, deep-throated woooooooo again. The dogs behind the house were not giving voice as dogs do on the trail. They were whimpering and yap-yapping. When we opened the door, the full volume of their sound struck us.

It was cold in the yard. John Henry was standing in the path listening. We went up to him. A sharp wind blew hard against us. We could hear the leashed dogs galloping at their chains in high excitement. To our right the woods began, rolling away like a giant brown wave. A little in front of us the land sheered away to an elliptical brown hollow, then rose again to form a vast, sandy amphitheater. As sharp and as lonely in the cold gray air as specimens seen under a microscope, three red-brown cabins stood in a hard row on the far lip of the hollow. These were the cabins in which the brothers lived.

"She's got him clear of the woods now," Millard said, listening.

"Far north. God spare me, I'm goin'a plant rutebeggers in 'at high field. That's 'bout where she's got him."

"Over by the sheep paster?"

"Further," John Henry said. "Where I sledged them stakes for the fence Friday. Better get you a gun."

"Stay with him, gal! Stay with him, ol' Glory," Millard said. He ran into the house and came out with a repeating rifle.

The brothers seemed to follow the sound with their eyes. Now it was distinct, and now adumbrated by the woods, but constantly coming nearer. As it moved from our right to center, the brothers fastened their eyes on the far ridge.

"Ain't many foxes lef'," John Henry said.

"Ain't, an' that's a fact," Millard said.

The three of us advanced to the near edge of the hollow and Millard and I sat down. John Henry stood above us. The sound streaked in with a thin solidity that made it seem almost possible to touch it. Before I could see anything moving on the opposite ridge, Millard raised his gun, and at the moment I heard the shot I saw a scarcely distinguishable shape bound high into the air and roll over and over down into the hollow. Then I saw the dog.

"He was fixin' to double," Millard said. He put his fingers into his mouth and whistled, and the dog trotted and slid down into the hollow, stopped to sniff at the dead fox, and then climbed up to us. She was an old dog, rib-thin and heavily dewlapped, and she came up wagging her stiff tail.

"Aren't you going to get the fox?" I asked.

"He ain't no good for nothin'," Millard said.

"Lawd," John Henry said, "if all the foxes we done shot was

good for something, we'd had us a tractor by now. Yes, sir. An' a whole trainload o' fertilize for them real po' acres behind the woods. Mill, I reckon we bes' ankle over there t'morrow an' snug up that sheep fol' some."

He went stomping sideways down into the hollow, and Millard and I returned to the house.

The old lady and Ras Toddy had not moved. The old lady looked at Millard, but the firelight played such tricks that I could not tell the expression on her face.

"It ain't only 'bout the boys John Henry ain't satisfied in his mind with," the old lady said. "It's 'bout you too."

"Ain't no need to worry 'bout me," Millard said. He sat down and took the clip out of the gun and laid it on the floor. The action made his words sound casual, like the words of a man who avoids an unpleasant subject.

"Ain't nothin' but little gals runnin' 'round this place," the old lady said. "I done said it a dozen times, an' I'm sayin' it again. John Henry an' Eddie Belle's got nothin' but gals. Joe an' Neonta got no . . ."

"Now, Maw."

"Who's goin'a bury you?"

"Don't start that again, Maw."

"Don't start it again! Don't start it again! S'pose Willie an' Ike don't come back here? Is the mules to phart in the gals' faces like they done in mine? Why'n' you jus' go'n an' take you a woman somewheres? No. You got a ha'nt in your mind. You got a ha'nt in your mind about Ciby!"

She had been holding herself with her forearms crossed over her breast and her hands tucked in her armpits. But now her hands dropped, and she seemed to let herself go. Her voice broke. She slumped tiredly, and her hands dropped into her lap.

"I 'clare 'fore God, Mill, she ain't nothin' but a ha'nt in your mind. I 'clare she ain't. Nine years now, an' it's still there. Nine years she been dead, an' you ain't buried her yet."

The mother just sat there with her hands fallen in her lap. Ras Toddy got up and went through one of the doors that led off the room. He did not come back. I got up also. Millard put the clip in his pocket and picked up the gun. He sat for a moment looking at his mother, then he, too, got up and put the gun in the corner.

"I must go now," I said.

The old lady said nothing.

"He's going, Maw," Millard said. "Tell him good-by, Maw."

The old lady nodded her head. Because of the flickering shadows on her face, I could not tell whether she smiled or her lips opened. Her nod was good-by. She did not say it.

It was very dark outside. Millard left me in the path while he went behind the house to get a lantern and to free the dogs. The dogs scampered away ahead of us, and pretty soon we heard them whining over the dead fox down in the hollow. Millard walked on ahead with the light. It was a quarter of a mile to the gate, which was in the sandy mouth of the narrow defile where the great central gully began. It was not until we reached it that Millard spoke.

"I ain't worried 'bout who's goin'a bury me. I know this. I ain't goin'a be the las' man on earth, an' somebody's bound to put me in the groun'."

7

I spent the night at Negro Alcorn College, where in 1815 Negro slave artisans built the beautiful chapel and Belles Lettres Hall, which once were the principal buildings of Oakland College. It was a school for rich planters' sons on both sides of the river then, and the river ran by Rodney. But now the river has moved away and houses stand in what was once its bed. The buildings of the college speak of those past days; every hall teems with memories, every brick is a muted tongue. But the old carriage sheds now house machinery. The playing field is a cotton patch. There are girls now, too, black and sweet-limbed. Black boys in white coats still serve the meals in the refectory, but now they serve other black boys in an atmosphere as decorous and as full of old-world manners as ever Oakland

College was. Among the moss-hung live oaks and the giant pecan trees the bell from the tower chimes as sweetly as ever it did over the heads of the planters' sons.

Young, hopeful, buoyant, a strange man in sand-hill Mississippi, though it is his home, President Bell said to me:

"We are proud of this place here. We feel that we are the not unworthy heirs of a proud tradition."

Indeed, they might well be proud. But they were also privileged, and privilege bred a tradition in which even Alcornians can feel no pride. But President Bell did not speak of this. I learned it from other sources.

I learned that there are two hundred and seventeen thousand Negro children of primary age who are not in school in Mississippi. I learned that there are one hundred and five thousand Negro children of high school age who are not in school. Negro schools run three to seven months. Directly controlling these schools are Negro trustees, and of the seven thousand Negro trustees, six thousand cannot read or write their names. An official told me this. He makes such facts his business.

"For twelve years the figures have not varied by a hundred either ways," the official said.

"Whose fault?" I asked.

He shrugged his shoulders in neither evasion nor excuse, but only because he saw it as a fact and facts are sometimes stubborn.

"No one's," he said. "That's just Mississippi."

It was not a casual statement uttered in dismissal of the subject. Beneath its old-world manners and its ancient, memory-flooded beauty, Alcorn College, more than any public school I saw, faced the world with courteous courage; with bulldog teeth sheathed in the rubber of discretion—but with bulldog teeth.

"We'll keep on fighting it, and one day we'll break it, and that will be that. It won't make much noise."

I also saw the Midgett boys, Willie and Ike. They were twin-like, brown as was their mother, slim of waist. I told them I had been to their home. "How's all?" they wanted to know.

They were undetermined whether to wait to be called up in the draft or to volunteer. They had been reading in the Negro papers of colored flying units. "This war," Ike said, "is li'ble to open up things for the colored." But Willie, who was more like John Henry, said, "It's a got-dawg shame it takes a war to do it."

All of Claiborne County is alive with more than memories. Here more than anywhere is one's mind susceptible to the impression of the total South as a land unified by its ancient passions, welded by its terrible contrasts. The Natchez Trace, long the most murderous trail in America, runs through here. On a back road stand the stately, melancholy ruins of Windsor, once the finest mansion in five counties, and the Presbyterian church where, legend says, General Grant broke into the stores of sacramental wine with which he rode drunk into Vicksburg. Here black Hiram Revels, whom the carpetbaggers sent to Congress, came eventually to live. Here also, just beyond the town of Rodney, was pointed out to me a row of neat white cottages where live the Negro concubines of men whose names are not unknown outside the South. In Louisiana, where a college president had to reach the ear of the governor through the governor's cook, I was told, "If the Negro wants to get somewhere, he's got to get the cooks and maids and butlers to thinking right. They're more potent than all the nigger big-shots." They say in Mississippi, "It is the concubines."

I stopped in Natchez only long enough to have a cup of chicory-bitter coffee with some friends and to be told again that Natchez-under-the-Hills was no place to miss. "Did you know that only women, and those the most beautiful mulattoes, were sold on the bluff there? Why, it's full of our history." But history sometimes is an instrument neither of evaluation nor of diagnosis, and I did not see Natchez-under-the-Hills. Instead I drove through the beautiful but spectral (made so by the Spanish moss weeping from huge oaks in innumerable country churchyards) country to Sibley, to Woodville, to Dolorosa, and into Louisiana.

At Lofton Villa, just north of Bains, I was attracted by what might have been a ghost. He stood leaning forward on a cane in front of the wrought-iron gates that guarded the driveway to what undoubtedly was an antebellum mansion hidden among the trees. His white hair flowed in a kinky cloud beneath his high plug hat. He wore a long, black broadcloth coat faced with satin. With his cane he waved me down, but when I stopped and he saw that I was a Negro, he stood motionlessly ignoring me, his eyes fixed on the ground. On the gate behind him was a painted sign: "Visitors From Ten to Three. Uncle Eph Will Show You Around."

I simply called at first, but he did not answer.

"Didn't you wave me down?"

With elaborate deliberateness, lifting his eyes from the ground and looking up and down the empty road, he ignored me. His face was the rusty brown of a late Kieffer pear. His arms, stiff as ramrods pressed downwards on the cane, trembled with the strain of his concentration.

"Uncle Eph," I called.

"Don' you call me dat!" he said. And then I knew he was trembling with indignation. He lifted his cane and beat it against the ground, while his old eyes blinked in exasperation. "Ah don' 'low no niggah-darky to call me dat. Ah'm Mister Spate to you, if you got some business wif me." It seemed a remarkably strong voice for such a pipelike throat.

"Excuse me, Mr. Spate," I said. "I'm really very sorry."

My apology took the edge off his anger, but his dignity was not shaken. I had never seen a man more deliberate, a man whose simplest movement was wrought with greater care.

"Has you some business wif me?"

"I'd like to see Lofton Villa," I said.

"Niggah-darkies ain't 'lowed," he answered shortly. Then for a moment he could not decide whether to ignore me again or to speak further. He took off his hat, drew a handkerchief from between the buttons of his coat, and slowly wiped his hair straight back. He wore a celluloid collar without a tie. His stiff shirt front was soiled.

"Dis is still de big gate. In de ol' times, darkies didn' much as stop to de big gate."

"Were you living then, Mr. Spate?" I asked, trying to put the proper respect in my voice.

" 'Co'se Ah was. Ah'm some sebenty-seben years ol'. Miss 'Legra's got de writin'. Miss 'Legra say Ah'm de las' bo'ned darky on dis plan'ation. Miss 'Legra say Ah'm de las' kinda darky she use to. Miss 'Legra say when she gawn an' Ah'm gawn, de good Lawd gawn' a close up His book an' leav de worl' to de ol' boy hisse'f. Dat's what she say."

I tried to picture this Miss Allegra wandering disconsolately through the dead, still time in the decaying mansion I could not see. What was she like? But I could not picture her, and I could never really know. Even of Ephraim Spate I had only an imperfect understanding. In time and history their place was fixed, but it was a measure of the weight of change that both in time and history they seemed as remote as the origin of the stars. I gazed at Ephraim Spate against the visible background of his times, and all I could see was a park, like an old, old cemetery full of weary trees.

"And do you believe this, too, Mr. Spate? That the Lord will close His book?"

"Ah cert'ny do, suh!" All this time he had stood in the recess before the gate, a dozen feet away from me. Now he took a step nearer. "De Lawd's gawn snap His gol' book shet an' dis ol' worl' gawn reel an' rock wif thunder."

"Suppose you die first, Mr. Spate?"

"Ah ain't gawn go firs'," he said, as if arrangements were already complete. "What kind' a triflin' darky you think Ah is? De Lawd know Miss 'Legra's min' on de matter, an' He know Ah got to look atter her. He wouldn' play no sech trick as dat." I thought his mouth quivered a little, perhaps in doubt. But he said, "Ah'm satisfied de Lawd know dat."

I had no chance to question him further, for just then another

car drove up—a car from Maine—and stopped. There were
white people in it, and Ephraim Spate waved me on impatiently.

On through Bains and St. Francisville, and at Dixie I sped
over the long Mississippi River bridge and went west and north
through the table-flat Louisiana countryside over the fine roads
built by Huey Long. Cane was being harvested. Great fields of
it, like giant marsh grass, dwarfed everything else in the landscape. Drawn by four mules, huge wagonloads of it trundled by
me on its way to the great refineries near New Orleans. The
raw-beefsteak smell of the immense marshes was in the air.

In the side yards of houses old-fashioned cane mills, drawn
round and round by mules or black men, ground out cane juice.
Fires blazed under cooking vats. Sorghum. Sorghum, corn bread,
and hog meat. Corn in Georgia, hogs in Tennessee. But in
Louisiana it was the cane. Men with machetes cut it, and women
in pants piled it. Black and white men, black and white women.
And at night around the cooking vats, black men on one side,
white on the other—the ring of men as evenly divided between
black and white as if some biologic law was at work—listening
to the wind moaning in the lonesome brakes, drinking last year's
fermented cane juice from stone jugs, they told tales.

"Yes, suh. Every good crop year, my grandfather told me,
just after planting time, this right young gal—maybe she was a
Cajun gal—would meet this great big man about midnight in
the middle of the field, and they'd lay down together. They
always knowed when they was there, 'cause the next mawning
they'd see the print of where they'd laid at in the ground. And
if the sorghum was goin'a be good an' thick, then just before
cutting time a nigger gal and a Indian would go to the same
place and lay down together. Nobody ever seen these people,
nor yet the other ones, but it was easy to tell when the nigger
gal and the Indian had been there, too, 'cause they'd beat down
about a six-foot square of cane and make a bed-like, and in the
mawning it would be there."

And from the other side, a voice:

"But, Cap'n, Ah ain't disputin' ya, y'un'erstan'. Ah jes' wud like ter know how dey knowed it wus a niggah gal an' a Injun man."

"You got me, boy. You sure got me."

Across the red Atchafalaya River the towns had colorful, haunting names: Sunset, Carenco, Opelousas, Breaux Bridge. Into Bayou Teche and the Evangeline country around St. Martinsville. Longfellow's Evangeline was here, the legend says, and here her people ended their long flight from Nova Scotia. They built the first steep-roofed houses. The houses and the fields kept by their descendants were as neat as picture postcards. The scale of things was smaller here. There was plenty of cane, but it grew only to man-height and well back from the road. Every house stood in a fence and every fence corner was neatly stacked with firewood. Even the sleek cattle were like pictures on a billboard.

The small dark people—sometimes so dark as to be indistinguishable from the Negroes who live among them—keep their ancient customs. The country is as distinctive of them as green is of postcard grass. They still build their houses high and gabled, still speak the ancient, liquid language, still bear such names as Le Beau, Broussard, Mouton, Fornet, Lefate, Rousseve. And they have given their names, and sometimes their blood, to Negroes.

They had given their name and blood to Menola Melancon, who waited on me in the restaurant where I took my meals in Gabriel. Menola's skin was the warm yellow color of a pumpkin. Luxuriant black hair glinted with blue lights and hung to her broad, square shoulders. Her breasts stood up aggressively, and in her gait there was a certain casual frankness. For two days she served me, smiling often at my ignorance of crayfish bisque, pompano, and the fried, delicious, gourdlike things stuffed with all manner of sea food. She seldom spoke to me beyond a good morning or a good evening, uttered in liquid, queer accent. But often she stood in the kitchen door and screamed in Creole patois at her mother, a little black woman, who screamed more loudly back again.

After an unusually violent and protracted bout of screaming the third morning, I asked Menola what the trouble was. I could hear her mother in the kitchen still talking excitedly to herself and throwing things about.

"Oh, it nothing," Menola said, shrugging her magnificent shoulders and jamming her hands into the pockets of her apron. Then in a burst of confidence, she put her hands on the back of the chair facing mine, and said:

"She say I too free-hand to you. I don't care for what she say, me. 'He eat it all,' I say, 'an' he pay for it. He hungry.' She say, 'Too much to eat. Too little bit money.' Pooh. Like dat. She say, 'Play seaburg too much. Seaburg take 'lectric. 'Lectric cos' money. Blues. Blues. Blues.' I say you like music. Then I say, 'Pooh.' Like dat." She threw up her hands in a liquid gesture and jammed them again in her pockets.

"But if you have been giving me more than my money's worth," I said, embarrassed. They were probably not having an easy time. In two days I had not seen another customer, except a white man who stopped in every evening to play all the trick slot machines, of which there were a dozen.

"Really," I said. And then I kept quiet, not knowing what to say.

"You like Creole food? You like music 'Do I Worry?' You like 'So Long'?"

Neither of us saw the mother until she was upon us and screaming in Menola's ear. Her words were unintelligible to me. She held a lighted, homemade cigarette between the middle fingers of her hand, and with this she seemed to be threatening Menola's eyes. Menola stood still, looking at her mother, her hands jammed in her apron. When the mother had screamed herself out, Menola began, shrugging her shoulders, gesturing violently with her head, her hands, her whole rich body. Any moment I expected to see them claw each other, but they did not; and the screaming ended as abruptly as it began. Menola marched away, only to stop in the kitchen door.

Smiling, showing remarkably even teeth, the mother leaned across the table close to my face.

"She full of tricks," the mother said, throwing a glance full of meaning at Menola.

"Shame!" Menola said, this time herself advancing and jabbing her forefinger through the air. "You full of tricks. Shame! Shame!" She stopped halfway and waited to see what her mother would say next.

"She full of tricks, her. She want big money, go to Louis Armstrong. She give 'way food, her," the mother said, smiling acidly over her shoulder at Menola. "Give food, play music, smile nice, get big tip, go Louis Armstrong. She full of conjure, her. She got plait-eye."

"Lie! Lie!" Menola screamed. But her mother only looked at her. Still smiling acidly, and now mouthing her clumsy cigarette, she brushed by Menola and went into the kitchen.

"She thinks you're giving me too much food," I said. My appetite was completely gone. I had eaten only one of the corn cakes with a little syrup and a small bit of the black, highly seasoned sausage.

"Pooh for her," Menola said. But she seemed less confident now. She looked past me through the big window into the narrow, shell-paved street.

Long wagons pulled by tractors or sleek mules and piled high with cane rumbled by at intervals. Black boys rode these mobile cane piles as if they were driving chariots on a dangerous course. Opposite the tiny restaurant stood a tiny fish market, and between it and a dark-windowed store, where long, black sausages, black hams, and black rubber boots hung from the eaves, rose a mound of oyster shells higher than either the fish market or the store.

"Do you want to hear Louis Armstrong?" I asked, thinking that perhaps I had been tricked after all. "Will you go with me?"

She looked at me, her eyes big with suspicion, disbelief.

"I mean it."

Her acceptance was casual, I thought, even a little cursory. But in the next moment she was at the table and breaking excitedly into the strange and beautiful and somehow emotion-compelling language of which I understood not a word.

Later I called her mother from the kitchen and paid her ten cents a meal extra, forty cents in all. Menola cried shame, but her mother, smiling and tucking the loose coins in the folds of her headcloth, only stroked her arms and called Menola a nice girl. "Nice girl, she." And Menola took this reversal of opinion with an indifferent shrug.

They lived in two small rooms over the restaurant, and that evening I simply ate later and stayed in the restaurant until Menola was ready. Every few minutes, while I wasted nickels in the slot machines, the mother came to the kitchen door and smiled at me. No one at all came in. When Menola came down, I could not see that she had needed time to get ready. She wore the same open-work sandals on her bare feet. Her hair was dressed in the same way, and under her cheap cloth coat she wore the same dress of green knitted stuff that she had been wearing all day. From the kitchen her mother brought a shoe box tied with string.

It was not far to the school on the edge of the town. There was a steady stream of people going. Their laughter and their gay voices rose all around us in the soft darkness. Frequently the words we heard were Creole words. In this section of the town there were no street lights, and pretty soon no sidewalks. Whenever the loaded cane wagons went by, the lights from their axles making weird patterns of shadows, everyone would scurry to the side of the road, and someone would yell something gay or obscene, and there would be a general laughter. Once Menola called out something to a passing wagon that I could not understand. All who heard her laughed.

"What did you say, Menola?" I asked.

"I say, 'Crow egg,'" she said. "It just something to say. He

might be white man, and I say crow egg. I feel good." She
laughed gaily.

"Tell me about yourself, Menola," I said.

"How you mean tell?" I could feel her looking at me in the
darkness, and I looked at her. Her eyes seemed to catch up all
the faint points and lines of light there were and to fling them
back at me.

"You know. Just things in general."

She turned her face from me, and we walked on in silence
for several paces. We had turned off the big road and now were
walking down the narrow road to the school. We could see the
dim lights in the many windows of the low schoolhouse and
many people standing in the yard around the door. The atmosphere, the whole scene seemed strangely foreign and exciting.
Menola put her hand lightly on my arm and turned to me again.

"I am born in Bayou Congo. Sometime, sometime too soon, I
die. Now I live. That is all."

And I knew that was indeed all she would answer to my direct
questioning. It was enough. She was born, she would die, but
now she lived. That was the great point, that now she lived. She
seemed to assume that I knew what her living was; that because
I, too, lived, her definition of life and mine were both the same.

We pressed into the crowd at the door where tickets were
sold. A great many people were not buying tickets, but were
just standing in the way, calling out to friends, shouting comments, making a gay, noisy crowd. Most of them were men and
young boys, but there were also women and young girls among
them. The two men at the door, one white and the other colored,
could do nothing with the crowd. At each entreaty to move
back and let the "paying customers in," the crowd laughed at
and jeered them.

"Treat, trade, ur travel," the colored man shouted to the
crowd. "If you can't pea, git off the pot."

Laughter and comments answered this. Behind me, Menola
fastened her arms around my waist and helped me press closer
to the door. The shoe box in one hand and money for the

tickets in the other, I let the crowd take me. Various voices called to Menola. A great many of them had a rising inflection and a foreign-sounding pitch. Menola answered them all with a gay, "Hi, you."

"Come on, y'all niggahs. Git out the way!" the colored man shouted. "If you ain't got no money, you can't git in yere."

"Dat what he think," someone said.

"Aw, go to hell, ol' niggah!" another said.

"Ain't dis a free country?"

"Yeah. Free schools an' dumb niggahs."

By the time we reached the door and I was stretching out my hand for tickets, the music started. The pressure behind grew stronger. The crowd was banked from the door to the road. The white ticket seller yelled for help. The Negro shouted obscenities at the crowd until his throat swelled and a great vein corded on his forehead. The crowd roared back at him and did a lot of playful shoving, a lot of purposeful pressing, and then I caught myself roaring, too, laughing, with the crowd. The music, which seemed untimed and without harmony, dripped through the air. The crowd heaved. The ticket seller grabbed for my money, missed, and I dropped it, and then we were forced through the door.

"Come on," Menola said, snatching my arm. The men at the door had their hands full. The white man was shouting for help; the Negro was cursing and shouting. They were trying to close the flimsy double doors against the crowd. "Come on," Menola said, and I followed her broad shoulders across the dim lamp-lighted hall and through the door to the auditorium.

It was not a large auditorium, and it was already well filled. There was a single row of collapsible chairs along each long wall. At the far end of the room, on a makeshift platform, sat the orchestra. Packed around the orchestra behind a wire screen was a crowd of white people. They had been let in a side door. Louis Armstrong's orchestra had played for whites the night before, but tickets had cost two dollars each. These were taking advantage of the dollar rates for colored. Now they were packed so tight behind the wire that they could not dance. On the main portion of the floor were people of all shades, from those as white as any behind the screen to the soot-black common to the isolated, inbred racial islands dotting the back country of Louisiana and Mississippi. They were dressed in a variety of styles. Women in long party dresses danced by with men in denim. Girls in gingham and calico house dresses, barelegged as was Menola, jumped the boogie with young men dressed in the long, tight-waisted coats and the narrow-bottomed trousers that were the latest style. Most of the older women wore the bright-colored headcloths which seemed to be standard among them. With godly impartiality, the music flowed over white and black alike.

Menola and I found seats near the screen. For a time she was content to watch, and refused several dances with youths who came up and simply held out their hands wordlessly. I had not the slightest idea that she was refusing dances on my account. My whole attention was centered in the dancers around me, in the absorbed faces and the strangely detached, recklessly flung bodies. The sudden bursts of laughter and snatches of talk enthralled me. The warm odors, at once sweet and yeasty, evoked memories beyond recalling and also beyond belief. A curious, throbbing, impersonal force flowed through me and around me in an unstemmable tide. It was in the music, in the soft, soft niggerskins, in the pale whiteskins.

"Come on. I want to dance, me," Menola said, rising suddenly and standing before me.

"But I don't very well," I said.

"Come on. Go with the music. Go how I go."

We moved onto the floor in the midst of the crowd. "See. It be's easy." And after a while it was easy, not unlike being carried along on the bosom of a stream, feeling the tug of its tide, becoming partaker of its strength and freedom. I could feel myself expanding, until it seemed that in a way almost as physical as my hand on Menola's waist, I touched the people around me. A few white couples had forced the screen and were also dancing on the edge of the crowd. Far from disturbing me, this fact gave a linear perspective to the scene, added piquancy to my jumbled feelings. Now, I thought, we have a microcosm of the American world. And then I tried to shut off my mind as one shuts a faucet off, for I realized the possibilities of dangerous absurdity in this symbolism. I gave myself up to the dance.

Louis Armstrong's trumpet dropped music with physical dimensions, notes as solid as golf balls. A kind of careless but controlled enthusiasm and gratification possessed the dancers.

"You like it?" Menola asked.

"Yes," I answered.

"To dance is easy."

She moved a pace from me and took a few independent steps, shaking her shoulders and her head as men and women were doing all over the hall. Her big, vital body weaved a fluid pattern before me. She swayed in the unmistakable vestige of a symbolic dance remembered by her blood. Her blood! Which blood of these: the Cajun, Indian, Negro, White in her? Her black hair clung to her neck. She moved easily in the crowd, parting from me with a twitch of her hips and joining me again, touching me lightly, and in that touch giving me to the crowd and to herself. Joining, parting to join again, and yet remaining free. Her upper lip beaded with perspiration.

When the music stopped, we got huge boiled crabs and eggplant stuffed with crayfish from the shoe box. Thus provided, we walked through the crowd. Everyone was eating, fish sandwiches and hot dogs, boiled crabs and hamburgers. We bought dripping bottles of soda water from the vendor, and we went up to have a look at Louis Armstrong and his band. Only a few white people were behind the screen now. The others were out on the floor.

"You feel good, like me?" Menola asked.

"Yes, I do."

"Everybody feel good. You like it, hunh?"

"I like it fine," I said.

When the music started again I did not dance, but sat against the wall near the orchestra. Menola swooped off with a yellow, flat-faced buck who moved as lightly as a breeze. I got swift glimpses of her moving through the crowd. I saw her everywhere, like an embodied essence. A part of the crowd, she melted into it, emerged again, and always she moved with absolute freedom.

Later that night, as I lay in bed and thought about that scene, it was this freedom that struck me, and I knew that every dancer in that crowd would have given me the same impression. It was not Menola alone, or something she alone possessed: it was in and of the crowd. It was that the crowd, living in the present, believed in it. "Now I live," Menola had said, and she was unbeholden to all that was sterile in the past. It was that she and they, the crowd, breathed the air of freedom. It was that they, emergent from the womb of slavery, sucked in the air of freedom, and they loved it.

But it was not this alone that I felt. I felt that I had come a far way, not in space and time alone, but in something which even to myself I feared to call understanding. I dared not boast anything so final and satisfying as comprehension. Only an utter fool would pretend to enough discernment and insight and to a sympathy sufficiently broad to embrace the total meaning of all I had seen and heard and of all that there was to be felt. Yet there are fools. I have heard them say, "I know and understand and love the Negro." The statement is usually made by someone in any discussion of the "Negro problem." It is meant by the speaker to indicate that he has all the answers to the problem. But it is an empty boast (it is also pure condescension), and it is based upon a fallacy. That fallacy is that the Negro is a problem both in vacuo and in toto, whereas in reality the Negro is only an equation in a problem of many equations, an equally important one of which is the white man. To know and understand and love the Negro is not enough. One must know and understand and love the white man as well.

It was in this direction—in the direction of knowledge and

understanding and love—that I felt I had come a little way. I do not boast of this. Under the circumstances it was almost inevitable. I had set out in nearly hopeless desperation to find both as Negro and as American certain values and validities that would hold for me as man. It is not enough in America to be Negro. It is not enough to be Negro American, or brown American, or colored American. There is an easily comprehensible mind-set, a psychosis, indeed, born of more than two centuries of slavery and inbred for dozens of generations. It was the point to Mike Chowan's bitter gibe, "There's a combine you can't beat—American, middle class, Negro." It was the burden of the bitter mouthings of innumerable men (and women) who had exhorted countless Negro audiences: "Be a man!" It is a phrase that has always meant more to a Negro American than non-Negro Americans can imagine. And so, in a bewilderment that years of planless seeking had increased, I had set out as Negro and American to find among my people those validities that proclaimed them and me men.

And I think I found them. Among all that was hollow and false and trifling (and there was much) I think I found those values and validities as quietly alive and solid, as deep-rooted as vigorous trees. They have simple names, and they have been called before. Other peoples have been said to have them, but that makes them no less good. Indeed, that they are the attributes of other peoples, men, makes them of the highest importance to me. That Negroes hold these values in common with others is America's fortune and, in a very immediate sense, the Negro American's salvation. For these things they hold valid and valuable are the highest common denominator of mankind. They are the bane of those who would destroy freedom, and they need no other justification than this. They are the intangibles in the scale of human values. They are, unmistakably, integrity of spirit, love of freedom, courage, patience, hope.

But that night, too, I thought of the meaning of where I had come from, of what I hoped I had left behind. I thought of the false and hollow things and people. I had been one of them,

I thought. They lived imbedded in a cocoon of memory and experience not their own. And this was cowardice. The traditions by which they lived were dried like husks. They clung to a tradition of freedom and of democracy, and not these themselves. And this was pride—pride in a past that had its roots in shame, mayhap, or in pure chance. Freedom was for them a thing of lineage, of ancestry—a free father, grandfather, great-grand-father. And the problem of living in a tradition was a problem in logic and pride. "Freedom," they say, "democratic freedom is a logical thing, a two plus two thing." It is rational, simply. They have no convictions about it. But they have the tradition. And one thing about a tradition is that it is the form of a thing completed, a finished thing. But freedom is not a finished thing. Democracy is not. That is why I saw so much pain, so much groping, so much growing. That is why there was Ephraim Spate and Mike Chowan, Leroy Stepteau and the cop in Memphis, because democracy and freedom are not finished, per-fected things. Freedom is a principle. And one thing about a principle is that it is an emotional thing. It may be logical, but it is also emotional. It takes conviction to live by a principle—a conviction that the principle is good, or honorable, or life-saving, or soul-saving. And conviction is emotional. And some day, I thought, these others may learn this: that something more than a free ancestor, or a tradition, or the law of the land must keep freedom and the love of freedom green.

That night as I lay in bed in the little town of Gabriel, a thousand miles from all that had meant refuge, I felt at home and at peace, even with all that lay ahead of unending struggle (for I was not blind to this) and remaking in the faintly glimmering future. This was victory for me, not triumph. No man alone can ever know such triumph as I had hope for in the years ahead.

The next morning I went to the restaurant. Menola served me thick, black, tough-skinned sausages, corn cakes, coffee gray with milk. I had told her the night before that I would be leaving after breakfast.

"Where you go now?" she asked.

"Texas. Oklahoma."

"Me, I always remember last night."

"So will I," I said.

The mother gave me a box crammed with pralines. Menola pressed a medallion of St. Christopher in my hand.